BERING'S VOYAGES

VOLUME II

AMERICAN GEOGRAPHICAL SOCIETY

RESEARCH SERIES NO. 2

W. L. G. JOERG, *Editor*

BERING'S VOYAGES

An Account of the Efforts of the Russians to
Determine the Relation of Asia and America

BY

F. A. GOLDER

IN TWO VOLUMES
VOLUME II:

Steller's Journal of the Sea Voyage from
Kamchatka to America and Return
on the Second Expedition
1741-1742

TRANSLATED AND IN PART ANNOTATED

BY

LEONHARD STEJNEGER

AMERICAN GEOGRAPHICAL SOCIETY

BROADWAY AT 156TH STREET

NEW YORK

1925

DOUGLAS C. MCMURTRIE
NEW YORK

Reprinted from plates by the
LORD BALTIMORE PRESS, BALTIMORE, MD.

CONTENTS

LIST OF ILLUSTRATIONS

PREFACE

Scholars will be ever grateful to Bering for persuading Steller to go with him on the *St. Peter*. Steller's account of his experiences is the most interesting of all the papers that have come down to us. The naval officers' log books contain the dry facts of the voyage, but Steller's journal gives the spirit of it, the "inside" story, the moral forces at work. The two records supplement each other, sometimes even in matters of navigation, and that is one reason why they are published together.

There are still other reasons. Steller was the first trained naturalist in the North Pacific, and he had opportunities for observation that were denied to his successors. He was the only scientist who saw a live sea cow. He studied the habits of the blue fox and the sea otter before they were frightened away by man. In all that relates to these animals as well as on other phases of natural history which he records, Steller was, is, and will be an authority.

Steller's journal, which is in German, his native language, was edited and published at St. Petersburg in 1793 by the naturalist P. S. Pallas, both serially in Volumes 5 and 6 of his *Neue Nordische Beyträge* and separately in booklet form (see the bibliography at the end of the present volume). Steller's description of Bering Island, which constitutes the end of the journal, Pallas had already published in 1781 in Volume 2 of the same series.

During the summer of 1917 I located in the archives of the Russian Academy of Sciences at Petrograd a manuscript copy of the journal. It seems probable that it is a direct transcript from the original. Pallas received the original in 1767 (or 1769), so he tells us in his two prefaces,[1] from Professor J. E. Fischer, one of the Academicians who took part in Bering's expedition in Siberia, and had it copied. That the manuscript I

---

[1] *Neue Nordische Beyträge*, Vol. 2, 1781, p. 256 ("einer andern kleinen Handschrift desselben [Steller], welche ich noch im Jahr 1767 nach der mir vom seligen Professor Fischer mitgetheilten Urschrift copiren liess"); *ibid.*, Vol. 5, 1793, p. 131, or book form, p. 3 ("Dieses merkwürdige

found is not the original seems apparent for two reasons: (1) it is not in Steller's handwriting, as a comparison with that handwriting[2] will show; (2) it does not lack the sheet containing the account of the happenings from August 4 to 11, 1741, nor is the sheet mutilated on which are described the events of September 15, 16, 19, 20, 21, and 24—defects which characterized the original, Pallas says,[3] when it was in his hands. That the present manuscript is also not the transcript made for Pallas from the original seems probable because it shows no trace of his many editorial changes or corrections, signs of which may plausibly be expected to have been evident on that transcript. On the other hand, that the manuscript is a direct copy from the original seems highly probable from the fact that, in the corresponding places, it is practically identical, word for word, with certain passages which J. B. Scherer quoted from the journal when he published Steller's "Beschreibung von dem Lande Kamtschatka" in 1774.[4] In a review of the book in 1775

Tagebuch . . . ist mir im J. 1769 von dem seeligen Professor der Geschichte Herrn Fischer . . . im Original mitgetheilt und eine Abschrift davon zu nehmen erlaubt worden"). The two prefaces are translated below as footnotes at the beginning of the description of Bering Island (footnote 1 on pp. 189-190) and of the journal (p. 9, footnote 2) respectively.

[2] Facsimile of portion of Steller's letter of November 4, 1742, to Gmelin, below, p. 248. Compare with specimen pages from manuscript also reproduced below (pp. 38, 165, 166).

[3] *Neue Nordische Beyträge*, Vol. 5, 1793, footnotes on pp. 174 and 206 (translated below, in the journal, as asterisk footnotes following footnotes 132 and 248 respectively).

[4] The following parallel passages from the manuscript, Scherer, and Pallas are typical and may serve as an example.

MS	Scherer	Pallas
die Ursache ist, dass wir während Zeit bey beständig *favorablen* Winde und Wetter nur imer fortliefen, Himmel und Wasser sahen, *particulas exclamandi* und *admirandi* von den Herren Officiren höreten. (fol. 8)	die Ursache ist, dass wir während Zeit bey beständig favorablem Winde und Wetter nur immer fortliefen, Himmel und Wasser sahen, *particulas exclamandi* und *admirandi* von den Herren See-Officiers hörten. (prefatory life of Steller, p. 10)	Die Ursache ist, weil man, bey beständig günstigem Wind und Wetter nur immer fortlief, nichts als Himmel und Wasser sahe und von den Officieren nur Ausrufungen und Bewunderungsausdrücke hörte: (*N. N. B.*, Vol. 5, p. 147; or book, p. 19)

Beckmann says[5] that Scherer lived for several years in St. Petersburg prior to 1774 and there, he has reason to believe, acquired the original manuscript of the "Beschreibung" through Professor Fischer or from his library. If Scherer had the original manuscript of Steller's description of Kamchatka it is not unlikely that he also had the original of the journal in his possession at that time. Having it, he would probably, especially in a short passage, quote it literally, to judge by the unedited condition in which he gave to the world the 450-page description of Kamchatka, a procedure for which Pallas[6] takes him to task.[7]

Whatever its exact status, the manuscript found in 1917 is of great interest because it evidently is a faithful rendering of Steller's words and thus makes it possible to restore the matter which Pallas omitted or abridged. Pallas, however, deserves much credit for editing the journal so well. In many places he improved on the reading of the original; in others he took liberties which may have had some justification a century and a third ago but do not have now. The pages reproduced in facsimile in the body of the present volume afford typical examples of the difference between corresponding portions of the manuscript and Pallas' version (cf. Fig. 1 with Fig. 2 and Fig. 18 with Figs. 19 and 20).

The present is the first complete English translation of the journal.[8] Even in German the journal has not been easily accessible, the existence in the libraries of the United States of only two copies in book form and six in serial form having come to

---

Although only the initials of J. B. S. are given on the title page of the "Beschreibung" it is known from the review of the book cited in the next footnote and from other sources that Scherer was the editor.

[5] *Physikalisch-ökonomische Bibliothek von Johann Beckmann*, Vol. 6, Göttingen, 1775, pp. 191–202; reference on p. 192.

[6] Preface to Steller's description of Bering Island, *Neue Nordische Beyträge*, Vol. 2, 1781, pp. 255–256 (translated, below, p. 189, footnote 1, at the beginning of Appendix A).

[7] The deductions in this paragraph are by the editor: Dr. Golder did not have occasion to see proofs.—EDIT. NOTE.

[8] The translation published by William Coxe in the fourth edition of his "Account of the Russian Discoveries Between Asia and America,"

my knowledge.[9] The translation was made from the printed
account; wherever there were essential differences in the manuscript these variants were translated and added as footnotes.
The present translation therefore has the advantage of whatever
clarification and improvement Pallas imparted to the narrative,
while, at the same time, it retains the full text of the journal as
written by Steller. A translation was at first made by me from
the printed version which, while not literally accurate, attempted
to render its spirit. I then had the good fortune to enlist the
coöperation of Dr. Leonhard Stejneger of the U. S. National
Museum. Dr. Stejneger, retaining as much as possible of the
phraseology of the first translation, made another which is as
near to the original wording as it is possible to make it. It is
this translation which is published herewith.

London, 1803, pp. 30–93 octavo impression, pp. 24–72 quarto impression, omits certain passages. The author himself says (p. 30, octavo; p.
24, quarto): "As it [Steller's journal] contains the only circumstantial
relation of that expedition, rectifies several errors in Muller's account,
and as it has never made its appearance in English, I deemed it necessary, for the complete elucidation of the Russian Discoveries, to submit
to the public a translation of those parts which detail the principal events
of the voyage; but have omitted several prolix accounts of his disputes
with the officers, and some of his frequent digressions concerning the
supposed situation of America." The inclusion of Steller's journal in the
edition of Coxe's book that followed the publication of the journal (the
third edition of the "Account" was published in 1787; see Bibliography,
Vol. 1, p. 363) is only additional evidence of Coxe's acquaintance with
the essential records on the Russian explorations of that period which he
acquired through his sojourn in St. Petersburg and contact with such men
as G. F. Müller. However, the progress in science and in the knowledge of
the region in the intervening century and a quarter afford ample justification, if any were needed, for offering the present translation.—EDIT. NOTE.

[9] According to H. C. Bolton: A Catalogue of Scientific and Technical
Periodicals, 1665–1895, 2nd edit., *Smithsonian Misc. Colls. 1076*, Washington, 1897, p. 1205, there were at that time sets of the *Neue Nordische
Beyträge* in the libraries of Harvard and Yale Universities, the Museum
of Comparative Zoölogy, Cambridge, Mass., and the Philadelphia
Academy of Natural Sciences. There are also sets containing Vols. 5
and 6 in the libraries of Dr. C. Hart Merriam of Washington and the
American Geographical Society. Copies in book form are in the Library
of Congress and the New York Public Library.

The translation is by no means all the work that Dr. Stejneger has done on this volume. His footnotes to the botanical and zoölogical references in the journal are a major contribution. Naturalists will agree that there is no man so well qualified to discuss these matters as he. During his repeated visits to the North Pacific region, including Kayak Island, Bering Island, and Kamchatka, in 1882–1883 (comprising an eighteen months' stay on Bering and Copper Islands), in 1895 and 1896–1897 (principally to study the fur seal question), and again in 1922, Dr. Stejneger has gone over the same ground, has studied the same plant and animal life that Steller did, and has in this way been able to verify Steller's observations.

It is a pleasure to record the encouragement and help given me by American men of science. This is particularly true of Dr. Charles V. Piper of the U. S. Department of Agriculture and the late Dr. Alfred H. Brooks of the U. S. Geological Survey, one an authority on plants and the other on the geology of Alaska. In making my translation of the journal I had the assistance of Professor O. C. Gebert of the State College of Washington in interpreting some of the more difficult passages in the German. To these and to the other scholars who have given me so generously of their time and learning I am sincerely grateful.[10]

F. A. GOLDER

[10] The editor is indebted to Professor Lucien Gallois of the University of Paris for locating Delisle's manuscript map of 1731 (Pl. I) and having it photographed, and to Professor R. DeC. Ward of Harvard University, Mr. F. W. Hodge of the Museum of the American Indian, Heye Foundation, and Dr. James T. Pilcher of Brooklyn, N. Y., for comment, incorporated in the footnotes, on certain climatological, ethnological, and medical questions respectively. He is also under obligation for help in the elucidation of material in Russian publications to Commander N. A. Transehe, Lieutenant-Colonel N. M. Kostenko, and Captain Nicholas George of the American Geographical Society's staff.—EDIT. NOTE.

BIOGRAPHICAL NOTE ON STELLER[1]

By F. A. GOLDER

GEORG WILHELM STELLER was born in Windsheim, Franconia, on March 10, 1709. After graduating from the schools of his native city he went to the universities of Wittenberg, Leipzig, Jena, and Halle, where he studied theology and the natural sciences and specialized in medicine and botany. In 1734 he went to Berlin to work under Professor Ludolf and to take an examination, which he passed with high honor. He was now ready for a position, but Germany had none to offer him. The only opening that presented itself at that time, and which he accepted, was that of surgeon on an army transport that was about to leave Danzig for Russia with a number of invalided Russian soldiers. This is how it came about that Steller found himself at St. Petersburg in the winter of 1734.

Soon after his arrival he became the physician of the Archbishop of Novgorod. This position provided him with a home, but it did not give him an outlet for his energy and an opportunity for his talents. Steller desired to go to Siberia as a member of Bering's second expedition and there make his reputation. With that in view he asked the Academy of Sciences to send him to Kamchatka as botanist. His friend the Archbishop, as well as others, backed him for the position, and in August, 1737, the Senate, on the nomination of the Academy, appointed him adjunct in natural history at a salary of six hundred and sixty rubles a year and ordered him to proceed to Kamchatka.

With such bright prospects before him Steller felt that he was in a position to marry the lady of his choice, the attractive

[1] Material for the study of the life of Steller may be found in the biographical publications listed in the bibliography at the end of the volume.

widow, Brigitta Messerschmidt. She assured him that she was ready to go with him to the ends of the world and share his hardships, but when the time came for leaving she decided to stay home and share his pay. Heartsick and alone he set out for the wilds of Siberia in the last months of 1737. He followed the much-traveled road to Tomsk, reaching there in the autumn of 1738, and hastened from there to Yeniseisk to join his two countrymen and fellow members of the expedition, the historian Gerhard Friedrich Müller and the naturalist Johann Georg Gmelin. With them he spent about seven weeks (January 20 to March 5, 1739) telling them his disappointments, his plans, and his ambitions, and receiving comfort and encouragement in return.[2] From Yeniseisk he pushed on to Irkutsk, Yakutsk, and Okhotsk, where he took ship for Kamchatka and landed at Bolsheretsk on October 2, 1740.

While on the way, at Kirensk Post on the upper Lena, Steller had met Captain Spanberg[3] and asked to be taken to Japan.

[2] Among the Steller papers in the archives of the Russian Academy of Sciences there is the following list of books which Müller and Gmelin gave Steller when he parted from them:

Caspari Bauhini Pinax. [Gaspard Bauhin: Pinax theatri botanici, Basel, 1596, 1623.]

Turnefortii Institutiones rei herbariae, cum corollario. [Joseph Pitton de Tournefort: Institutiones rei herbariae, 3 vols., Paris, 1700.]

Thomae Willis Opera omnia. [Thomas Willis: Opera omnia, 2 vols., Geneva, 1680 (later imprints also).]

Ioann Ray Methodus emendata et aucta, 1710. [John Ray: Methodus plantarum emendata et aucta, Leyden, 1703 (first publ. London, 1682).]

Ej.—De variis plantarum methodis dissertatio. [John Ray: De variis plantarum methodis dissertatio, London, 1696.]

Ej.—Stirpium Europearum extra Britannias nascentium sylloge. [John Ray: Stirpium europearum extra Britannias nascentium sylloge, London, 1694.]

Ej.—Synopsis methodica animalium quadripedium et serpentini generis. [John Ray: Synopsis methodica animalium quadrupedum et serpentini generis, London, 1693, 1696.]

[3] On Spanberg and his expeditions to Japan see below, in the journal, footnote 18.

Spanberg agreed to do so provided the Senate gave its consent. On April 30, 1740, Steller had sent a petition to that body and then proceeded to Bolsheretsk to wait for a reply. Before it came, Bering, who was at Avacha Bay on the eastern coast of Kamchatka, notified him that he had a proposal to make to him. Steller immediately crossed the peninsula and presented himself before the Captain Commander on March 20, 1741. As a result of the interview Steller agreed to go to America. That which happened to him on his voyage is recorded in his own journal and need not be repeated here.

On his return in August, 1742, he set about completing his Kamchatkan investigation. During the winter of 1742–1743 he made his headquarters at Bolsheretsk and worked out from there in different directions. In the spring and early summer months of 1743 he explored several of the Kurile Islands. After that he went to Lower Kamchatka Post, where he built a boat, engaged a small crew at his own expense, and sailed for Bering Island and wintered there, returning early in July, 1744. A month later, loaded with boxes of specimens of all kinds, he bade Kamchatka goodby forever and set out for Okhotsk. He stopped but a short time at this post, then proceeded to Yakutsk, where he spent nearly a year studying natural history, and then went to Irkutsk, reaching there in December, 1745. In January, 1746, he was at Krasnoyarsk, in March at Tobolsk and Tyumen, in April at Solikamsk, and in the summer months at Perm and in the adjoining country, making botanical researches.

While at Bolsheretsk he had a quarrel with one of the officers, who made a complaint to the Senate that Steller meddled in affairs that did not concern him and that he had freed certain Kamchadal prisoners who were held on the charge of rebellion. That complaint came to the hands of the Senate early in 1744, and at once instructions were despatched to Irkutsk to look into the matter. When Steller wandered into the city in December, 1745, and was faced with the charges, he cleared himself without trouble and was allowed to go about his business. Unfortunately the officers in charge of the investigation delayed in making a report of their findings until some time after Steller had departed on his way to the capital. When the Senate heard again of Steller he was in the Urals. Thinking that he was trying to evade the law, a special messenger was sent to take him back to Irkutsk to stand trial. The messenger found him in the neighborhood of Solikamsk and made him retrace his steps. In the meantime the acquittal of Steller reached St. Petersburg (August 20, 1746), and a special courier was ordered to proceed in all haste to tell him that he was at liberty to go where he pleased. By that time he was some distance to the east of Tobolsk. He faced about once more, and when he had reached the neighborhood of Tyumen he was taken ill and died on November 12, 1746, being then only thirty-seven years of age.

The nine years of strenuous life, the hard summer of 1746, and the marching back and forth as a prisoner had much to do in undermining Steller's vigorous constitution, but the greatest single factor in causing his death was strong drink. It is said that after his return from Bering Island in 1742 Steller took to drinking. Each year the habit grew stronger and fastened itself on him. More than once his friends had to put him to bed. He was drinking heavily during the summer of 1746 and gradually ruined his health and lowered his vitality. When in the fall of 1746 he had come as far as Tobolsk he was already a sick man burning up with fever. His friends tried to persuade him to go no farther and to give up drinking, but he would do neither. He hired a sleigh and started for Tyumen. It was very cold weather, and on the way the driver stopped at an inn to warm himself, leaving Steller in a drunken stupor outside. After a long time the driver returned and found Steller almost frozen. He was hurried to Tyumen, but nothing could be done for him. His strength was gone.

Steller was an interesting man and a great scientist. His discoveries in America and Bering Island assure him eternal fame. He was blessed with a retentive memory, a keen power of observation, and an ability to generalize and to interpret his data. The facts which he recorded and the conclusions which he drew from his observations on the voyage have, on the whole, stood the test of time. He sometimes erred in matters of detail; he occasionally, owing to his strong prejudices against the naval officers, made erroneous assumptions, but he was seldom wrong in his scientific reasoning. Modern scientists may not wholly accept his theories, but they cannot altogether sweep them aside.[4]

Not only intellectually but physically and temperamentally Steller was well fitted for exploration. He was strong, tireless, and devoted to his work. He accomplished more in one day than the average investigator did in a month. His wants were few and easily satisfied. His fellow scientists had cooks, servants, supply wagons, and camping outfits, but Steller was his own cook and servant and lived off the country. One plate, one cup, one pocketknife, and his blankets constituted his personal baggage. Traveling light, he covered much ground and went to places where his more dignified and encumbered colleagues could not follow, and in the end he achieved more than they. Gmelin and Delisle de la Croyère had to be provided with European foods and European wines, but Steller purposely lived on native foods in order to ascertain their nutritive values and their effects on white men. In a report to the Yakutsk commandant he stated that during the winter and spring (1743–1744) which he and his men spent on Bering Island not one of them tasted bread and not one of them was the worse for it, and he thus convinced himself that European food was not essential for the Russians in Kamchatka.

Steller's weak point was his inability to work with other people. He lacked tact, sympathy, and appreciation of the other man's point of view. He was always quarreling and making enemies. Sometimes it was with his fellow German scientists but more often with the Russian officers in Siberia, on whom he looked down as beneath his notice. He was ever sending complaints against them, the burden of his charges being that they

[4] For Steller's published works see the bibliography at the end of the volume.

did not show him proper respect and did not consult him enough. He offered advice, not only to the Siberian governors and to the naval officers but also to the Senate and to the Synod, on navigation, military strategy, commerce, agriculture, conversion of the heathen, education of the natives, building of forts, and more such subjects. It is interesting to note that most of his suggestions were good, and the reason for their rejection must be sought in a large part in the manner of their presentation. His very insistence to be heard and his air of wisdom aroused opposition.

His cutting remarks about the officers of the *St. Peter* show what a poisonous pen he had; there is reason to believe that he had a sharp tongue as well. In describing to the Senate[5] the scene that took place on board the ship, when he asked to be allowed to land on Kayak Island, Steller says: "Then I turned on Captain Commander Bering and in no gentle words told him what I thought of him and what I would do if he did not let me go."

If Steller treated Bering in this manner we can easily guess what he did to Khitrov, Waxel, and to some of the smaller fry from whom he had no favors to expect. They hated him and he despised them, and their life on board was as disagreeable as can be imagined. It would be worse than a waste of time to sit in judgment and try to decide the rights and wrongs. In the first place, we have only one side of the story, Steller's; the other men have left no memoirs.[6] In the second place, they were all living under abnormal conditions and were not altogether responsible. They all suffered from disease, vermin, cold, hunger, thirst, and despondency, and their actions and quarrels are psychologically

[5] Steller's report to the Senate, dated Bolsheretsk, Nov. 16, 1742, published in P. Pekarski: Arkhivniya razyskaniya ob izobrazhenii nesushchestvuyushchago nynye zhivotnago Rhytina borealis, Suppl. No. 1 to *Zapiski Imp. Akad. Nauk*, Vol. 15, St. Petersburg, 1869, pp. 13-24; reference on p. 18. See also, below, footnote 67 and passage in the journal to which it refers.

[6] The "Lettre d'un officier de la marine russienne," Berlin, 1753 (see bibliography in Vol. 1, p. 362), whose author is with great probability

interesting and nothing more, showing as they do how men will act under certain conditions.   In reading of their voyage it would be much better to think less of their quarrels and more of their glorious deeds.

---

identified as Lieutenant Waxel, is mainly a refutation of J. N. Delisle's claims concerning his part in the origin of Bering's second expedition and Delisle de la Croyère's achievements on that expedition. It does not deal with Steller.

The present translation, as previously stated (p. ix), was made from the journal as published by Pallas in 1793. The wording of the manuscript copy of the journal located in 1917, wherever it differs essentially from the published version, is indicated in footnotes.

The manuscript copy of the journal located in 1917 is referred to throughout as "the MS;" the 1793 edition, as "the published version," "Pallas edition," etc.

In paragraphing and in the separation of sentences within a paragraph by a dash the present translation follows the published version.

Interpolations by the translator are indicated by brackets [ ]. The parentheses ( ) used occur in the published version.

Transliteration from the Russian has been made directly from the Russian words and names themselves and essentially according to the Library of Congress system. This accounts for the differences from the spellings used by Steller and Pallas, which are transliterations into German and which are in addition sometimes based on Russian pronunciation and not spelling.

Kamchadal and other native words have been spelled so as to reproduce in English the pronunciation indicated by the German or Russian-through-German transliteration used in the journal.

All dates in the journal itself are Old Style; in 1741–1742 they were eleven days behind the Gregorian calendar.

Publications not cited in full in the footnotes can be identified in the Bibliography of Vol. 1 or Vol. 2; the location of these entries can be determined through the index, under the author's name or otherwise.

Asterisk footnotes are footnotes by Pallas in the published version. Unsigned footnotes dealing with variants of the MS from the published version and footnotes followed by (S) are by Dr. Stejneger; footnotes followed by (B) are by the late Dr. A. H. Brooks of the U. S. Geological Survey; by (G), by Dr. Golder; by (J), by the editor.

Units of Measure and Weight Used in the Journal

1 arshin (Russian ell) = 28 inches (Engl.) = 71.19 centimeters
1 sazhen (land fathom, for measuring length) = 7 feet (Engl.) = 2.1336 meters
1 sea fathom (for measuring depth) = 6 feet (Engl.) = 1.8287 meters
1 verst = 0.6629 English statute mile (⅔ mile in round numbers) = 1.0668 kilometers

3 arshins = 1 sazhen
500 sazhens = 1 verst

1 German, or Dutch, mile = 4 nautical miles = 4.6106 English statute miles = 7.4204 kilometers

15 German miles = 1°

1 Russian pound = 0.903 pounds avoirdupois = 0.4095 kilograms
1 pood (pud) = 36.113 pounds avoirdupois = 16.38 kilograms

40 Russian pounds = 1 pood

G. W. STELLER'S

FORMER ADJUNCT OF THE IMPERIAL ACADEMY OF SCIENCES

JOURNAL

OF HIS SEA VOYAGE FROM THE HARBOR OF PETROPAVLOVSK
IN KAMCHATKA TO THE WESTERN COASTS
OF AMERICA AND THE HAPPENINGS
ON THE RETURN VOYAGE[1]

INTRODUCTION[2]

Having lived to set foot once more upon the sacred soil of
Russia after the conclusion of a hard voyage of fourteen months[3]

[1] The title page of the MS reads:

II

Second Kamchatka Expedition Undertaken by
Russian High Imperial Orders
that is
Description of the Voyage
of Captain Commander Bering which was
undertaken for the exploration of the lands
lying to the northeast of Kamchatka, also of the
island on which there was opportunity to land
and on which we wintered in 1742, with which
are described, in addition to what befell us, the objects
in the three natural kingdoms that are to be found there
by
Georg Wilhelm Steller, Adjunct in Natural History
of the Academy of Sciences
of St. Petersburg
1743

[2] This heading is supplied by Pallas; it is not in the MS.
Pallas introduces the journal with this "Preface by the Editor.—This
noteworthy journal by the late Steller, whose loss can never be too
greatly deplored, was communicated to me in the original [Original] in
the year 1769 by the late professor of history Fischer, a friend of the
industrious Steller, and I was allowed to make a copy of it. I have
communicated a part of it, which contains the description of Bering

undertaken for the exploration of the shore of America situated northeasterly from Kamchatka[4] and after despairing more than once of either surviving or serving Russia again, I deem it my duty to precede my further reports with a brief, impartial, and true account of my voyage, its happenings, and the fate which befell the ship's company.

The great monarch Peter I, of glorious memory, was influenced by the discovery of Kamchatka as well as by the representations of the Paris Academy of Sciences[5] to cause an investigation to be made, by sending out the then Captain Bering in 1725, as to how far America is distant from Kamchatka, the extreme northeastern corner of the Empire, or whether it [America] might not in the north be nearer to the extreme Chukchi headland, which the old map makers[6] called Promontorium Tabin, or even be continuous with the latter.

Island, in Vol. 2 of *Neue Nordische Beyträge*, p. 255 and ff., and here publish the journal itself, from which it will appear how correct Steller's judgment was in that early period of discovery about many matters relating to the position and nature of the west coast of America and how much it is to be regretted that the celebrated Bering on this, his last voyage no longer had the energy and health which caused him on his earlier voyage toward the northern strait that is named after him to merit the praise of the great Cook."

[3] June, 1741, to August, 1742.

[4] The MS reads "des Nordostlichen Ufer von America," the northeastern coast of America, but what is meant is of course the coast of America lying to the northeast of Kamchatka, as literally stated in the title of the MS version (cited in footnote 1) and as implied by Pallas' change of this phrase to "des nordostlich liegenden Ufers von Amerika."

[5] Also by the desire to find precious metals and to win for Russia "glory along the lines of the arts and sciences" (see Vol. 1, pp. 8–9, footnote 10). (G)

[6] e. g. Mercator, 1587, Quadus, 1608 (see A. E. Nordenskiöld's "Fac-simile-Atlas to the Early History of Cartography," transl. by J. A. Ekelöf and C. R. Markham, Stockholm, 1889, Pls. 47 and 49); map B, dated 1610, on plate between pp. 966 and 967 in Vol. 2 of Witsen's "Noord en Oost Tartaryen," 2nd edit., 1785; Witsen, 1687, in Frederik Muller and Co.'s "Reproductions of Remarkable Maps," No. 4, Amsterdam, 1897; and Witsen, 1692, in Teleki's "Atlas zur Geschichte der Kartographie der Japanischen Inseln," 1909, Pl. 13, map 2. (G)

Although at the time of the first attempt in the ship *Gabriel*[7] it would have been an easy matter, without further costs or loss of time, by sailing on a northeast or east course, between the parallels of 51° and 64°[8] north latitude, i. e. as far as the Kamchatkan shore extends from its extreme end at Cape Lopatka[9] to Chukchi Cape, to touch at the American islands by going twenty or thirty miles[10] or at the mainland itself by sailing fifty to seventy miles,* nevertheless the officers in command at that time were satisfied with a short exploration of Kamchatka from Lopatka to the so-called Serdse Kamen,[11] which is not the same by a considerable distance as the Chukchi Promontory, during

[7] The ship used by Bering on his voyage of 1728 (see Vol. 1 of the present work, p. 18, footnote 34, and Fig. 6, opp. p. 20). (G)

[8] The MS has 61°. The correct latitude of Chukchi Cape is 64°, however.

[9] The southern tip of Kamchatka (see Vol. 1, Pl. I).

[10] German miles, fifteen to a mean degree of latitude. One German mile therefore equals 4 nautical miles, or 4.61 English statute miles.

* As may be noticed from various passages, Steller imagined the American coast [to be] quite near towards the northeast and east, while at the present time we are quite firmly convinced of the opposite through the discovery of the islands, their distances from each other and from Kamchatka.—P.

[11] By this is meant the equivalent of East Cape, i. e. the cape near which Bering turned back on his first expedition, having been informed by the Chukchis that the land turned west from here (see also Vol. 1, pp. 18–19). According to the conception illustrated on the map by the St. Petersburg Academy of Sciences (a redraft of which, our Fig. 14, accompanies the English translation by Jefferys, 1761, of the account of this expedition by Müller in Sammlung Russischer Geschichte, Vol. 3, 1758), a conception which Steller shared, to judge by the next words in his journal (see, however, below, p. 19, line 10), this was not the northeastern extremity of Asia. This extremity was represented, as shown on the aforesaid map, by a great protuberance extending northward almost to the 75th parallel and designated Chukchi Promontory. These conceptions are best illustrated by quoting from Jefferys' translation of Müller (p. 4; in German edition, pp. 117–119):

"At last they arrived, on the 15th of *August*, in 67 deg. 18 min. North latitude, at a promontory, behind which the coast extended towards the West, as the former *Tschuktschi* had said. From this the captain drew a pretty plausible conclusion, that now he had reached the extremity of

which they followed the Kamchatkan coast in a northerly direction and never lost sight of it except in foggy weather.—The object of the voyage[12] was consequently anything but achieved, for, if America were situated so close to Siberia, it would have been discovered before then by the cossacks who in their *baidars* (skin boats) had at various times sailed over this course from the mouth of the Anadyr; as also the geodesist (surveyor) Gvozdev[13]

Asia towards the North East. He was of opinion that from thence the coast must continually run to the West; and was this the case, no connection with *America* could take place; consequently he believed that he had fulfilled his orders. . . . It must be allowed that the circumstances, on which the captain founded his judgment, was [*sic*] false; for it was afterwards found that this was the promontory which, by the inhabitants of *Anadirskoi Ostrog*, is called *Serdze Kamen*, on account of a rock upon it in the form of a heart. And, although the country behind it winds to the West, yet this winding composes only a large bay, in the innermost part of which the rock *Matkol* lies, according to the above account given by the Cossack *Popow*. But here the coast begins again to run regularly to the North and North East, till in the 70th degree or more, of North latitude, the proper *Tchuktschian Noss*, as a great peninsula, appears; where, and not before, it might be said, that there was no connection between the two parts of the world, but who on board that ship could know this?"

Today the name Serdze Kamen is applied to a cape, 90 statute miles northwest of East Cape, on the side of the (modern) Chukchi Promontory facing the Arctic Ocean, in the position indicated by Captain Cook in the following quotation (his reference to Müller is to the passage just cited): ". . . and that thus far Beering proceeded in 1728; that is, to this head which Muller says is called Serdze Kamen, on account of a rock upon it, shaped like a heart. But I conceive that Mr. Muller's knowledge of the geography of these parts is very imperfect. There are many elevated rocks upon this Cape, and possibly some one or other of them may have the shape of a heart. It is a pretty lofty promontory, with a steep rocky cliff facing the sea; and lies in the latitude of 67° 3′ and in the longitude of 188° 11′ [E.]" (James Cook, A Voyage to the Pacific Ocean, Vol. 2, London, 1784, p. 470). (G)

[12] To investigate how far America is from Asia and whether it joins the Chukchi Peninsula (see items 2 and 3 of the instructions for the expedition, Vol. 1, p. 11).

[13] For an account of this voyage, see Vol. 1, Ch. III.   (G)

and his cossacks in the ship *Gabriel* later on, in 1735,[14] went much farther, viz. to 66° north latitude.

On Captain Bering's return the eager world consequently received nothing more than a chart and a defective account of the already well-known Kamchatka, besides a few verbal reports of the Anadyr cossacks, according to which the Chukchi Promontory was really separated from America by open sea, but that on the 51st parallel, opposite Lopatka, there was a chain of islands stretching out towards Japan, to which [islands] the cossacks, with a few surveyors, had ventured out sometime before in very frail vessels and [of which islands they] had actually explored thirteen.[15]

On Captain Bering's return to Moscow in 1730 it was at once realized how little the object had been attained and yet how much reason there was still left for supposing the mainland of America to be near. At the same time there arose a desire to secure information about the islands lying south of Kamchatka towards Japan. Out of these considerations, therefore, grew the second, great Kamchatka Expedition, so costly and arduous on account of the great distances, the remote and toilsome transportation of provisions and materials, besides many other causes which might perhaps have been reduced considerably if an unbiased and conscientious report on the farthest parts of Asia and their resources, based on all the information then at hand, had been submitted. In particular, it must have been well known to the officers employed on the first expedition how oppressive and injurious the transportation of the provisions, at that time relatively so insignificant, had been to the few inhabitants of the Lena regions and of Kamchatka and how many hundreds of the latter lost their lives in the journeys from the Bolshaya River to the harbor of Avacha.[16] It would then have been easily seen

[14] 1732, not 1735. (G)

[15] The most northerly of the Kurile Islands were visited by Ivan Kozirevski and companions in 1713; in 1720 or 1721 Luzhin and Evreinov examined a number of these islands at the order of Peter the Great (see Vol. 1, p. 6). (G)

[16] Across the southern part of Kamchatka from its western to its eastern side (see Vol. 1, Fig. 3 and Pl. I).

that additional and much larger transportation would completely exhaust these desolate regions and be the ruin of the poor
natives there, as subsequent events have shown.[17]

I pass over the ten years of laborious preparation which preceded the second voyage—the innumerable difficulties encountered, the expenses, the losses of men and beasts, etc., which took
place during the years from 1733 to 1741, as well as the circumstances relating to Captain Spanberg's separate expedition,[18]

[17] The last two sentences do not occur in the MS and seem to be an
elaboration by Pallas.

[18] Spanberg's voyages to Japan constituted one of the two expeditions
subsidiary to Bering's second expedition, the second being explorations
along the Arctic coast of Siberia. Spanberg, using the Bolshaya River
as a point of departure, made three voyages, one in 1738, one in 1739,
and the last in 1742. On the first he explored the Kurile Islands as far
as 45° 30', on the second he skirted the eastern coast of Yezo and northern
Hondo as far as 39°, on the third he reached 39° 35' without touching
land or accomplishing any new discoveries. (On Spanberg's voyages see
the pages indicated in the following works cited in the bibliography of
Vol. 1: Müller, Sammlung Russischer Geschichte, Vol. 3, 1758, pp. 166–
185, English transl. by Jefferys, 1761, pp. 26–34; Sokolov, *Zapiski
Hydrogr. Depart.*, Vol. 9, 1851, pp. 345–365 and 416–422, with map of
1738 and 1739 voyages; Lauridsen, Vitus Bering, Chicago, 1889, pp.
117–126, with copy of Sokolov's map; Golder, Russian Expansion on
the Pacific, 1914, pp. 220–231.)

Steller's reference, immediately below in the journal, to his request
in 1740 to join Spanberg's second voyage to Japan relates to the voyage
which was ultimately carried out in 1742. The voyages of 1738 and 1739
were considered as a single undertaking, in which that of 1738 was a
preliminary effort which fell short of the mark.

The news of Spanberg's 1739 voyage had at first been received with
satisfaction by the authorities in St. Petersburg, but later doubts arose
as to whether he had reached Japan at all, inasmuch as the current conception, as reflected on contemporary maps, was that Japan lay on the
same meridian as Kamchatka and Spanberg reported his discoveries to
lie 11° to 12° farther west (see the works cited, e. g. Müller, p. 183).
For this reason Spanberg was ordered to repeat the voyage. The order
reached him at Kirensk Post on the upper Lena while he was on his way
to St. Petersburg to report. Here Steller seems to have met him and asked
to be taken to Japan. Spanberg made his preparations during the
winter of 1740–1741 and actually set sail from Okhotsk in the summer

none of which properly come under my plan, and I shall turn my attention solely to what relates to the expedition of Captain Bering and of Captain Chirikov, which started on June 5, 1741, as long as the two packet-boats fitted out for this voyage kept together, and later to the fortunes of Bering's crew alone until their return to Kamchatka on August 26, 1742.

As it is well known, however, in what capacity in the year 1738 I was sent from St. Petersburg to Kamchatka only for the purpose of making an investigation of the three natural kingdoms and consequently was not to have the slightest share in the enterprises of the naval officers, it is necessary for me to explain briefly how I came to be in their company nevertheless. In the year 1740 I had addressed from Kamchatka[18a] an application to the High Governing Senate humbly petitioning to be permitted to accompany Captain Spanberg on a second voyage to Japan which he was planning, in order that, considering the great expense incurred, thorough information about the islands along the route as well as about Japan itself might be secured through me. When in the meantime Captain Commander Bering learned of my insatiable desire to see foreign lands and to investigate their resources and curiosities, he sent me,[19] in the month of February, 1741, from the Harbor of St. Peter and St. Paul, or Avacha, a special letter requesting me to journey to him for the purpose of discussing certain matters with him. Perceiving at once that the intention was to persuade me to undertake the voyage to America in company with him, I did not hesitate long, and with only one *sluzhiv* (cossack of the Siberian militia) I traveled to him by dog team. As soon as I arrived he represented to me with many arguments the important and useful service I could render and

---

of 1741, but the unseaworthiness of his newly built vessel forced him to winter at the Bolshaya River and postpone the voyage to 1742. (J)

[18a] The words "from Kamchatka," not in the MS, were probably added by Pallas. Indeed, Steller seems to have sent his application from Kirensk Post in the interior of Siberia (see the preceding footnote and, above, p. 2). (J)

[19] Steller was then at Bolsheretsk Post.

how much my undertaking would be appreciated in high places, if I should consent to go along with him. I replied that I had no orders to do so and that I should not dare to take that decision upon myself, especially as I had already approached the High Governing Senate for permission to go to Japan; that consequently such a decision might be regarded as a very bold and thoughtless offense, particularly if the American voyage should become so protracted that I should not be at hand in case the order to go to Japan should arrive. The Captain Commander, however, swept aside all my objections by taking upon himself the responsibility for all the consequences. He also promised to write about it himself to the High Governing Senate and pledged himself to give me all possible opportunities so that I might accomplish something worth while and to give me as many men as I should want whenever needed, since I should have to leave those of my own command behind. Subsequently he also sent me a formal document, after having held a sea council of all the officers attached to the expedition, officially charging me, it is true, with the observation during the proposed voyage of the mineral kingdom only. In consideration of all this I decided to accept the offer, seeing that it could not interfere with my Kamchatka investigations, with which I was particularly entrusted. I hope therefore that my venture, devoid as it was of all personal gain, will be received the more graciously the more exclusively it will be found to have been based upon the general good and the advantage of the Imperial Academy of Sciences as well as upon my own prescribed duties. I consequently expect anything but punishment for undertaking something without orders, since the great distance did not permit me to submit extensive representations and then await instructions for carrying out an enterprise which could wait only a few days for my own arbitrary decision but not for orders from far away. For this reason I venture beforehand to promise myself a gracious pardon, when, after an absence of fourteen months and a six months'[20] miserable and dangerous sea voyage, I reappear with few useful discoveries,

[20] June to November, 1741.

through no fault of mine but because the Captain Commander kept his promise to me so poorly that he only let me see the American mainland from a distance and was finally persuaded at last to put me ashore on three islands,[21] though only for a few hours, without any assistance, like a malefactor, and with great reluctance and many sarcastic remarks not encouraging to my honest zeal. Moreover, no proposal of mine, not even the most insignificant, was considered worthy of being accepted, because those in command were too much imbued with their own wisdom, until the disastrous end and a just dispensation exposed their unfortunately too naked vanity.[22] It was the resentment at having already been so long in Siberia and having to stay there still longer which spurred these gentlemen[23] on to do in one summer's voyage and in one attempt that which, according to a moderate calculation, would necessarily require two summers.

They did not take it into consideration that during the beginning of July the Kamchatkan coast between 56° and 51° is often beset with ice and that this ice cannot come, as they alleged, from the strait between the Chukchi Promontory and

[21] Kayak Island (see, below, p. 41), and Nagai (p. 77) and Bird Islands (p. 93) of the Shumagin group, although Steller did not actually set foot on Bird Island.

[22] Pallas has modified this sentence so as to make the criticism apply to the other officers as well, while in the MS Steller refers to Bering only. The MS reads: "Likewise, he did not accept even the most insignificant proposal of mine from a too exalted opinion of his own counsel, although the end and the divine judgment afterwards very plainly demonstrated how far the reason of the one [Steller] differed from the unfounded guesses of the other [Bering] and what great respect the one [Steller], even when most obstructed, entertained for the other [Bering], his services, and the general good resulting therefrom." The translation of the last clause is not certain, as this clause is somewhat obscure in the original. The translation seems plausible, however, in view of Steller's fair-minded estimate of Bering at the time of his death (see the journal, below, pp. 155–157). The obscure clause reads in the original: "und wie grose Hochachtung einer vor den andern auch in den grösten Wiederwärtigkeiten vor seine Dienste und das daraus fliesende Interesse geheget." (S)

[23] The MS reads "him," i. e. Bering.

America, because ice is absent to the northeast of the mouth of the Anadyr and very rare from the Anadyr to Olyutora,[24] while on the other hand from Uka or Ukinski Bay[25] to Kamchatka [Bay] and from there to Lopatka it is seen every year. From this, I say, must necessarily follow: (1) that this ice is drift ice from the American rivers; (2) that the American continent must lie nearest to the region where this drift ice ordinarily is observed every year; (3) that, because this ice usually drifts ashore after three days of continuous east wind, the nearest land in this region must necessarily be supposed to be directly to the eastward; (4) that when 56° north latitude is passed there is no drift ice and consequently no further obstacle is to be feared from it. On the contrary, it was erroneously assumed[26] that this ice comes from Chukchi Promontory and consequently would obstruct navigation during June and July in case it was decided to turn in a northerly direction or even to conduct a survey opposite the Chukchi Promontory, where everybody thought America to be nearest. It was decided, therefore, at the start, to assume gradually a course between east and south in order to be able, after going about 20° of longitude from Avacha, to discover, somewhere between 45° and 46° north latitude, the alleged Company Land discovered by the Dutch,[27] from which

[24] River flowing into bay of same name in 61° N. (see Vol. 1, Pl. I, where bay is spelled "Olyutorski").

[25] River and bay in 58° N. (see Vol. 1, Pl. I, where bay is spelled "Ukinskaya").

[26] Steller was mistaken in regard to the ice on the coast of Kamchatka. It is part of the winter ice floes of Bering Sea and not river ice from Alaska. The council of officers was right in not taking a northeasterly course, as the northern part of Bering Sea is usually not clear of ice until July. (B)

[27] This was really Urup, the third island in the Kurile chain counting from the south (see Vol. 1, Pl. I, correlated with Fig. 3), discovered by Vries in 1643 (*ibid.*, p. 2). Lack of knowledge of all but its southwestern end, which Vries had coasted, led to its exaggerated extension eastward into a large land mass and, in some cases (as in Vol. 1, Fig. 1), the identification of its hypothetical southern coast as that of Juan de Gama Land (see next footnote). (J)

it was believed with certainty that it would be easier to discover
America or the coasts of America projecting towards the west
reported by Gama[28] in this neighborhood. If, however, no land
were made on this course, it was the intention to proceed farther
between east and north, turning more and more northerly, because it was hoped towards the middle of July to find the sea
there clear of all ice and thus to lose no time. If in doing so
America should be reached, it was proposed to follow the coast
in a northerly direction until we came to the parallels of 64°
to 66°, where the farthest point of Asia, or the Chukchi Promontory, is situated, toward which it was then intended to turn in a
westerly direction and, after having determined the distance between both continents in the north, to make ready for the return
to the home port. However, in view of the winds and the distance, the necessary proviso was made that the coast should be
followed only long enough for the time to admit of the port
[Avacha] being reached again by the end of September, when
it was intended to let the remaining part of the investigation be
conditioned on a second voyage the following year.

It is admittedly true that originally Captain Commander
Bering had firmly resolved to pass a winter in America and in
the spring to finish from America the remainder of the task,
which on account of the shortness of the summer and the long
distance would not have been accomplished in one [outward]
trip, and then embark upon the return voyage. In that case not
only would have been prevented the great disaster to the crew,

[28] Juan de Gama, a Spanish navigator, whose discoveries of islands
on a voyage from China to New Spain appear on a map for the first time
in 1649 (see bottom inset on Buache's map of 1754, reproduced in
Teleki's "Atlas zur Geschichte der Kartographie der Japanischen Inseln," 1909, p. 141; also Vol. 1 of present work, pp. 2–3 and Fig. 1).
The fact that De Gama Land was sometimes merged with Company
Land (see preceding footnote), which in two passages of the log book
of Vries' voyage (under June 21 and August 5: Leupe's edit., 1858, pp.
100 and 157–158; Teleki's "Atlas," pp. 118 and 126) is characterized as
part of America (see also Graaf's map, derived from Vries' voyage, in
Teleki's "Atlas," Pl. 8, map 2), accounts for Steller's statement. (J)

many of whom because of the too protracted voyage in the late autumn died from scurvy and exposure, but an exact knowledge of the land and information as to its people and products would also have been obtained, while the whole expedition could have been finished in excellent condition and to the greatest advantage of the Empire. However, the execution of this plan had already been rendered impossible by Fleet Master Khitrov[29] and [his] two misfortunes. First, through him all the ready supply of biscuits for both packet-boats was lost in Okhotsk in 1740 at the mouth of the Okhota River. Secondly, later on the supplies destined for Avacha in place of the former had to be unloaded at the Bolshaya River; because of the transportation of these, which was to be undertaken by dog teams during the winter, the Koryaks on the Tigil[30] rebelled even before a start was made, since it became necessary, in order [to be able] to deliver five poods[31] of supplies per man at the port [Avacha], to gather natives from a distance of five to six hundred versts at Bolshe-retsk Post. During this process they were treated very harshly by the men sent out for the purpose [of gathering them in], and they were also led to suspect that something else might be intended.—Owing to these circumstances the Captain Commander as well as the other officers, in order not to incur a shortage, found themselves compelled to organize two separate voyages for the accomplishment of this task, as, even so, the delays caused by the investigation of the rebels and the constant drunken state of Kolessov, the commander of Kamchatka, brought it about that we could not leave the Harbor of St. Peter and St. Paul before the beginning of June, while in other respects the month of May was suitable and [originally] determined on.

[29] As the reader will very readily discover, Khitrov was Steller's *bête noire*. (G)

[30] The Tigil River flows into the west coast of Kamchatka in 58° N. (see Vol. i, Pl. I).

[31] One pood, containing 40 Russian pounds, equals about 36 pounds avoirdupois.

Account of the Sea Voyage from Kamchatka to America [32] [and Return]

Towards the end of May, in the year 1741, all the necessary preparations for the voyage to America were at last completed, and the packet-boats *St. Peter* and *St. Paul* moved out of the harbor on May 29 and anchored in the roadstead of Avacha Bay to wait for a fair wind in order to clear the entrance. On the *St. Peter*, which I also boarded, there were [33] Captain Commander Bering as commanding officer, Lieutenant Waxel, Fleet Master Khitrov, mate Hesselberg, second mate Yushin, assistant surgeon Betge, assistant constable Roselius, guard marine Sint, boatswain Nils Jansen, assistant navigator Khotyaintsov, commissary Lagunov,[34] surveyor Plenisner, the rest of the crew, viz. sailors, soldiers, five sons of Kamchatkan cossacks as sailor-apprentices, interpreters, and men supposed to be familiar with all places on the Kamchatkan coast, one of whom was in my service as a hunter, making a total, including the son of the lieutenant, of 76 men.[35]—On the other packet-boat, the *St. Paul*,

[32] This heading is supplied by Pallas; it is not in the MS.

[33] The names of members of the expedition are here and elsewhere throughout the journal spelled in the standardized form established for Vol. I. The spellings used in the MS in some cases differ considerably from these, such as Chytrew for Khitrov. Some of the differences are doubtless due to copyists' errors; most of these are eliminated by Pallas' skillful hand. There would still remain the differences resulting from transliteration from Russian into German in the one case and from Russian into English in the other, not to speak of the instability and lack of definiteness in the spelling of proper names prevalent in the eighteenth century.

Hesselberg's name is spelled thus instead of Eselberg as in Vol. I (pp. 226, 282, 312) because this is probably the preferable form. It is so spelled both in the MS and the published version of the journal, in which more information is given about him than in the cited passages in the log book and Waxel's and Chirikov's reports.

[34] Between Lagunov and Plenisner the MS lists "a trumpeter."

[35] This agrees with the figure to be arrived at by adding the number (45) of survivors on Bering Island as given in the list in Khitrov's version of the log book (Vol. I, p. 235) to the number (31) of deaths as given

were Captain Chirikov, Lieutenants Chikhachev and Plautin, Professor of Astronomy Delisle de la Croyère, Fleet Master Dementiev, mate Elagin, one guard marine, one commissary, the assistant surgeon Lau, sailors, soldiers, as well as sons of Kamchatkan cossacks, likewise [a total of] 76 men.[36]

On June 4, about nine o'clock, we sailed at last out of Avacha Bay into the ocean and entered on our real voyage with favorable wind and weather. We sailed with southwest and south-south-west winds on the initial ESE and SE by E courses, so that on the eighth day of our journey, that is to say on June 11, we found ourselves 155 Dutch miles[37] from Avacha in latitude 46° 47'.[38]

On June 12 we noticed for the first time rather distinct signs of land to the south or southeast of us. The sea being quite calm we observed various kinds of seaweed suddenly drifting about our ship in large quantities, especially the sea oak,[39] which do

in Waxel's report (*ibid.*, p. 282). If account be taken of the death seemingly overlooked by Waxel (p. 282, footnote 6) the total complement of the *St. Peter* would seem to have been 77. This was the figure arrived at by Captain Bertholf (Vol. 1, p. 341).

[36] This likewise agrees with the figure resulting from the addition of the number (54) of men present on the return of the *St. Paul* to Kamchatka as given by Chirikov in the list accompanying his supplementary report (Vol. 1, p. 326) to the number (22) of men who died or were lost as itemized in Chirikov's journal and summarized in his report (*ibid.*, pp. 321–322). This was also the figure arrived at by Captain Bertholf (*ibid.*, p. 348).

[37] Designated German miles in the log book in Vol. 1; fifteen to a mean degree of latitude (see, above, footnote 10).

[38] The log book (Vol. 1, p. 56) has 156½ miles and latitude 46° 40'.

[39] In the MS: "verschiedene Seegewächse, *quercum marinum.*" "Meereiche" (sea oak), the word used in the published version, is only a literal translation of *quercus marina*. In pre-Linnaean botanical literature *quercus marina* is the name of the common alga, *Fucus vesiculosus* Linnaeus, of the Arctic Atlantic. The representative form of this species in the North Pacific appears to be *Fucus evanescens* Agardh (Kjellman, *Kongl. Svenska Vetensk.-Akad. Handl.*, Vol. 20 (N. S.), 1882–83, No. 5, pp. 200 and 202, and Vol. 23 (N. S.), 1888–89, No. 8, p. 34), which is common around the Commander Islands.

The clause "which do not . . . towards the land" does not appear in the MS. (S)

not as a rule occur very far from the coast, inasmuch as the tide always carries them back towards the land. We also saw gulls, the large gulls (*Diomedea exulans*), and the ducks called rock ducks in Kamchatka (*Anas histrionica*),[40] all birds which are never seen in the open sea or very far from land. From all these [indications] it might be inferred that if the initial course were continued still farther, land would be reached shortly.[41] Just at the time, however, when it was most necessary to apply reason in order to attain the wished-for object, the erratic behavior of the naval officers began. They commenced to ridicule sneeringly and to leave unheeded every opinion offered by anybody not a seaman, as if, with the rules of navigation, they had also acquired all other science and logic. And at the time when a single day—so many of which were afterwards spent in vain— might have been decisive for the whole enterprise, the course was suddenly changed to north. On this course for the first time we experienced a slight storm, and our first misfortune occurred when, owing to foggy and dark weather, the other ship, the

[40] The published version reads: "So sahe man auch Seemöwen, die grossen Möwen (*Diomedea exulans*) und auf Kamtschatka sogenannte Klipp-Enten (*Anas histrionica*)." In the MS, however, this reads: "So sahe man auch *Laros, Aernas Turneri* und Enten *kamenni utki*." By *Laros* Steller probably meant only gulls in general, but by *Aernas Turneri* he certainly did not mean the albatrosses—"die grossen Möwen (*Diomedea exulans*)." Pallas has here committed a most absurd blunder in guessing what "Aernas Turneri" might mean, absurd because nobody, and Steller last of all, would claim that the albatross is a bird which is never seen in the open sea or very far from land. Aernas is plainly a misreading for Sternas, the S being so joined to the t in the manuscript as to have the appearance of A. Turner was the first author (in 1544) to apply that word to a tern, and *Sterna turneri* a hundred years after became a generic denomination for terns in general (see Alfred Newton: A Dictionary of Birds, London, 1893–1896, p. 955, footnote 2). The terns seen by Steller were probably *Sterna paradisaea*, which is known both from Bering Island and several of the Aleutian Islands (Stejneger, *U. S. Natl. Museum Bull. 29*, 1885, pp. 85–86). "Klipp-ente," or rock duck, is the harlequin duck (*Histrionicus histrionicus*) which is still known to the natives of Bering Island as *kamenushka* (Stejneger, *op. cit.*, p. 168). (S)

[41] On this point, see the next footnote.

St. Paul, under the command of Captain Chirikov, became separated from us and was not seen again during the entire voyage.—Because even thus early a beginning had been made to carry out another scheme, namely not to let the Captain Commander, who constantly stayed in the cabin, know more than was considered advisable, another misfortune occurred, in that the story told by some of the men who thought that they had seen land to the north—a story, if not infallible, at least apparently very probable—was neither listened to nor considered worthy of any consideration, until during the return voyage, on August 24,[42] unexpectedly and to the terror of all, land was sighted on the 51st parallel, whereupon the voices of the penitents were heard too late. This, according to the ship's

---

[42] Both Pallas and the MS read thus. The date should, however, be September 24 (civil time): see the log book of the *St. Peter* (Vol. 1, p. 168) and Waxel's report (*ibid.*, p. 275), also, below, p. 112, under September 24.

Steller's whole argument in this paragraph is fallacious, and in this instance his contempt for the naval officers was not justified. A continuance of the original SE by E course after June 12 would not have led to the discovery of land, as a glance at any chart of the North Pacific will show.

The statement that the land sighted on September 24 "according to the ship's reckoning must have been the land where we lost Captain Chirikov" must be understood as referring only to the general location. The log of the *St. Peter* for June 20, the day of separation of the two vessels (Vol. 1, p. 65) gives her position as lat. 49° 22′ and long. 18° 06′ from Vaua lighthouse at the entrance to Avacha Bay; for September 24 (*ibid.*, p. 167) as lat. 51° 27′ and long. 20° 45′ from Vaua. These two positions are about 160 nautical miles apart; but, owing to the accumulated error in longitude in the ship's reckoning (see Vol. 1, p. 210, footnote 124), the two positions were really about 215 nautical miles apart, as shown on Pl. I in Vol. 1. The land sighted on September 24 was probably Adak and Atka Islands with the intervening islands (see, below, footnote 260). Even assuming the distance of 160 nautical miles, they would not have been visible from the *St. Peter's* position on June 20.

As to the belief of some of the men that they had seen land to the north where the two vessels lost sight of each other, there was no basis for it in fact, as the nearest arc of visibility, that of Amatagnik Island, did not reach to within 40 nautical miles of the ships' northernmost position, just before separation, on June 19 (see Vol. 1, Pl. I). (J)

reckoning, must have been the land where we lost Captain Chirikov, and already then it seemed to several persons as if they had seen land, a circumstance at that time regarded as a trivial matter since none of the naval officers themselves had seen it. Moreover, they considered it then a greater honor to run farther, along the land, so as to be able to boast of having traveled very far and suffered much unnecessarily.

After having searched several days in vain for the lost packet-boat and any further hope of finding it had vanished, we sailed once more south from the 50th to the 46th degree in the hope of finding the *St. Paul* or Company Land on this course. However, having failed in both, and as the appearance of Company Land had now been awaited in vain a second time without its having ever come into view in the place demanded, the conclusion to regard it as an imaginary land—an invention of the Nuremberg map makers,[43] over which either our ship or Captain Spanberg's [44] necessarily must have sailed, if it had a real existence—became unavoidable. As if those gentlemen had not laid themselves open to the suspicion of being capable of committing just such a geographical blunder, by the fact alone that one of them pointed out our course on the map of the world in the sea off Canada,[45] while another asserted with all his might against me that Canton lies on the 45th parallel and the Maldive Islands lie in the Mediterranean Sea.—They consequently now began to repudiate utterly said Company Land, although they could have had no other reason for going so far south than to search for it in all seriousness. On June 18[46] the beginning was made in earnest to go east and gradually north, so that for every two or three degrees in longitude one degree of latitude was gained.

After we had sailed on this course for several days and had come once more as far as the 52nd parallel, there appeared again

[43] Particularly Johann Baptist Homann (see Vol. 1, p. 3).   (G)

[44] On his voyage of 1739 (see, above, footnote 18, and maps there mentioned accompanying Sokolov's and Lauridsen's accounts).

[45] i. e. in the Atlantic Ocean.

[46] Should be June 26, astronomic time (see log book, Vol. 1, p. 71, and footnote 20 on that page; also *ibid.*, Pl. I).

very many signs of a land situated not far from us to the north, along which we ran for exactly four weeks until July 18 in such a way that on said day, on which we actually saw land for the first time,[47] we were in north latitude 59° and some minutes and 49° of longitude from Avacha, consequently nearly 500 Dutch miles away.

It should cause no wonder that I have summarized the happenings of a four weeks' voyage over such a long distance thus briefly. The reason is that, running steadily along with constantly fair wind and weather, we saw nothing but sky and sea and heard only from the officers exclamations and expressions of amazement over how we could have erred so fundamentally as to believe Kamchatka to be separated by a narrow channel from America, which now was found to be so remote. The brazen and very vulgar snubs by the officers, who coarsely and sneeringly rejected all well-founded and timely admonishings and propositions, thinking that they were still dealing with cossacks and poor exiles freighting provisions from Yakutsk to Okhotsk, who had simply to obey and keep still without talking back, had been the cause of closing the mouth of myself as well as of others long ago. No matter what we observed and might discuss for the benefit of the general good as well as the public interest, the answer was always ready: "You do not understand it; you are not a seaman; you have not[48] been in God's council chamber!"— For the first time[49] I had here the sad occasion to see how it happens that often the greatest and most useful undertakings may in the end, in spite of all care given and great expenses [involved] and although granted all possible resources, accomplish very much less, as far as the public good is concerned, than was planned for originally; while on the other hand the smallest beginnings, through mutual and earnest coöperation in word and

[47] Land was actually sighted on July 16, civil time (see Vol. 1, pp. 93 and 332). Steller himself says below, p. 33, "July 16, the Thursday on which the land became for the first time clearly visible." On the chronology of the first sightings in general see, below, footnote 58

[48] The "not" does not occur in the MS but is added by Pallas.

[49] The MS reads "For the first time in the Russian service I had" etc.

deed, of minds devoid of all egotistic aims and gain, may grow into mighty achievements which pay interest on the outlay a thousandfold.—It should be stated here that during the ten years in Siberia, when every one lived as he pleased and demanded and received so much homage from the ignorant mob as suited his notions, the greater number of our officers completely forgot themselves and, through habit, fell into the delusion of being infallible or feeling insulted when anyone mentioned anything of which they were ignorant. Even Captain Spanberg's attitude gives a clear proof of this, as he conducted himself towards the representatives of the Academy of Sciences in a similar manner. [50]

The reasons for which I long ago concluded that we had been sailing close to and along the land I shall now place before everybody for intelligent judgment, just as I presented them so often on our trip, but in vain, to the naval officers, viz.: We saw frequently floating from the north, and many times in large quantities, various seaweeds [51] (*Fuci*), especially the sea oak (*Quercus*

[50] Instead of "in a similar manner" the MS reads "in such a manner that, while it might be said he knew he was a captain, nevertheless he had not yet forgotten the lowest tricks of a sailor."

[51] Dr. Marshall A. Howe, of the New York Botanical Garden, to whom I submitted the list of seaweed names used by Steller, has very kindly furnished me with valuable notes on their identity, from which I quote the following: "I have considered the evidence presented in your letter, and I think you may be quite right in believing Steller's *Quercus marina* [the MS. has "*quercum marinum glandiferam Bauhini*"] to have been *Fucus evanescens* [see, above, footnote 39]. *Alga dentata* Raji was probably a species of *Odonthalia*, as you suggest." (As *Odonthalia aleutica* (Mart.) seems to be more common than *O. kamtschatica* I. G. Ag., I suppose the former species may have been meant.)

By *Fuci membranacei calyciformes* Dr. Howe thinks Steller is most likely to have meant *Constantinea Rosa-marina* (S. G. Gmel.) Post. et Rupr., referring to S. G. Gmelin's "Historia fucorum," St. Petersburg, 1768, p. 102, Pl. 5, Fig. 2.

According to him the *Fucus clavae effigie* was probably *Nereocystis Priapus* (S. G. Gmel.) Saunders, and Pallas' footnote on Gmelin could doubtless be completed by adding that the reference is to be found on p. 231.

Tournefort's *Fucus lapathi sanguinei foliis* is the Atlantic *Hydro-*

marina); the *Alga dentata* Raji, which grows on rocks in two or three feet of water; the *Fuci membranacei calyciformes* already opened, which was a certain indication that they had been lying for some time on the beach and had again been carried off by the tide; the *Fucus clavae effigie*,* which grows in two fathoms of water but nowhere around Kamchatka; the *Fucus lapathi sanguinei foliis* Tournef., which, if it had been drifting long at sea, would on account of its tenderness have been quickly torn to pieces by the waves or eaten by the sea animals which were constantly seen in large numbers and are very fond of it. We observed also red and white sea nettles (*Priapi* Lin.),[52] which cling to the rocks at low tide in at least five or six feet of water and, according to my experience in the Sea of Penzhina,[53] are never met with until one has approached the coast to within fifteen to twenty miles.—One time[54] it even happened that there came drifting by the ship a large mass of the large reed

---

lapathum sanguineum (L.) Stackh. Dr. Howe suggests that the species seen by Steller may have been *Delesseria crassifolia* Rupr., which is recorded from the Pribilof Islands and is the only species "in that region that suggests *Hydrolapathum sanguineum*." (S)

* Gmel. hist. Fucorum.—P. [For identification see preceding footnote, second paragraph.]

[52] Steller in the MS has "*Urticas marinas rubras* und *albas*," by which I take it he means the stinging jelly fishes, the North Pacific varieties or subspecies of *Cyanea capillata* (Linn.) (*ferruginea* and *postelsii* if distinct) and *Aurelia aurita* (Linn.). Linnaeus in first describing the former (Fauna suecica, Stockholm, 1st edit., 1746, No. 1287) expressly says "vulgo *Urtica marina*." It is true that Pallas in the published text adds in parenthesis "(*Priapi* Lin.)," but these are sessile actinians. Thus Gmelin's *Actinia crassicornis* (Carolus Linnaeus: Systema naturae, 13th edit., edited by J. F. Gmelin, 2 vols. in nine, Leipzig, 1788–93; reference in Vol. 1, Part VI, p. 3132) has among its synonyms *Priapus senilis* Linn. and *P. ruber* Forskål as well as *Urtica rubra* Aldrovandi, and it is probably these quotations which misled Pallas, for surely Steller refers to floating organisms and not to those attached to the bottom. (S)

[53] This name was at that time applied to the whole of the Sea of Okhotsk (Krasheninnikov, Histoire et description du Kamtchatka, Amsterdam, 1770, Vol. 1, p. 236).

[54] The MS has "often."

grass**[55] common in Kamchatka, which was a most infallible indication of a near coast, because this grass grows everywhere along the beaches of the ocean, both in Kamchatka and America, and on account of the smoothness of its straw would long have been scattered if it had not been carried by the tide immediately from shore towards us. Other vegetable objects which from day to day and from hour to hour were noted down in my diary need not be mentioned.

Even though such irrefutable indications of a near land were submitted with reason, great respect, and patience to the officers and they were advised to lay the course toward the north in order to reach land sooner, and even though the Captain Commander had always himself been of the same opinion but, being outvoted by the other officers, had felt himself constrained to yield without necessity and in spite of his rank and authority, nevertheless he considered it, as did the other officers, ridiculous, beneath his dignity, and annoying to receive such advice from me, a man not versed in nautical matters. Therefore he used to answer me offhand that I did not know how to judge such affairs; in many parts of the ocean the whole sea was overgrown with weeds; what could I say to that? It did no good to reply that I was as fully aware of this fact as I was of the places near the Cape Verde and the Bermuda Islands where these seaweeds,

** *Gramen paniculatum arundinaceum, panicula densa spadicea* Stell.—P.

[55] "grosses Schilfgras" in the text of the published version, to which words the above footnote by Pallas refers. This Latin name, omitting the attribution to Steller, is the term used in the MS. Pallas transferred it to a footnote and supplied a German equivalent in his text.

Professor A. S. Hitchcock, the well-known agrostologist, to whom I submitted the matter, writes me "that the grass referred to is probably *Calamagrostis scabra* Presl. The phrase name you quote is the one applied by pre-Linnaean authors to the European reed, *Calamagrostis epigejos* (L.) Roth. The corresponding plant on the Alaskan coast is the one mentioned, which, however, is usually reported as *C. langsdorfii* Trin., a Siberian species." Both *C. langsdorfii* and *C. arundinacea* (Linnaeus) are recorded from the Commander Islands (Fedtschenko, Flore des Îles du Commandeur, 1906, pp. 122 and 123). (S)

the names of which I also knew, were drifting about; or that I knew the reason why plants could grow in those regions but not here in the north, where the sea water, on account of the different effect of the sun, was quite differently constituted; or finally that it is no secret what the nature of these [seaweeds] is and in what manner they have been transplanted.

It seemed to everyone absurd and incredible that anyone should maintain the existence of a current* in the sea, although we clearly observed its effects, inasmuch as the objects floating in the sea kept to a definite direction frequently even contrary to that of the winds, so that during the southwest and southeast winds which we were having these things drifted toward us from the north. On account of this incredulity the necessary precautions which have to be observed in the ship's reckoning on account of the currents were not taken, either on the outward or return voyage; consequently through cocksureness many errors, because of the great distance between the two continents, may have crept in.[56] Afterwards, indeed, on the return voyage, they saw with their own eyes how often—almost continuously—they had previously been sailing close to land; that the sea was full of islands, and that consequently such currents were entirely possible; also that even the reckoning itself had failed.

Another argument from which it was to be infallibly concluded that we were under the lee of the land and not far from it was furnished by the frequent occurrence of marine animals which are not commonly met with in the open sea. It is known that the heart of the hair seals has the so-called *foramen ovale* as well as the *ductus arteriosus Botalli* open, in consequence of which these animals are enabled to remain a long time under water and,

* This very current, however, in connection with the other circumstances, should have caused Steller to reflect that it did not come from the continuous coast of a mainland but from a channel or from several straits between islands.—P.

[56] How eminently valid this criticism was is evidenced by the error in longitude which actually did result, amounting in the case of the *St. Peter* to about 6° and in the case of the *St. Paul* to over 11° (see, on this topic, Vol. 1, pp. 210, 276, 308, 322, and 332). (J)

as fish-eaters, to secure their food in all parts of the ocean, even at a considerable distance from land. Nevertheless, it has been observed that they seldom venture ten miles from land and never more than twenty. As we frequently caught sight of seals, it might easily have been surmised that land must be near.

The constant occurrence of the Kamchatkan sea beaver,* or more correctly sea otter, furnished a still stronger proof. This animal lives solely and entirely on crustaceans and shellfish and cannot, because of the structure of its heart, remain under water more than two minutes without inhaling air, and it is therefore compelled to keep close to the shore, as it is not able to look for food at depths of sixty to a hundred fathoms, nor would it find any even if it were able to. From all this evidence the conclusion was inevitable that land was near. As the strongest evidence that America was nearest to the east of and opposite the coast of Kamchatka between 51° and 56°, I have always regarded the fact that in Kamchatka the sea otter is found in this latitude only, in the sea which is therefore called the Beaver Sea, but not farther north nor farther south.** Otherwise there would seem to be no good reason why the sea otter should not also be found as far north as 57° or 58°, about Olyutora, or as far south as 49° or 50°, among the farther Kurile Islands, since in America we met with these animals almost in latitude 60°, in the neighborhood of Cape St. Elias, [and since] it is also well known that they occur in latitude 10° on the American coast, and even in Brazil, from which country Marggraf has described them. The fact is that the sea otter is an animal peculiar to America and only a newcomer and stranger in Kamchatka. Owing to the wide expanse of sea and the lack of food it cannot, on account of its organization, get across above 56° north latitude or below 50° south latitude, but only through the so-called Beaver Sea, where in a straight line it may not have more than

* *Lutris* Lin.—P.
** The now discovered chain of islands is a more probable explanation of this coming over of the sea otter from the American seas to the Kamchatkan coast here specified.—P.

twenty miles from shore to shore, a distance it can cover comfortably in thirty-six hours without suffering from hunger.[57]

Moreover, at different times, we saw sitting on the water large flocks of gulls which, particularly in June, always keep close to the coast where the fishes approach the land and ascend the streams from the sea in the greatest number and thus afford them the most abundant food supply. We saw these gulls always fly in a northerly or northwesterly direction until lost to our view. How easy and necessary would it not have been to have convinced oneself of the correctness or incorrectness of such an obvious supposition as to the nearness of land by sailing a few hours in a northerly direction, especially since the constant fogs did not permit a view of more than a few miles, while the winds on the outward trip were so fair that we could not have wished them better for the accomplishment of a great venture.

I pass over several circumstances which gave enough occasion for conjecture. But while other navigators on expeditions of discovery, such as one reads of in accounts of travels, paid attention to all details and tried to profit by them, in our case on the contrary the biggest and plainest signs and most evident reasons were disregarded and made light of. As a result of this state of affairs we reached land six weeks after leaving Avacha, whereas if we had sailed on a northeast course we might have made it in three or four days, or in ten days at the most if we had followed the course originally agreed on, provided the above-mentioned signs and indications of the nearness of land had been taken

[57] The southern Kurile Islands were so little known that Steller was not aware of the fact that the sea otter at that time was quite common as far south as Yezo, or latitude 45°. Nor can he be blamed for believing that it was the same animal which Marggraf (1610–1644) had described from Brazil. The whole argument is therefore more or less futile. As a matter of fact, the sea otter (*Latax lutris* (Linn.)) is a North Pacific species which in Steller's time occurred all the way from Lower California north along the coast to the Aleutian chain and thence westward to Kamchatka and south to Japan. The greatest gap in the distribution of the sea otter was the stretch of open ocean between Copper Island and Attu, the westernmost of the Aleutian Islands proper, approximately 185 statute miles. (S)

advantage of.* In fact, even on July 16, the Thursday on which the land became for the first time clearly visible, it was as good as decided that, if land were not sighted by July 20, we would return to Avacha because our supply of water was already more than half consumed.

We saw land as early as July 15,[58] but because I was the first to announce it and because forsooth it was not so distinct that a picture could be made of it, the announcement, as usual, was regarded as one of my peculiarities; yet on the following day, in very clear weather, it came into view in the same place. The land was here very much elevated; the mountains,[59] observed extending inland, were so lofty that we could see them quite plainly at sea at a distance of sixteen Dutch miles. I cannot recall having seen higher mountains anywhere in Siberia and

* It is true that under these suppositions islands might have been reached within the time mentioned, but not the mainland of America.—P.

[58] In Yushin's version of the log book there is a statement (Vol. 1, p. 89, 4 P.M. entry) that the course was modified on July 14 toward "the land sighted." This date is according to the astronomic time used by the navigators, which for that hour would correspond to July 13, civil time. In view of the probable position of the *St. Peter* at that hour in latitude 54° 34′ (see "Decision to Change Course," *ibid.*, p. 90), it would have been impossible to see land then or earlier, as in this position the vessel still had to go 190 nautical miles before entering the circle of visibility projecting farthest out to sea in that region, namely that of Mt. St. Elias (see map accompanying George Davidson: The Tracks and Landfalls of Bering and Chirikof on the Northwest Coast of America, San Francisco, 1901; or radius of circle may be computed if altitude is known—in this case 18,008 feet—from the standard formula, e. g. in Hermann Wagner: Lehrbuch der Geographie, 10th edit., Hanover, 1920, p. 95). It is quite probable, however, that in view of her rate of progress (see log book, Vol. 1, p. 92) the *St. Peter* had entered that circle before the end of July 15, civil time (according to which Steller reckoned; see, below, footnote 131), which would bear out Steller's statement. Even the official announcement of the discovery of land at 12.30 P. M. on July 17, astronomic time (July 16, civil time) took place only 12½ hours later, inasmuch as the end of July 15, civil, represents the middle of July 16, astronomic. (J)

[59] Mt. St. Elias and other mountains in that region. For identifications see Vol. 1, pp. 92ff.

Kamchatka. The coast was everywhere much indented and therefore provided with numerous bays and inlets close to the mainland.[60]

Once having determined to tell the truth and be impartial in all things, I must not fail to mention one circumstance which perhaps may not escape the notice of the high authorities but may receive an interpretation different from the actual facts.— It can easily be imagined how happy every one was when land was finally sighted; nobody failed to congratulate the Captain Commander, whom the glory for the discovery mostly concerned. He, however, received it all not only very indifferently and without particular pleasure, but in the presence of all he even shrugged his shoulders while looking at the land. Had the Commander survived and had he intended to take any action against his officers because of their misdoings, they would have been ready to point to his conduct then as evidence of his evil-minded disposition. But the good Captain Commander was much superior to his officers in looking into the future, and in the cabin he expressed himself to me and Mr. Plenisner as follows: "We think now we have accomplished everything, and many go about greatly inflated, but they do not consider where we have reached land, how far we are from home, and what may yet happen; who knows but that perhaps trade winds[61] may arise, which may prevent us from returning? We do not know this country; nor are we provided with supplies for a wintering." —Now that we were close to land it was great fun to listen to the conflicting expressions of great self-conceit and expectations of future reward and pathetic effusions. Some would at once make for the shore and search for a harbor. Others represented this as very dangerous. However, everybody acted for himself, and no one made any representations to the Captain Commander.

[60] The MS reads: "and therefore provided with many islands close to the mainland and with numerous bays and inlets in the mainland itself."

[61] In the sense of persistent winds (see also footnote 144, second paragraph); in the present case, persistent westerly headwinds.

Councils and commissions, that were so often called on shore in case of trivial matters, were neglected now when we had come to the most important business and the culmination of the ten years' Kamchatka Expedition, and it was quite plain that we had nothing in common and nothing to keep us united except that we were locked up together on the same ship.

Since after July 16 more noteworthy happenings occurred daily than during the six preceding weeks, I shall from now on continue my record according to what took place each day.[62]

On the 17th, the wind being light, we gradually drew nearer the land. On Saturday, the 18th, we were so close to it towards evening, that we were enabled to view with the greatest pleasure the beautiful forests close down to the sea, as well as the great level ground in from the shore at the foot of the mountains. The beach itself was flat, level, and, as far as we could observe, sandy. We kept the mainland to the right and sailed northwesterly in order to get behind a high island[63] which consisted of a single mountain covered with spruce trees only. This had to be accomplished by continuous tacking, as the wind was contrary, the coming night being consumed with this.

On Sunday, the 19th, we were opposite the northwestern[64] end of the island, about two miles distant. This morning there arose again a petty quarrel. We had already noticed the day before the channel between the mainland and the island, and the thought occurred at once to me that a notably large stream must be flowing from the land into the channel, the current of which could be observed two miles from shore while the difference in the water could be inferred partly from the floating matter and partly from the lesser salinity; it was consequently my opinion

[62] It will be found helpful in following this record to refer to the daily entries in the log book in Vol. 1, as the log book and Steller's journal often supplement each other. In so doing the overlapping of the astronomical dates used in the log book and the civil dates used by Steller (see, below, footnote 131) should be borne in mind.

[63] Kayak Island.

[64] Northeastern or southwestern?

that an attempt could have been made to enter this channel,[65] where it would have been just as safe to anchor as, if not safer than, in the place under the lee of the island selected on the 20th. It might even have been possible to find a harbor for our ship, with its nine feet draught, in the mouth of the river, which was large enough and therefore probably also deep enough. But the retort I got was, Whether I had been there before and made certain of it? Yet in uncertain things it is better to act on even the slightest indication than for no reason at all and only trusting to good luck.

The day was spent in tacking in order to get close to the island, to enter the large bay seen from the distance, and at the same time to come under the lee of the land. This was also accomplished, with the greatest apprehension, when on Monday the 20th we came to anchor among numerous islands. The outermost of these had to be named Cape St. Elias, because we dropped our anchor under the lee of it on St. Elias' day. For the officers were determined to have a cape on their chart notwithstanding the fact that it was plainly represented to them that an island cannot be called a cape,[66] but that only a noticeable projection of land into the sea in a certain direction can be so designated, the same meaning being conveyed by the Russian word *nos* (nose), while in the present case the island would represent nothing but a detached head or a detached nose.

Orderly management as well as the importance of the matter

[65] As mostly, Steller's observation of physical phenomena was excellent, in thus deducing the presence of the river now called the Bering River and other glacial streams descending from Bering Glacier; the naval officers, however, were correct in their decision to sail around the southern end of Kayak Island, as the channel between it and the mainland, according to the modern chart of the region (U. S. Coast and Geodetic Survey Chart No. 8513; a section reproduced in Fig. 4), shoals to four feet before reaching the mouth of Bering River channel (Okalee Channel). (J)

[66] The officers called the island St. Elias and its southern cape Cape St. Elias (see Vol. 1, p. 96, footnote 36, and map mentioned in *ibid.*, p. 99, footnote 42, i.e. our Fig. 3). The cape is still so called (see Fig. 4). (G)

would now have demanded a harmonious consideration of what ought to be done, how to utilize the time and opportunity to the best advantage, what to explore on shore and how to go about it; furthermore, whether, considering the season and the provisions as well as the distance, the following up of the coast should be continued at this late time of the year, or whether we should winter here, or, finally, try the straight way for home. However, all this was not considered worthy the calling of a council, but everyone kept silent and did as he pleased. Only on one point were all unanimous, viz. that we should take fresh water on board, so that I could not help saying that we had come only for the purpose of bringing American water to Asia.* It was agreed, besides, that the small yawl should be used for the transportation of the water, while the larger one should be given to Master Khitrov with a sufficient crew and ammunition in order that he might explore the country, a task for which he possessed the best qualifications. I asked to be sent with Khitrov, since after all he himself did not know everything, but in spite of his making the same request permission was refused. At first an attempt was made to scare me with dreadful tales of murder, to which I answered that I had never been so womanish as to fear danger and that I could not guess why I should not be allowed to go ashore, especially since that was in the line of my principal work, my calling, and my duty and that it was my determination to serve the Crown to the best of my ability in the future, as I had done in the past; moreover, that, if for reprehensible reasons I were not given the permission, I would report this action in the terms it deserved. For this I was called a wild man, who would not let himself be held back from business even when treated to chocolate, which was just then being prepared. Seeing now that

* It is incomprehensible that there was no thought of a real exploration and taking possession of the land discovered; one might almost conjecture that the general instructions issued must have been insufficient, or that in so distant parts all subordination and discipline had vanished.—P.

[As to the instructions issued, see Vol. 1, pp. 29-32, especially the end of Article 6 and Article 13.]

FIG. 1—Reduced facsimile of fol. 15 of the MS copy of Steller's journal located by F. A. Golder in 1917 in the archives of the Academy of Sciences at Petrograd. (The MS consists of 111 leaves besides the title page.)

The equivalent of this section is included between the words "the larger one should be given to Master Khitrov," p. 37, and "ship's doctor and physician in ordinary, since with an," p. 41, of the present translation.

mein fester Wille sey, der Krone wie bisher, also auch
ferner nach Vermögen zu dienen; ja daß ich, wo man
mich aus nachtheiligen Absichten nicht ablassen wollte,
dieses Verfahren unter dem verdienten Titel angeben
würde: so nannte man mich einen wilden Menschen,
der sich auch nicht durch Bewirthung mit Chocolate, die
eben damals in der Arbeit war, von Verrichtungen wollte abhalten lassen.   Weil ich nun sahe, daß man mich
mit Gewalt und wider meinen Willen zu unverantwort-
licher Verabsäumung meiner Dienste zwingen wollte,
sezte ich endlich alle Achtung aus den Augen, und betete
ein besondres Gebet, wodurch sich der Herr Commandeur sogleich erweichen ließ, mich mit den Wasserträgern,
ohne die geringste Hülfe, und ohne einen Menschen, als
den Casaken Thomas Lepechin, so ich selbst mitgenom-
men hatte, zuzugeben, nach dem Lande fahren zu lassen.
Beym Abschiede vom Fahrzeug machte er noch eine Pro-
be, wie weit ich Schimpf und Ernst verstünde, indem
er mir mit Trompeten nachblasen ließ; da ich denn ohne
mich zu bedenken die Sache eben so annahm, als sie be-
fohlen war. Ich sahe jezt mehr als zu klar, warum man
mich mitzureisen hatte überreden wollen. Ich sollte nemlich mit meiner Person einen Punkt der Instruction aus-
füllen, auf welchen man sonst die Antwort schuldig ge-
blieben wäre, nemlich was die Untersuchung der Mine-
ralien durch gewisse, dazu bestandne Personen anbelang-
te. Dergleichen Leute aus Catrinenburg zu fordern hatte
man nun seit acht Jahren vergessen, und der in Ochozk
sich aufhaltende Probiermeister Hartepol war nach Ja-
kuzk, den Capitain Spangberg zu begleiten abgelassen,
so daß man ihn bey der Abreise nicht mitnehmen konnte.
So sollte ich auch, nur dem Namen nach, der ganzen
Sache ein größeres Ansehn geben, und übrigens die
Stelle eines Schif-und Leibarztes vertreten, weil man
sich mit einem Unterwundarzt zu schlecht versehen sahe.

FIG. 2—Facsimile of page from the published version of Steller's journal, as
edited by Pallas (*Neue Nordische Beyträge*, Vol. 5, 1793, p. 158, or book
form, p. 30), corresponding to the lower three-quarters of the section from
the MS journal reproduced on the opposite page.

it was the intention to force me against my will to inexcusable neglect of my duty, I finally put all respect aside and prayed a particular prayer,[67] by which the Commander was at once mollified so as to let me go ashore with the water carriers, without any assistance whatever and with no other person but the cossack Thomas Lepekhin, whom I myself had brought with me. On my leaving the ship he again made a test as to how far I could distinguish between mockery and earnest, by causing the trumpets to be sounded after me, at which, without hesitation,[68] I accepted the affair in the spirit in which it was ordered.[69] By this time I saw only too clearly why he had wanted to persuade me to go along. I was to fulfill in my person one point of the instructions,[70] in regard to which it would otherwise have been impossible to give an accounting, namely that which related to the investigation of the mineral resources by certain properly qualified persons. For eight years it had been forgotten to requisition them from Ekaterinburg,[71] and the assayer Hartepol, who was staying at Okhotsk, had been sent to Yakutsk in order to accompany Spanberg, so that at the departure he could not be taken along. Under the circumstances it was intended that I, though only in name,

[67] The meaning of this passage is scarcely doubtful. It is plain that Steller was very much wrought up by the refusal to let him go ashore, and a few lines above he had threatened to report the officers for their action. Lauridsen (Vitus Bering, Danish edit., p. 136; American edit., p. 151) therefore—and probably correctly—regards the "particular prayer" as a euphemism for an oath. (S)

Steller, in his report to the Senate (for reference, see, above, p. 6, footnote 5), said that he swore at Bering, "Upotrebil uzhe zhestokiya slova" (I now used harsh words). (G)

[68] The published version has "ohne mich zu bedenken," without hesitation. The MS has "ohne mich zu bedancken," without returning thanks!

[69] In the MS this sentence is completed by the clause, "as I had never been a braggart, nor would I care for such [attentions] even if they were really intended to honor me."

[70] See Vol. I, p. 31, Article II.

[71] Ekaterinburg, in the Urals, was founded by Peter in 1723 and named in honor of the Empress. This city soon became an important mining center. (G)

should confer upon the whole affair a greater distinction and at the same time fill the office of ship's doctor and physician in ordinary, since with an assistant surgeon it was considered that [the expedition] was too poorly supplied.

The events of the day consequently relate to four distinct parties: Half of the command, including all of the officers except the master [Khitrov],[72] remained on board as watch, busying themselves with hauling out the empty and stowing away the filled water casks. With another party I was sent off after water, to make watery observations, while others were out on a windy expedition.

As soon as I, with only the protection and assistance of my own cossack, had landed on the island[73] and realized how scant and precious was the time at my disposal, I seized every oppor-

[72] The words in this paragraph up to this point, except "Half of the command," do not occur in the MS. They are editorial additions by Pallas.

[73] The landing place and other points of Steller's route were identified by me during a visit to Kayak Island on June 30, 1922. This visit was made as a side trip while I was a member of the party which accompanied the Assistant Secretary of Commerce on a voyage in the U. S. Coast Guard vessel *Mojave* to examine into the conditions of the fisheries and other industries of Alaska. From Cordova, at which port the *Mojave* had called, Katalla was reached by motor boat. From here another motor boat was used for the trip to the island. Six hours, from 6 P. M. to midnight, were spent on the island, during which the western shore was followed on foot northeastward for 2 statute miles from our landing place.

This landing place was chosen after inquiring of the owner of the boat, a local resident, where a ship wanting to take in water would be most likely to find it. He pointed out the mouth of a creek about 7 statute miles from the southern end of the island (see reproduction of coast chart, Fig. 4, where marked "Watering Place"). On landing there we found a small stream of clear, cold water rushing out of a dark wood of spruce (Figs. 9 and 10). These conditions, together with the fact that there is no other suitable watering place along this stretch of shore and that this point is about 6 versts, or 4 miles, from a hill descending abruptly into the sea, all of which closely agrees with Steller's statements (see, below, pp. 47 and 49), makes it highly probable that the mouth of the creek was the spot where Steller landed. With this point established, it was possible to identify other points on Steller's route. (S)

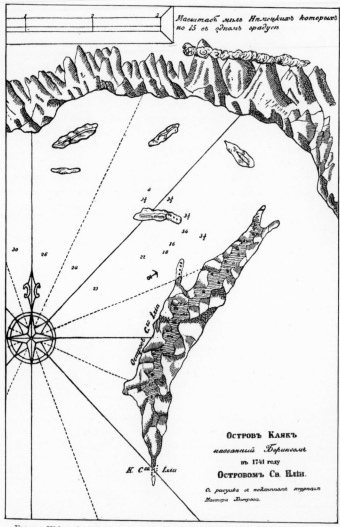

Fig. 3—Khitrov's sketch map of St. Elias (Kayak) Island (see Vol. 1, p. 99), reproduced from Sokolov, *Zapiski Hydrogr. Depart.*, Vol. 9, St. Petersburg, 1851.

Note the representation of the mountains as seen from the side, laid down on the ground plan of the coasts. The cloud-capped mountains on the mainland are Mt. St. Elias and adjacent peaks.

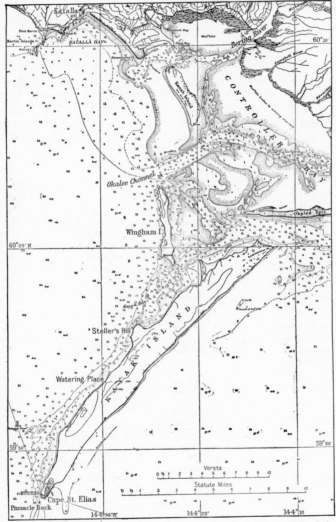

FIG. 4—Modern map of Kayak Island (section from U. S. Coast and Geodetic Survey Chart No. 8513). Scale, 1: 345,000.

tunity to accomplish as much as possible with the greatest possible dispatch. I struck out in the direction of the mainland in the hopes of finding human beings and habitations. I had not gone more than a verst along the beach before I ran across signs of people and their doings. Under a tree I found an old piece of a log hollowed out in the shape of a trough, in which, a couple of hours before, the savages, for lack of pots and vessels, had cooked their meat by means of red-hot stones,[74] just as the Kamchadals did formerly.[75] The bones, some of them with bits of meat and showing signs of having been roasted at the fire, were scattered about where the eaters had been sitting. I could see plainly that these bones belonged to no sea animal, but to a land animal, and I thought myself justified in regarding them as reindeer bones,[76] though no such animal was observed on the island but was probably brought there from the mainland. There were also strewn about the remains of *yukola*, or pieces of dried fish, which, as in Kamchatka, has to serve the purpose of bread at all meals. There were also great numbers of very large scallops[77] over eight inches across, also blue mussels similar to those found in Kamchatka and, no doubt, eaten raw as the custom is there. In various shells, as on dishes, I found sweet grass*

[74] There are of course no signs of the fireplace now, especially as the shore at this point is being constantly undermined by wave action. (S)

[75] Thus in the published version—"nach vormaliger Kamtschadalischer Art." The MS has "nach anderwerts beschriebener Kamtschatkischer Art," "just like the Kamchadals, as described elsewhere." The reference is to Steller's "Beschreibung von dem Lande Kamtschatka," still in manuscript only when he wrote these words and not published until 1774.

[76] Steller was probably correct in identifying the bones found as those of reindeer, or caribou. The region is a typical caribou country. The species is probably *Rangifer stonei* Allen, originally described from the Kenai Peninsula. (S)

[77] "Jacobsmuscheln," Jacob's mussel, a scallop (*Pecten caurinus* Gould). The blue mussel mentioned immediately after is *Mytilus californianus* Conrad. The true "Jacob's mussel" is *Pecten jacobaeus*. (S)

* *Sladkaya trava* [sweet grass in Russian] are the peeled stalks exuding a sugary substance in drying.—P. [See the next footnote, second paragraph.]

FIG. 5—Kayak Island seen from the southeast. Cape St. Elias is cloud-capped. The detached rock is Pinnacle Rock (see Fig. 4).

FIG. 6—Cape St. Elias and Pinnacle Rock seen from the west.

FIG. 7—The western shore of south-central Kayak Island seen from the west. The hill in the left background is the one Steller climbed, which it is here proposed (footnote 92) to call Steller's Hill.

(Figs. 5 and 6 from photos by The Alaska Shop, Cordova; Fig. 7 from photo by L. Stejneger, June 30, 1922.)

Fig. 8—Rock fall on western shore of Kayak Island, a mile and a half south-west of the base of Steller's Hill, seen in the middle distance. Wingham Island faintly visible in the left background.

Fig. 9—Mouth of a creek on the western shore of Kayak Island, presumably at the spot where Steller landed on July 20 (O. S.), 1741 (marked "Watering Place" on Fig. 4).

Fig. 10—The same spot closer by.

(From photos by L. Stejneger, June 30, 1922.)

completely prepared in Kamchadal fashion, on which water
seemed to have been poured in order to extract the sweetness.[78]
I discovered further [not far from the fireplace][79] beside the
tree, on which there still were the live coals, a wooden apparatus
for making fire,[80] of the same nature as those used in Kamchatka.
The tinder, however, which the Kamchadals make from a species of grass, was here different, namely a species of fountain

[78] The MS from here on is confused, and Pallas has taken considerable
liberty in editing it so as to make sense. The person copying Steller's
original seems to have transposed part of the matter, inasmuch as the
argument derived from the fire-making apparatus precedes the finding
of it. (S)

This argument, which Pallas has abridged in the passage below, reading in translation "From all this I think . . . in their miserable
craft," in the MS is inserted at this point, between the sentence ending
with "in order to extract the sweetness" and the one beginning with
"I discovered further." The meaning of the first part of this argument
might possibly be rendered thus: "This grass is known to the Kamchadals
as *kattch*, to the Russians as sweet grass, and is a true species of Sphondylium. The outer part of the grass is scraped with mussel shells; in this
as well as in other ways of preparing and using it for food the Kamchadals
and Americans are one. In this respect they differ from the Tungus and
the Deer Koryaks (near neighbors of the Kamchadals), who do not know
about the grass and do without it, just as, for lack of steel, they do
without steel in making fire." Steller gives a detailed description of sweet
grass, or *sladkaya trava*, in his "Beschreibung von dem Lande Kamtschatka," 1774, pp. 84–87. Stejneger pictures and describes it from
Bering Island (*Bull. U. S. Fish Comm.*, Vol. 16, 1896. p. 25 and Pl. 15a);
likewise Suvorov in his "Komandorskie Ostrova," 1912 (p. 79 and
Fig. 13). It is the cow parsnip, *Heracleum lanatum* Michx. The fact that
the pre-Linnaean name of the European species was *Sphondylium* accounts for the reference in the MS.

The second part of the argument is represented by Pallas' sentence
beginning "But if this is so" and by the statements translated below in
footnote 82. (G)

[79] The bracketed words are in the MS only and help clarify the meaning.

[80] The MS here has this additional characterization: "with which,
for lack of steel, they are in the habit of making fire by friction, just as
in Kamtchatka and other places in America,"—in other words, a fire
drill.

moss (*Alga fontinalis*),[81] which was bleached white by the sun and of which I have kept a sample to be forwarded.—From all this I think I may conclude that the inhabitants of this American coast are of the same origin as the Kamchadals,[82] with whom they agree completely in such peculiar customs and utensils, particularly the preparation of the sweet grass, which have not been communicated even to the Siberian natives nearest to Kamchatka, for instance the Tunguses and Koryaks. But if this is so, then it may also be conjectured that America extends farther westward and, opposite Kamchatka, is much nearer in the north, since in view of such a great distance as we traveled of at least 500 miles, it is not credible that the Kamchadals would have been able to get there in their miserable craft.

The chopped-down trees, as I came across them here and there, were miscut with many dull blows in such a way that in all likelihood the cutting of trees must be done by these savages, as in Kamchatka, with stone or bone axes similar to those used by the Germans of old[83] and known today as "thunderbolts."

[81] I owe to the kindness of Mr. R. S. Williams of the New York Botanical Garden a note from Dr. M. A. Howe to the effect that "*Alga fontinalis*, etc. Bauhin is quoted by Linnaeus as a synonym of *Conferva glomerata*, now known as *Cladophora glomerata*, a freshwater filamentous alga." Mr. Williams in addition expressed the opinion that some species of Sphagnum must have been referred to by Steller as being used for tinder. In this opinion he is upheld by Dr. Howe and Dr. Setchel. The latter has collected algae along the Alaskan coast, and he informed Mr. Williams that *Cladophora* does not occur in sufficient quantities to be collected for tinder and that it is doubtful if it could be used as such, even if obtainable in quantity. (S)

[82] Pallas completely ignores Steller's concurrent argument from the identity of the fire-making apparatus given towards the end of the transposed passage in the MS: "This is an almost certain proof that this invention came from Kamchatka, consequently that both peoples formerly had intercourse with each other or even that this people [the American] is one with the Kamchatkan and has emigrated from it." Steller finally concludes: "Be that as it may, most of the American objects and inventions are identical with or only slightly different from the Kamchatkan, or Asiatic, ones." (S)

[83] The MS has in addition "before the discovery of iron."

After having made a brief examination of all this I pushed on farther for about three versts, where I found a path leading into the very thick and dark forest which skirted the shore closely.[84] I held a brief consultation with my cossack, who had a loaded gun, besides a knife and ax, as to what we should do in case we met one or more persons, and I commanded him to do nothing whatever without my orders. I myself was only armed with a Yakut *palma* (dagger)[85] for the purpose of digging up rocks and plants. No sooner had we taken this path than I noticed that the natives had tried to cover it up but had been prevented by our quick approach and as a result had made it only more conspicuous. We saw many trees recently bared of bark and conjectured that they must have used it for houses or *ambars*[86] and that these must be near by, since in whatever direction we looked there was no lack of fine forests. However, as the first

[84] This place was identified during my visit in 1922 as the point where the shore changes its direction from northeast to north-northwest (see chart, Fig. 4) in swinging around the hill that projects into the sea. (S)

[85] Pallas uses the German "Dolch," dagger, as an equivalent. The word *palma* seems to be of Tungus origin (see M. A. Czaplicka: Aboriginal Siberia: A Study in Social Anthropology, Oxford, 1914, p. 360), signifying "a long knife with a wooden handle." In R. Maak's "Vilyuiskii okrug Yakutskoi oblasti," St. Petersburg, 1887, Vol. 3, p. xvi, it is stated that the *palma*, or *batas*, as it is also called, is a large knife, distinguished by its long handle, used by the Tungus in bear hunting. An illustration is given (*op. cit.*, Pl. 9, Fig. 14) one-tenth natural size, which would make the handle of the specimen figured about 17 inches and the blade about 11 inches. A copy of this illustration is presented herewith (Fig. 11). The *palma* with which Steller, when first landing on Bering Island, killed a large number of blue foxes (see, below, footnote 323) is obviously the same as that he used on Kayak Island.

According to Admiral Ferdinand von Wrangell (Expedition to the Polar Sea, New York, 1841, p. 167) the Kolyma Yakuts also used the word *pal'ma* for their large hunting knife.

FIG. 11

I am under obligation to Dr. T. Michelson of the Bureau of American Ethnology for having put me on the track of the references in the first paragraph. (S)

[86] Russian word meaning storehouses or sheds.

trail broke up into a number of paths through the forest, we explored some of them for a little distance into the wood, and after half an hour we came to a spot covered with cut grass. I pushed the grass aside at once and found underneath a cover consisting of rocks; and when this was also removed we came to some tree bark, which was laid on poles in an oblong rectangle three fathoms in length and two in width. All this covered a cellar two fathoms deep in which were the following objects: (1) *lukoshkas*, or utensils made of bark, one and a half ells[87] high, filled with smoked fish of a species of Kamchatkan salmon at Okhotsk called *nerka* in the Tungus language but in Kamchatka known by the common name *krasnaya ryba*.[88] It was so cleanly and well prepared that I have never seen it as good in Kamchatka, and it also was much superior in taste to the Kamchatkan;[89] (2) a quantity of *sladkaya trava* [or sweet grass,] from which liquor is distilled; (3) different kinds of plants, whose outer skin had been removed like hemp, which I took for nettles, which grow here in profusion and perhaps are used, as in Kamchatka, for making fish nets; (4) the dried inner bark from the larch or spruce tree done up in rolls and dried; the same is used as food in time of famine, not only in Kamchatka but all through Siberia and even in Russia as far as Khlynov and elsewhere on the Vyatka;[90] (5) large bales of thongs made of seaweed which, by making a test, we found to be of uncommon strength and firmness.[91]

Under these I found also some arrows in size greatly exceeding

[87] The MS has 1½ arshins. This would be about 42 inches.

[88] The MS has *nerka;* the Pallas text has *sterka;* the former is correct. *Krasnaya ryba* (red fish) is the usual name in Kamchatka for the red salmon (*Oncorhynchus nerka* (Walbaum)). (S)

[89] The position of this sentence in the MS is as here given; in the published version it is under (2), but probably incorrectly so.

[90] The MS reads "as far as Khlynov or Vyatka." In Steller's time Khlynov and Vyatka were two neighboring towns; in 1781 they, with two others, were combined to form the present city of Vyatka, on the river of that name, in about lat. 58° N. and long. 50° E. By "as far as Vyatka" is probably meant "westward as far as Vyatka." (G)

[91] The "thongs" of seaweed were probably *Nereocystis priapus* (Gmelin). According to Saunders, the Harriman Expedition, although

those in Kamchatka and approaching the arrows of the Tunguses and Tatars, scraped very smooth and painted black, so that one might well conjecture that the natives possessed iron instruments and knives.

In spite of my fear of being attacked in the cellar I continued my search but, discovering nothing more, took away with me, as proof, two bundles of fish, the arrows, a wooden implement for making fire, tinder, a bundle of thongs of seaweed, bark, and grass and sent them by my cossack to the place where the water was being taken on, with instructions to bring them to the Captain Commander; at the same time I asked once more for two or three men to help me further in my investigations of nature; I also had those on shore warned not to feel too secure but to be well on their guard. I then covered over the cellar as it had been and proceeded, now all alone, with my project of investigating the noteworthy features of the three kingdoms of nature until my cossack should return. However, when I had gone about six versts, I came to a steep rock extending so far into the sea beyond the beach that it was impossible to go farther.[92] I determined to climb the rock and after much diffi-

keeping a constant watch for *Macrocystis pyrifera* (Turner), did not see this species north of Sitka (Harriman Alaska Expedition, Vol. 5, 1904, p. 195). (S)

[92] This rock, later in the journal referred to as a mountain, was identified during my 1922 visit as the hill about 250–300 feet high which is shown on the chart (Fig. 4) as a bold projection from the western shore of the island in 59° 56′ N. and which appears in the background of two of the photographs (Figs. 7 and 8). Although I was not able to approach its base nearer than a mile and a half, because of a comparatively recent rock fall (Fig. 8) which made progress along the shore impossible at this point, the general topographical relations and the agreement of distances with those given by Steller made the identification practically certain.

This hill is without a name. It would seem eminently fitting that it should bear the name of the naturalist who first set foot here on Alaskan soil, and it is herewith proposed, as was previously done in regard to a similar feature on Bering Island (*Deutsche Geogr. Blätter*, Bremen, Vol. 8, 1885, p. 226 and Pl. 5), that this piece of classic ground in the history of American discovery be called "Steller's Hill" (the name has thus been inserted on our map, Fig. 4). (S)

culty reached the top, where I discovered that the east side was steep as a wall and that it was impossible to proceed farther. I therefore turned south in the hope of getting to the other side of the island in order to follow the beach there to the channel and thus investigate my theory regarding the existence there of a river and harbor. However, as I descended the mountain, which was covered with a thick and dark forest, without finding any trace of a path, I saw that I could not get through here. Considering at the same time that it would be impossible for my cossack to find me, also that I was too far away from the others in case something should happen, and that it might be impossible for me to return before nightfall, not to mention other dangers, which I should not have feared had I had the least assistance of companions, I climbed the mountain again and looked once more sorrowfully at the barrier to my investigations, with real regret over the action of those who had in their hands the direction of such important matters, for which nevertheless all of them had let themselves be rewarded with money and honors.

When I was once more on the top of the mountain and turned my eyes towards the mainland to take a good look at least at that country on which I was not vouchsafed to employ my endeavors more fruitfully, I noticed smoke some versts away[93] ascending from a charming hill covered with spruce forest, so that I could now entertain the certain hope of meeting with people and learning from them the data I needed for a complete report. For that reason I returned in great haste and went back, loaded with my collections, to the place where I had landed. Through the men who were just ready to hurry back to the ship in the boat I informed the Captain Commander and asked him for the small yawl and a few men for a couple of hours. Dead tired, I made in the meantime descriptions on the beach of the rarer plants which I was afraid might wither and was delighted to be able to test out the excellent water for tea.

[93] The MS reads "one verst away"; according to this version the location of the smoke must perforce still have been on Kayak Island.

In an hour or so I received the patriotic and courteous reply that I should betake myself on board quickly or they would leave me ashore without waiting for me.—I reflected that God gives to each one the place and the opportunity to do that which he is ordered to do, so as to enable one to present one's services favorably to the highest authorities and after long waiting and untold expenses to the Empress [i. e. Government] work out one's destinies. However, as matters now stand, it is probable that at our departure we all saw Russia for the last time, since under the present circumstances it is impossible to expect the divine help on the return voyage, if wind and weather were to become as hostile [toward us] as we have been to the general object of the expedition and thereby to our own good fortune.—However, since there was now no time left for moralizing, only enough to scrape together as much as possible before our fleeing the country, and as evening was already nearing, I sent my cossack out to shoot some rare birds that I had noticed, while I once more started off to the westward, returning at sunset with various observations and collections.—Here I was given once more the strict command that, unless I came on board this time, no more notice would be taken of me. I consequently betook myself with what I had collected to the ship and there, to my great astonishment, was treated to chocolate.—

Although I did not need to trouble myself for the benefit of anybody except those who were capable of judging what I was doing, I nevertheless showed some of the objects and made known my ideas about various things, but only a single one of these was accepted. Namely, an iron kettle, a pound of tobacco, a Chinese pipe, and a piece of Chinese silk were sent to the cellar, but in return the latter was plundered to such an extent that, if we should come again to these parts, the natives would certainly run away even faster or they would show themselves as hostile as they themselves had been treated, especially if it should occur to them to eat or drink the tobacco, the correct use of which probably could be as little known to them as the pipe itself.—A couple of knives or hatchets, the use of which was quite obvious, would have aroused the interest of these savages much more.[94]   But to this it was objected that such presents might be regarded as a sign of hostility, as if the intention were to declare war. How much more likely was it, particularly if they attempted to use the tobacco in the wrong way, for them to conclude that we had intended to poison them! On the other hand, we learned later how gladly the savages had accepted a few knives from Captain Chirikov[95] and how eager they were to have more.

I had been on the ship scarcely an hour when Khitrov with his party of about fifteen men also returned in the great boat and made the following report:[96] He had discovered among the islands lying close to the mainland a harbor where one could anchor without any danger. Although he had seen no human beings on land, he had nevertheless come across a small dwelling built of wood, the walls of which were so smooth[97] that it seemed as if they had been planed and in fact as if it had been done with cutting tools.[98] Out of this building he brought with him various tangible tokens, for instance, a wooden vessel, such as is made in Russia of linden bark and used as a box; a stone which perhaps, for lack of something better, served as a whetstone, on which were seen streaks of copper,[99] as if the savages,

[94] Sarychev (Voyage, St. Petersburg, 1802, Vol. 2, pp. 52–53; English edit., London, 1806–07, Vol. 2, p. 25) relates that the natives near Nuchek told him that an expedition like Bering's came to Kayak and that the people of the ship came ashore and left some knives (see also Vol. 1, p. 98, footnote 38). In the account of this incident in the log book (Vol. 1, p. 97, 4 P. M. entry) and also in Khitrov's report (ibid., p. 99) it is stated that two knives were ordered to be left in the cellar.   (G)

[95] See the journal of the St. Paul (Vol. 1, p. 304).

[96] Khitrov's report is printed in Vol. 1, p. 99. In the log book (ibid., p. 97, 9 P. M. entry) there is also a brief account of his reconnaissance.

[97] The MS has "the walls of which were so smooth on the inside."

[98] Instead of "and in fact as if it had been done with cutting tools" the MS reads "wherefore it would almost appear that they have instruments of iron and must know the use and working of iron."

[99] The stone on which Steller thought he recognized some stains of copper was probably a whetstone which had been used on some copper

like the ancient Siberian tribes, possessed cutting tools of copper;[100] further a hollow ball of hard-burned clay, about two inches in diameter, containing a pebble[101] which I regarded as a toy for small children; and finally a paddle and the tail of a blackish gray fox.

These, then, are all our achievements and observations, and these not even from the mainland, on which none of us set foot, but only from an island which seemed to be three miles long and a half mile wide[102] and the nearest to the mainland (which here forms a large bay studded with many islands) and separated from it by a channel less than half a mile wide. The only reason why we did not attempt to land on the mainland is a sluggish obstinacy and a dull fear of being attacked by a handful of unarmed and still more timid savages, from whom there was no reason to expect either friendship or hostility, and a cowardly homesickness which they probably thought might be excused, especially if those high in authority would pay no more attention to the testimony of the malcontents than did the commanding officers themselves. The time here spent in investigation bears

---

implement. It is, however, possible that the whetstone originally contained pyrite or chalcopyrite, which Steller mistook for native copper. Some native copper was obtained by the coast natives by trade with the interior natives. This copper came from two localities, one at the head of the White River and the other in the Chitina basin, tributary to the Copper River. In 1899 I met a party of natives searching for native copper nuggets on Kletsandek Creek, tributary to the upper White River. They used caribou horns for digging in the gravel banks of the streams. (B)

[100] The reference to the whetstone is in the MS here amplified as follows: "from which I concluded that their instruments, like those of the Kalmuks and the Asiatic Tatars of Siberia in former times, must be of copper, because the smelting of an iron ore so rich in copper requires more intelligence and experience than one could expect these people to have, apt as it is to ruin the best smelting ovens."

[101] The MS has in addition: "making a noise when the ball was shaken."

[102] German miles are meant. For the true dimensions and locational relationships see Fig. 4.

an arithmetical ratio to the time used in fitting out: ten years the preparations for this great undertaking lasted, and ten[103] hours were devoted to the work itself. Of the mainland we have a sketch on paper; of the country itself an imperfect idea, based upon what could be discovered on the island and upon conjectures.

What can be said from comparison and observations at a distance may be summed up about as follows: The American continent (on this side), as far as the climate is concerned, is notably better than that of the extreme northeastern part of Asia.[104] For, although the land, wherever it faces the sea, whether we looked at it from near or far, consists of amazingly high mountains,[105] most of which had the peaks covered with perpetual snow, yet these mountains, in comparison with those of Asia, are of a much better nature and character. The Asiatic mountains are thoroughly broken up and long since deprived of their coherency, consequently too loose for the circulation of mineral gases and devoid of all inner heat, accordingly also without precious

[103] The MS reads "20 hours." According to the log of the *St. Peter* (Vol. 1, pp. 96 and 97) Khitrov was out from the sixth morning hour to the ninth evening hour—about 15 hours; the yawl (with Steller on board) from the tenth morning hour to presumably the same time in the evening (Steller says, p. 51, above, "at sunset")—about 11 hours. The *St. Peter* was at anchor from the sixth morning hour to the seventh morning hour of the next day—about 25 hours.

[104] Steller, though he speaks of "the extreme northeastern part of Asia," in fact refers to the Kamchatka Peninsula and not to the Chukchi Peninsula, which is actually the northeastern part of Asia. Had he compared the Chukchi Peninsula on the Siberian side of Bering Strait with the Seward Peninsula on the Alaskan side he would have found the physical conditions very much the same. He saw neither of these regions. (B)

[105] Steller refers to the high mountains of the St. Elias region, which is the part of Alaska he had best opportunity to see. The mountains of the Alaska Peninsula and Aleutian Islands, which he had some glimpses of, have somewhat similar topography and vegetation to those of the Kamchatka Peninsula. (B)

metals.[106] On the other hand the American mountains are solid; not naked rocks covered with moss but everywhere with good black soil,[107] and therefore not, as are the former, barren, with stunted dwarf trees among the rocks, but densely covered to the highest peaks with the finest trees; also they are decked with short grass and herbs, some succulent, some drier, but not with moss, marsh vegetation, and water plants.[108] The springs, of which I discovered so many, flow out of the valleys at the base of the mountains, and not as in Siberia everywhere among the rocks, often up to the summits and in stagnant hollows.[109] The plants are about the same size and appearance whether found on the summit of the mountains or lower down, owing to the equally distributed interior heat and moisture. In Asia, on the other hand, the plants are often so different according to their station that one is tempted to make different species of the same plant if one is not mindful of this general difference, because a plant which in the valley is two ells high often on the mountains reappears scarcely half a foot high.—In America on the 60th parallel one sees most beautiful forests directly on the shore, while in latitude 51° in Kamchatka willow and alder bushes only begin 20 versts from the sea, birch woods not nearer than 30 to 40 versts, not to mention that no conifers are found there but are first seen 60 versts inland from the mouth of the Kamchatka River.[110] In latitude 62°, for instance from Anadyrsk

[106] The student of the history of science will be interested in these and other obsolete views, such as that immediately below on the geothermal control of plant distribution (see also footnote 113), expressed by Steller in this summary of the physical geography of Kayak Island.

The clause in the next sentence, "with stunted dwarf trees among the rocks," in the MS occurs at this point but in the fuller form of "without trees or vegetation, except here and there among the rocks a few low and hardy shrubs." (J)

[107] The MS reads: "their rocks not covered with moss but with good black soil."

[108] The MS here has "as in Asia."

[109] In the MS the second half of the sentence reads: "and not as in Siberia everywhere, even on the summits of mountains and as lakes."

[110] In about 56½° N. (see Vol. i, Pl. I).

on, no tree is to be met with for 300 or 400 versts inland. I therefore hold that continuous land must extend northwards from Cape St. Elias to about 70° or farther,[111] which by furnishing shelter against the north wind promotes the fertility of the coast, which moreover, towards the east, is protected by the mountains.[112] On the other hand the Kamchatkan shores, particularly on the Sea of Penzhina, are directly exposed to the north winds; while the eastern side is somewhat better provided with trees, because of the protection of the Chukchi Promontory.[113]—Owing to the milder temperature it also comes about that in America the fishes go up from the sea[114] earlier than in Kamchatka. On July 20 we found there the fish supply already stored, while in Kamchatka this, the day of St. Elias, indicates the time only for the beginning of good fishing. That plants which only start to bloom in Kamchatka at this time already have mature seed here in America is only a partial argument, because in the northern regions the usually longer days and the sudden great heat and dryness contribute greatly to this result, as I had already observed in Yakutsk in 1740.

Whoever stops to consider how much one man, without assistance, can accomplish in ten[115] hours on a small island will

[111] It is of interest to note the remarkable accuracy of this deduction of Steller's.

[112] In the MS the words following "farther" read as follows: "which, because of its protection as well as its being sheltered from the west, causes this luxuriant growth of forest."

[113] The climate of Kamchatka is somewhat colder than that of Alaska lying between the same parallels of latitude. Steller's theory that the geologic constitution of the mountains directly controls the distribution of vegetation is without merit. Kamchatka lies within the region of permanent ground frost, which is not true of the Pacific littoral of Alaska. This to some extent influences the distribution of springs. The comparisons between the soil and vegetation of Kamchatka and the part of Alaska which he knew best are in general correct. The differences are largely due to differences of climate. (B)

[114] The MS has in addition "into the rivers."

[115] The MS here also reads "10 hours" although it reads "20 hours" above (see footnote 103).

easily see that my failure to discover any minerals is not due to carelessness or laziness on my part. I confess freely that I observed nothing else than sand and gray rock. It is also well known that close to the beach Nature is neither able nor accustomed to produce anything outside of marcasites and pyrites.[116]

Of fruit-bearing shrubs and plants I only met with a new and elsewhere unknown species of raspberry[117] in great abundance, although not yet quite ripe. This fruit on account of its great size, shape, and delicious taste had well deserved that a few bushes of it should have been taken along in a box with soil and sent to St. Petersburg to be further propagated. It is not my fault that space for such was begrudged, since as a protester I myself took up too much space already.—Such well-known berries[118] as the *Chamaecerasi*, red and black whortleberries, the scurvy berry, *Empetrum*, and such like were here as plentiful as

[116] The geology of Kayak Island is not well known. The formation of the island is probably chiefly graywacke and slate, with some igneous rocks (see G. C. Martin: Geology and Mineral Resources of the Controller Bay Region, Alaska, *U. S. Geol. Survey Bull. 335*, 1908). I am unable to understand Steller's reference to the occurrence of marcasite, etc., on sea beaches. (B)

[117] The unknown species of raspberry is undoubtedly *Rubus spectabilis* Pursh, which according to Funston (*Contr. U. S. Natl. Herbarium*, Vol. 3, 1896, p. 329) is known all along the Northwest coast as the salmon berry. According to Steller the berries were not quite ripe at the end of July (July 20 O. S.). This agrees well with Funston's account to the effect that at Yakutat "it begins to ripen at sea level about August 5, and at higher altitudes two weeks later." (S)

[118] By *Chamaecerasi* Steller undoubtedly meant *Lonicera coerulea* L. In his "Catalogus" (see next footnote) he enumerates it as "Chamaecerasus montana fructu singulari caeruleo. C. B." and adds "in magna copia habetur." This seems strange in view of the fact that *L. coerulea*, although variously credited to Alaska, is not represented in the collections from there. Steller was so well acquainted with this species from Siberia and Kamchatka, however, that it does not seem likely that he can have been mistaken.

Red and black whortleberries: *Vaccinium vitis idaea* L. and *V. ovalifolium* Smith. In his "Catalogus" Steller enumerates them as "Vitis

in Kamchatka. The other plants collected by me in America I have recorded in a separate list.[119]

The animals occurring there and supplying the natives with

---

idaea baccis rubris" and "Vitis idaea fol. oblongis crenatis fr. nigricanti. C. B. P."

What Steller means by "Scharbocksbeeren," scurvy berries, is difficult to make out. Among berries enumerated by him in the "Catalogus" as having been observed on Kayak Island there are three in addition to the above, viz. "Sambucus racemosa rubra. C. B. P. In maxima copia, occupat montes"; "Vitis idaea magna, quibusdam sive Myrtillus grandis, I. P. Parce" (*Vaccinium uliginosum* L.); and "Chamaeneri clyminum Norvegicum" (*Cornus suecica* L.). As the berries of *Sambucus* in that region (Yakutat) do not ripen until about the first of September (Funston, *Contr. U. S. Natl. Herbarium*, Vol. 3, 1896, p. 329), it is not likely that this species is meant. I am not aware that the *Cornus* has ever been designated as an antiscorbutic.

On the other hand it seems strange that Steller does not include *Oxycoccos* in his list. The cranberry might perhaps have been considered by him as *the* scurvy berry. It is equally strange that this plant is omitted in his list of Bering Island plants, though it occurs there plentifully (Fedtschenko, Flore des Îles du Commandeur, 1906, pp. 23–29). It has also been suggested that *Streptopus amplexifolius* (L.) D. C. may have been the scurvy berry. Although occurring in the region (*Contr. U. S. Natl. Herbarium*, Vol. 3, 1896, p. 346) I do not find it in Steller's "Catalogus" unless it be the "Smilax altera," but in his catalogue of the Bering Island plants (No. 4 in the archival designation mentioned in the next footnote) it is enumerated as "Polygonatum idem quod ad prom. Eliae."

Empetrum is *Empetrum nigrum* L. (S)

[119] The MS here continues "at the end, which is appended to the description of the rarer and peculiar plants of the region." This list is one of five manuscript documents in Latin in the archives of the Academy of Sciences at Petrograd (Arkhiv Konferentsia, Bundle 13 C, Nos. 4–8, Q), four of them lists of plants and the fifth the description of the rarer plants just referred to. The list here in question (Bundle 13 C, No. 5 Q) is entitled "Catalogus plantarum intra sex horas in parte Americae septentrionalis iuxta promontorium Eliae observataram anno 1741 die 21 Iulii sub gradu latitudinis 59." Photostatic copies of these documents are now in the Library of Congress and the library of the American Geographical Society. Mr. Litvinov, the curator of the Academy's herbarium, told me in 1917 that only a few of these specimens are now in the Academy; the greater part of them were sold to the British Museum by Pallas. (G)

their meat for food and with their skins for clothing are, so far as I had opportunity to observe, hair seals,[120] large and small sharks,[121] whales, and plenty of sea otters, the excrements of which I found everywhere along the shore; from this circumstance it may also be concluded that the natives, because otherwise sufficiently provided with food, do not trouble themselves greatly about them, since otherwise these animals would not have come ashore, any more than they now do in Kamchatka, where there are so many people interested in their pelts. Of land animals, aside from what has been inferred above about the reindeer, I, as well as others, saw at various times black and red foxes[122] and did not find them particularly shy, perhaps because they are hunted but little.—Of birds I saw only two familiar species, the raven and the magpie;[123] however, of strange and unknown ones I noted more than ten different kinds, all of which were easily distinguished from the European and Siberian [species] by their very particularly bright coloring. Good luck, thanks to my huntsman, placed in my hands a single specimen, of which I remember to have seen a likeness painted in lively colors and described in the newest account of the birds and plants of the Carolinas published in French and English, the name of the author of which, however, does not occur to me now.* This bird

[120] The "Seehunde" mentioned are probably referable to the Pacific harbor seal (*Phoca richardii* Gray), which occurs from California to the Aleutian Islands and eastern Bering Sea (see Allen, *Bull. Amer. Museum of Nat. Hist.*, Vol. 16, 1902, pp. 459–499). (S)

[121] The number of species of sharks known from Kamchatkan and Alaskan waters is not great. The large and small sharks seen by Steller may well have been the mackerel shark (*Lamna cornubica* (Gmelin)) and the dogfish (*Squalus sucklii* (Girard)), both common in the region. (S)

[122] Black and red foxes, probably *Vulpes kenaiensis* Merriam. (S)

[123] Raven: *Corvus corax principalis* Ridgway; magpie: *Pica pica hudsonia* (Sabine). (S)

* The late lamented [Steller] refers to the work of the English traveler Catesby [Mark Catesby: The Natural History of Carolina, Florida, and the Bahama Islands, etc., 2 vols., London, 1731–43] and to Plate 15 in Vol. I of the English edition, on which the North American blue jay

proved to me that we were really in America. I would have enclosed the drawing herewith, were it not that I had to leave it behind, as my return voyage had to be made on foot from Avacha to the Bolshaya River, and consequently it will have to be forwarded at some future time.[124]

After this brief sketch of the discovered land, I proceed with the account of our voyage.

On July 21 in the morning, two hours before daybreak, the Captain Commander, much against his usual practice, got up and came on deck and, without consulting anyone, gave orders to weigh anchor. Although Lieutenant Waxel earnestly requested that we might stay long enough at anchor until all the casks were filled with water, twenty being as yet empty, and nothing but homesickness compelled us to hurry, nevertheless and in spite of all the order was carried out, and we stood out of the bay, gradually gaining the sea. It was considered reason enough that the wind just then blew favorably for getting out

---

[Cyanocitta cristata (Linn.)] is figured, to which the bird observed by Steller, it is true, has considerable resemblance, but is a different species, as is sufficiently clear from Steller's description which will be published elsewhere. This bird, consequently, could give no proof as to America. But nobody, notwithstanding, will doubt that Steller really has been in America.—P.

Pallas is right with regard to Catesby, but singularly wrong in denying that Steller's bird furnished proof of its American origin. It was described by Gmelin, 1788, as Corvus stelleri and is a member of the same genus as our blue jay, which genus, Cyanocitta, is exclusively American, Cyanocitta stelleri, consequently, furnished conclusive proof that the expedition had reached America and vindicates Steller's excellent judgment. He must have had not only a wonderful memory to be able to remember Catesby's figure so well, but also a fine appreciation of zoögeographical relations to draw the above conclusion in 1741. (S)

[124] Steller sent twelve drawings of American and Asiatic birds, but when the package reached the Academy Müller examined it and made the following note: "es sind nur 5 Zeichnungen von Vögeln and fehlen sieben" (see Pekarski, Zapiski Imp. Akad. Nauk, Vol. 15, Suppl. 1, 1869, pp. 26–27). While in Petrograd in 1917 I made a search for the five but could not locate them. (G)

and contrary for going into the harbor. When a few days later a light gale arose, there was consequently no little rejoicing over the fact that we were out of the bay and far from land. The Captain Commander then announced his opinion, which was to the following effect: Because of the approach of August and our ignorance of the land, the winds, and the sea, we should be satisfied for this year with the discovery already made and should not follow up the land farther nor hug the coast closely in making the home trip but should sail back on our former course. Although it might now be inferred that the land continued farther in a westerly direction, nobody could know whether it did not extend farther south towards Kamchatka, in which case we might run blindly on land at night or in a fog or be wrecked during the autumn gales on islands in an unknown sea. However, as this decision was given only in conversation and without being submitted to a sea council and though I did not hear the reply, I could clearly see from the subsequent actions of Lieutenant Waxel and Master Khitrov that they were not pleased with the project, and consequently we continued to keep near land until July 26, as these gentlemen thought it necessary always to follow the land along the coast, instead of which it might have been sufficient every time after sailing a hundred versts[125] to try to go north one or two degrees. Thus it happened that during the night of July 27 with a light gale we got bottom at 60 fathoms, being a bank extending from shore into the sea, though fortunately for us the land itself was so far away that it was not seen.[126]

On July 28 and 29 we had continuous stormy and wet weather. We had signs of the nearness of land by the same kind of floating

[125] The MS has "miles" (i. e. German miles), which seems more plausible.

[126] The MS here continues: "and they might then already have been able to understand the danger, to which, by running too close to land, we all were afterwards wantonly exposed to no purpose whatever and without there being exercised even a semblance of experience in nautical affairs." The location was probably south of Tugidak Island (see Vol. I, p. 335, end of footnote 5).

objects as on the outward voyage, and I noticed them afterwards always prior to and before our coming in sight of land, which happened very often.

During July 30 and 31, as well as on August 1, we had beautiful, clear weather, a quiet sea, a favorable southeast wind, and made pretty good progress. About one o'clock in the night of August 1[127] it was discovered on sounding that the ship was in four fathoms of water, though it was reported differently to the Captain Commander. The weather being calm, the ship was finally worked out so far from land that we reached eighteen and twenty fathoms, where we dropped anchor and waited for daylight.

We found ourselves on the morning of August 2 only about three versts distant from a rather large and wooded island.[128] The weather was unusually pleasant and warm, sunshiny, and absolutely calm. Towards noon a sea lion[129] appeared near the ship and swam continuously around it for more than half an hour. I asked the Captain Commander, as the wind and weather were so favorable, to let me go ashore for a couple of hours in the small boat to continue my investigations, but we got into a slight altercation on the subject with the result that he finally called a sea council in which it was agreed that in the future nobody should upbraid me, as if I, on my part, had not wanted to do my duty most zealously, to the best of my ability, and at every opportunity; this everybody promised, and I let it go at that. Towards evening I caught with the hook two unknown fishes of the same genus as the so-called *Scorpii marini* (*Cottus*).[130] I made at once a description of them and preserved them in spirits, but

[127] i. e. 1 A.M., August 2, even according to Steller's reckoning by civil time. For a parallel account see the log book entry of that hour (Vol. 1, p. 111); for comment see Vol. 1, pp. 334–335.

[128] Chirikov Island, not so named by this expedition (see Vol. 1, p. 111, footnote 53).

[129] The northern sea lion (*Eumetopias jubata* (Schreber)), usually known as *E. stelleri* (Lesson)). (S)

[130] The two unknown sculpins are evidently the *Hemilepidotus hemilepidotus* (Tilesius) and *Megalocottus platycephalus* (Pallas), both names based, at least in part, on Steller's descriptions. (S)

they, with other rare collections, were lost during the disastrous stranding of the vessel in November. Towards evening we weighed anchor, passed by the island, and went out to sea in a westerly direction.

On August 3[131] the mainland once more came into sight in latitude 56° and we saw it in NNW½W about fourteen miles from us, yet uncommonly distinct, owing to the high, snow-covered mountains.[132] With an easterly wind we headed south because on the west the land was in our way. In fact we found ourselves, as it were, in a bay, since to the west and north we had the mainland and on the east the island under the lee of which we stood on August 2.

* On August 4, going on the southerly course, we finally sighted also between south and west, about two or three miles from us, many high, large, and wooded islands,[133] so that we were hemmed in by land all around. Wherever we wanted to get out there was land in the way, but the winds, which at this time and until August 9 were mostly east or southeast and could have advanced us several hundred miles on the straight course to Kamchatka, were now utilized fruitlessly in tacking up and down.

During all this time (until the 9th)[134] we saw large numbers of hair seals, sea otters, fur seals, sea lions (*Phoca ursina* and *leonina*), dolphins, and storm fishes.[135] On this occasion as well

[131] The MS has in addition "towards noon." This sighting of land is the same as that recorded in the log book on August 4 just after midday (Vol. I, p. 113). This and other references indicate that Steller's time reckoning is according to civil time.

[132] Mt. Chiginagak (see Vol. I, p. 113, footnote 57) and others at the head of Chiginagak Bay (57° N. and 156¾° W.; see Vol. I, Pl. I).

* What follows from here to August 11 had to be taken from a Russian translation of this journal, because a whole sheet was missing in the original.—P. [On this point, see the Preface, p. viii, above; see also Pallas' footnote, between footnotes 248 and 249, below.]

[133] Semidi Islands (see Vol. I, p. 113, footnote 58).

[134] Instead of "(until the 9th)," which is probably an interpolation by Pallas or the Russian translator and is less plausible, the MS reads "that we were near land or surrounded by it."

[135] The published text has "Delphine und Sturmfische," the MS "See-

as later on I learned from repeated experience that whenever these animals were to be seen unusually often in a very quiet sea, a storm followed soon after; and that the oftener they came up and the more active they were, the more furious was the subsequent gale.

On August 10 we saw a very unusual and unknown sea animal, of which I am going to give a brief account since I observed it for two whole hours.—It was about two Russian ells in length; the head was like a dog's, with pointed, erect ears. From the upper and the lower lips on both sides whiskers hung down.[136] The eyes were large; the body was long, rather thick and round,[137] tapering gradually towards the tail. The skin seemed thickly covered with hair, of a gray color on the back, but reddish white on the belly; in the water, however, the whole animal appeared red, like a cow.[138] The tail was divided into two fins, of which the upper, as in the case of roosters,[138a] was twice as large as the lower. Nothing struck me as more surprising than the fact that neither forefeet[139] nor, in their stead, fins were to be seen. In default of a more detailed description one can do no better than compare the shape of this animal with the picture which Gesner received from a friend and which he has published under the name of *Simia marina danica* in his book on animals. At any rate, our sea animal deserved this name because of its resemblance to Gesner's

Schweine, Phocaenen." "Seeschwein" or "Meerschwein" is the ordinary German equivalent for *Phocaena*, the porpoise. The Russian equivalent according to Pallas (Zoogr. rosso-asiat., Vol. 1, 1811, p. 284) is, changed to English transliteration, *morskaya svinya*. "Sturmfisch" is evidently meant for the same, for in another place (passage at footnote 253) we find "Swinki oder Sturmfische." Steller consequently only meant porpoises and not also other species of dolphins. (S)

[136] The MS has besides: "which made it look almost like a Chinaman."

[137] Instead of "long, rather thick and round" the MS reads "longish round and thick."

[138] Instead of "red, like a cow" the MS reads "entirely reddish and cow-colored."

[138a] The MS reads "wie bey den *gallis*" which Pallas literally turns into "wie bei Hahnen," as in roosters. *"Gallis"* is probably a copyist's error for *galeis*, sharks (see, below, p. 117 at note 265). (S)

[139] The MS has in addition: "as in the marine amphibians."

sea monkey as well as on account of its wonderful actions, jumps, and gracefulness. For over two hours it swam around our ship, looking, as with admiration, first at the one and then at the other of us. At times it came so near to the ship that it could have been touched with a pole, but as soon as anybody stirred it moved away a little farther. It could raise itself one-third of its length out of the water exactly like a man, and sometimes it remained in this position for several minutes. After it had observed us for about half an hour, it shot like an arrow under our vessel and came up again on the other side; shortly after, it dived again and reappeared in the old place; and in this way it dived perhaps thirty times. There drifted by a seaweed,[140] club-shaped and hollow at one end like a bottle and gradually tapering at the other,* towards which, as soon as it was sighted, the animal darted, seized it in its mouth, and swam with it to the ship, making such motions and monkey tricks that nothing more laughable can be imagined.[141] After many funny jumps and motions it finally darted off to sea and did not appear again. It was seen later, however, several times at different places of the sea.[142]

[140] Instead of "a seaweed" the MS reads "a large American seaweed 3 to 4 fathoms long."

* Gmelin histor. fucor.—P. [For identification see, above, footnote 51, second paragraph.]

[141] The MS here has in addition the following passage, the last words of which replace the next sentence in the published version: "once in a while biting a piece off and eating it. Having now observed it for quite a while I had a gun loaded and fired at this animal in order to get possession of it for a more accurate description, but the shot missed. Though somewhat frightened it reappeared at once and gradually approached our vessel. However, it went off to sea as a second shot was fired at it without effect or perhaps only slightly wounding it and did not appear again." The MS then continues like the published version with the words, "It was seen later," etc.

[142] It is very difficult to explain satisfactorily Steller's account of this extraordinary occurrence. Various animals have been suggested as possible objects of Steller's description, as for instance the sea otter, hair seal, sea lion, etc. But with all these Steller was so familiar that it is not easy to believe that in his sober senses or by daylight he could have failed

On August 11, as we were by now out of the bay, we sailed
westerly with a light southeast wind. On the 12th, however, it
was calm, and a sea council was held in which it was decided,
because of the approaching autumn and of the long distance, to

---

to recognize any of them after watching it for two hours, sometimes so
near that it could be reached with a pole. It is hardly necessary to
affirm that there is no animal in the sea or on land which combines the
characters assigned to it by Steller. But if purely imaginary, from where
did he get the general idea and the details of his vision?

Steller suggests the resemblance of the alleged animal to Gesner's
account in his "Historia animalium" of a *Simia marina danica*, or
Danish sea monkey. A search through Gesner's work (Konrad von
Gesner: Historia animalium, 4 vols., Zurich, 1551–58) fails to disclose
any description or illustration which even remotely recalls the general
habitus of Steller's creature. In the chapter headed "De simia marina"
(p. 1053), it is true, Gesner speaks of a "fish" of which a picture is given
which was sent from Denmark (i. e. Dania) to his friend Io. Kentmann
under the name of "Meeraff," or sea ape. The woodcut (on p. 1054)
unquestionably represents the chimaera (*Chimaera monstrosa* Linn.)
and in no feature whatever recalls Steller's account, as it has large front
fins, a long whip-shaped tail, no mustache, and no ears. Moreover, the
chimaera is not a surface fish at all. It is evident that Steller did not
have this picture in mind, and that his wonderful memory failed him in
this particular. However, Steller had a faculty for remembering just
such things (Pallas' note, pp. 59–60, above). It was therefore natural to
search Gesner's book for the prototype of Steller's sea ape. No single
picture, however, corresponds to it, but several of the most prominent
features are recognizable in various woodcuts. Thus the pointed ears
are a very prominent feature in the "monstrum marinum" on p. 522,
which also has hair on the head, if not on the body. On p. 1248 there is
a chapter "De vulpe marina, Bellonius, ipse quidem simiam marinam
appellavit" with a picture of a shark showing a most extravagantly
elongated upper lobe of the caudal fin, exactly as described by Steller.
In none of Gesner's figures of sea monsters do we find the "beard hanging down from both the upper and the lower lips," except possibly in the
grotesque figure on p. 246 of the "bearded whale." The only feature
which cannot be matched is the lack of fore limbs.

The behavior of the strange creature, it should be added, recalls other
accounts of the playfulness of the sea otter. Are we permitted to suppose that Steller had this fantastic vision at dusk and that, having had
up to that time no opportunity to watch a sea otter at close quarters,
though otherwise familiar with it, he did not recognize the details of the

enter at once upon the return voyage to Avacha without making any attempt to search for the direction in which the mainland might extend. I confess that this council and what was decided in it seemed highly remarkable to me. The immediate return was decided upon, and the report[143] to that effect was signed by all the officers down to the boatswain's mate, though, as usual, not by me; consequently they were intent upon Avacha; however, the straight course was not taken, but we sailed along the land, which of course amounted to following the American coast. On account of the contrary west winds the intention was to attempt advancing in a more westerly direction by tacking between south and north on the 53rd parallel; the mainland could be suspected at least in latitude 54°, since it had been seen in latitude 55°.[144] It could also be clearly inferred from the con-

---

strangely acting animal's make-up and supplied these from his fragmentary recollection of Gesner?

In this connection it is interesting to note that the "large American seaweed" with which this remarkable creature played is apparently the one named *Ulva priapus* by Gmelin (S. G. Gmelin, Historia fucorum, St. Petersburg, 1768, p. 231) from a description furnished by Steller, who found it "about the Kamchatkan coasts" (ad littora Kamtchatica Stellerus invenit). Pallas, in the footnote, also refers to Gmelin's "Historia fucorum." Gmelin's description refers to a fragment of the species formerly generally known as *Nereocystis lutkeanus* Mertens, which according to Saunders (*Proc. Washington Acad. of Sci.*, Vol. 3, 1901, p. 431, Pl. 58; *idem*, Harriman Alaska Expedition, Vol. 5, 1904, p. 195) should be recognized as *Nereocystis priapus* (Gmelin). The floating fragment here described by Steller was evidently quite similar to the one described by Gmelin and credited to Kamchatka. Is it significant that in the latter description there is no reference to its having been observed in American waters? It should be noted in justice to Steller that the species is abundant on the American side from Puget Sound to the Shumagin Islands. (S)

[143] For the text of this report see Vol. 1, p. 120.

[144] Steller's meaning appears more clearly when the MS version of the passage from "consequently they were intent" down to this point is restored. The MS reads: "And they did not want to give up their old plan and, in view of the contrary west winds, go several degrees farther south but [persisted in wanting to go] to Avacha along the Avacha

stant signs of animals and drifting objects that we were still near land and could expect it yet farther south; while at the same time the adverse west wind was an indication of land ahead of us. On the contrary, other and more favorable winds could with all the more certainty be hoped for in latitudes 49° and 50° as there is no instance of trade winds in such latitudes or outside the tropics at all. However, although the Captain Commander came to agree with me, nevertheless he would not issue any order accordingly but merely talked about it and allowed his opinion to be rejected without contradiction.[145]

---

parallel of 53°, although it could certainly be assumed that land, since it had been found in latitude 54°, might extend farther south, which [plan] thus amounted to constantly sailing along the land and refusing to avail oneself of the shortest way home at a distance away from the land America."

Steller's argument was that it would have been wiser to go south to latitude 49° or 50° before turning west, as the land probably extended farther south and the winds would at least not be persistent head winds (it is in the sense of persistent and not of easterly winds that the subsequent reference in the journal to trade winds is to be understood).

The likewise immediately subsequent reference to the west wind as evidence of land ahead, as well as similar statements later in the journal (passages to which refer footnotes 242 and 289), seem to indicate that Steller believed that such a relation existed. What was the basis of this belief is, according to Professor R. DeC. Ward of Harvard University, to whom the question was submitted for comment, hard to say. The prevailing winds of the region in summer are southwesterly and southerly, and the generally westward course of the *St. Peter* would naturally cause her to meet with land constantly because of the southward sweep of the Aleutian Islands arc. Although this simple combination of existing conditions accounts for the actual circumstances it is probable that Steller's deduction was based on a conception of local winds commensurate with meteorological knowledge at the beginning of the eighteenth century. Steller's view that northwestern North America approaches Asia as a much larger and more compact land mass than is actually the case (see, below, footnote 418) may have had something to do with his deduction. (J)

[145] The MS continues: "If I now draw the logical conclusion, from a comparison between the object of the sea council and their subsequent acts, it must certainly be as follows: 'These gentlemen want to go home, and that by the shortest road but in the longest way.'"

Meanwhile it is singular that the winds had never been so steadily contrary before as they were after August 12. From the 13th to the 17th the time was spent in constant tacking between north and south without gaining much thereby.

On the 18th another singular event took place. About four o'clock in the morning I heard those on deck speak about land. I rose at once and went above. However, it may already have been agreed that no one should say anything about having seen land, especially in such a singular place, namely in the south. Although this land, which before sunrise had been seen plainly, was hidden later on by a fog, nevertheless it could still be distinctly recognized.[146] That it was not far from us could also be inferred from the quantities of kelp floating from that direction. The fact that the westerly wind died down suddenly served as an additional proof that we were sailing between America and some island to the south of us. Our officers were long since weary of meeting land; but it was nevertheless indefensible to leave it without an investigation to assure themselves of its existence and to plot it on the chart. When I inquired of them

[146] There is of course no land in this region (about $52\frac{1}{2}°$ N. and 158° W.; see Vol. I, Pl. I). Whatever Steller may have heard said on deck, it is not known whether the officers thought there was land there. At all events they did not record it in the log book (see Vol. I, p. 128), although, to be sure, according to Steller's view of their duplicity, this would not necessarily prove their disbelief in the presence of land. That, on being asked what land they thought it was, they said Juan de Gama Land, as Steller states immediately below, may simply have been to send him about his business, impatient as they were of his constant insistence on his point of view. In spite of what Steller goes on to say about their alleged misconception of Juan de Gama Land, from all the records it would appear that they did not consider this land (about which see Vol. I, pp. 2–3 and Fig. I, and, in this volume, footnotes 27, 28, and 148, last paragraph) at the most to extend farther east than longitude 180°, where they had disproved its existence on June 25 (see Vol. I, Pl. I and p. 71).

Whatever the merits of the case, it seems probable that Steller was partially led into this error of judgment, as he had been in his belief that a continuance of the ESE course after June 12 would have led to the discovery of land (see, above, footnote 42), by his contempt for the opinion of the officers. (J)

what land they considered it to be, as incontestably it must be a large island (of which on this voyage we had seen so many that America cannot be less provided with them on this side than in the Western Sea[147]), I received the answer that it must be Juan de Gama Land. From this answer I could judge how splendidly they had understood the large chart of Monsieur Delisle[148]

[147] i. e. the Atlantic Ocean. The last clause reads in the MS as follows: "that America on the western side is provided with as many islands near shore as on the eastern side."

[148] A photograph of this manuscript map, which has hitherto never been reproduced, is presented herewith as Pl. I. This map was prepared in 1731 at the request of the St. Petersburg Academy of Sciences by the French astronomer and geographer Joseph Nicolas Delisle, a member of the Academy, to show what was then known of the relation of eastern Asia to America. The order to procure this information came to the Academy from the Senate. In 1731 the map was presented to the Empress Anna and to the Senate (so stated in a note, not in Delisle's handwriting, on the back of one of the Delisle MSS in the archives of the Service Hydrographique de la Marine, Paris, marked Vol. 115, XXVI, 3, B, according to information received from Professor Gallois, mentioned below; this statement, together with the date 1731 on the map itself, would seem to refute Müller's denial in Sammlung Russischer Geschichte, Vol. 3, 1758, p. 139, Jefferys' transl., 1761, p. 15, that the map was made as early as that year). Delisle prepared an accompanying memoir in French, which he read before the Academy of Sciences in 1732, in which he described the sources on which the map was based and discussed feasible routes between Asia and America. This memoir has been published with a translation as Appendix F (pp. 302–313) to Golder's "Russian Expansion on the Pacific," 1914. Whether the map still existed and, if so, where, was not known.

At the request of the American Geographical Society M. Lucien Gallois, senior professor of geography on the Faculté des Lettres of the University of Paris, kindly made a search for the map in various archives in Paris. It was finally found in the archives of the Service Hydrographique de la Marine, where it is preserved in Portefeuille 172, Division 2, as Pièce 1. That it is the original map compiled by Delisle is practically certain when it is compared with statements made in the memoir, often identical in phraseology with those appearing on the map. De Gama Land is stated in the memoir (Golder, *op. cit.*, pp. 308, 312) and is shown on the map to lie east of Company Land, with a number of islands between the two and with Company Land limited on the east by a coast, as on the last maps of Guillaume Delisle (died 1726), and not left in-which [their] stupidity had scoffed at so often; for De Gama Land was hitherto the name of the unknown coast of America, located in the north and extending from east to west and could not be regarded as a land separate from America. Nor could this land be more than fifteen [German] miles wide, as otherwise we should have sailed over it, or at least seen it, on our outward voyage.

---

definitely open, as on the Dutch maps. Yezo, which on the Dutch charts is similarly unbounded on the west, is described (*ibid.*, p. 312) and shown as an island separated by a strait from the Asiatic mainland. Japan is described (p. 310) as being plotted from the accurate observations of the Jesuits and subsequently the Dutch; the use of this accurate material is attested by the detailed mesh into which the normal grid of the map has been subdivided in this region. The coasts of northeastern Asia are stated (p. 310) to be shown, and are so shown, according to the results of Bering's first expedition (cf. Vol. 1, Fig. 5). On the American side attention is called (p. 304) to the opening on the Pacific coast discovered by Martin Aguilar (the mouth of the mythical River of the West), shown on the map, and (p. 306) to the fact that the gulfs and bays followed in the search for the Northwest Passage, such as Hudson Bay and Baffin Bay, are essentially closed at their heads—a condition which is portrayed on the map. Two routes of vessels are stated (p. 302) to be indicated, that of Juan de Gama from China to New Spain and that of a French vessel called the *St. Antoine* in the reverse direction: the latter route appears clearly and so designated on the map, the former faintly without designation along the coast of De Gama Land. Longitude is stated (p. 310) to be, and is, reckoned from the prime meridian of Ferro. All the correspondences so far enumerated can be established by comparing the memoir with the photograph of the map (Pl. I). Comparison with the map itself, so Professor Gallois informs us, furnishes seemingly conclusive corroborative evidence in that the different countries are colored exactly as stated in the memoir: red for China including Korea (p. 308), green for the Russian dominions (p. 310), yellow for Japan (p. 310), and blue for Yezo and the adjacent islands (p. 310).

Whether the map in the archives of the Service Hydrographique de la Marine is the identical map that Bering had with him on the *St. Peter* is open to question. The passage in Müller, *op. cit.*, p. 194, reading in Jefferys' translation, p. 38, "*de Lisle's* map . . .", of which I have mentioned above that it had been presented by the academy to the Senate; the Senate had given it to the captain commander, that he might be directed by it. *De la Croyere* had also a copy of it, which he produced in the council" would seem to imply that Bering had the original map. Lauridsen, however, says (Vitus Bering, Chicago, 1889, p. 132) "When the

Meanwhile, I pass over the fact that there was no desire to make sure about this land [island] or to indicate it on the chart, but I am greatly astonished that the officers did not yet guess the reason for the constant west wind or let themselves be induced

---

second Kamchatkan expedition left St. Petersburg a copy of De l'Isle's map was given to Bering as well as to La Croyère." This, on the whole, seems more probable. The Service Hydrographique map seems to have been folded by its users, to judge by the tears along its creases; a navigator is more likely to have kept a map in the form of a roll, possibly mounted on cloth. But a more cogent reason than this for believing that the original was not used by Bering is the fact that the present map was found in Paris, with other Delisle documents dating from Delisle's sojourn in Russia (1726–1747), while most of the Bering documents are, or were before the war, in Petrograd. In this connection it should be noted that Golder (Guide to Materials for American History in Russian Archives, 1917, p. 131) lists an enlargement to 10 by 8 feet of Delisle's map (the Service Hydrographique original measures 7 by 4 feet along the black-line border, exclusive of title, etc.) as being in 1914 in the archives of the Hydrographic Section of the Ministry of Marine in Petrograd under MS charts, 1732–1742 (?), No. 2990, on which the new discoveries had been added subsequently. This is probably the copy that Sokolov says he used in his studies (*Zapiski Hydrogr. Depart.*, Vol. 9, 1851, p. 437).

Whatever the exact status of the Service Hydrographique map here presented in Pl. I, there is no doubt that the map that Bering had with him and to which Steller refers in the above passage was, in *content*, its exact equivalent and that it may therefore illustrate his remarks. Steller's immediately following statement that De Gama Land was the east-west trending coast of northwestern North America is entirely in consonance with one view that prevailed with regard to this land and which is reflected in the text of Delisle's memoir (Golder, Russian Expansion, p. 304). This passage reads: "Ces côtes vues par Dom Jean de Gama . . . font peut être partie d'un grand continens qui seroit contigu à l'Amérique et qui iroit rejoindre au nord de la Californie la côte septentrionale de l'entrée decouverte par Martin Aguillar: au moins trouve-t-on dans quelques anciennes cartes une longue côte marquée dans tout ce trajet." This view goes back to Texeira's map of 1649, the first on which De Gama Land was shown (see Vol. 1, p. 2; the map is reproduced as the bottom inset of Buache's map of 1754 in Teleki's "Atlas zur Geschichte der Kartographie der Japanischen Inseln," 1909, p. 141). That Delisle did not on the map show De Gama Land extending so far eastward as to join California is probably due to the fact that even he considered this phase of the problem conjectural. (J)

thereby to try a more southerly course, until according to the reckoning we should be opposite the open strait,[149] where other winds might be looked for, the more so as in the fall continued north and northeast winds have been observed in Kamchatka as well as during the Captain Commander's first voyage.

About three hours after midnight on August 19 we got a favorable east wind with which we sailed due west, but towards noon it began to go down. The horizon cleared, enabling us to recognize rather distinctly the mainland to the north of us.[150] We were also warned of its nearness by the sudden drift towards us of seaweeds and refuse from shore, as well as by many animals

[149] The MS reads "Canal Uries" (i.e. Vries; "Det[roit] d'Uriez" on Delisle's map, Pl. I). Vries Strait was the name given to the strait between Company Land (the modern Urup; see, above, footnote 27) on the east and State Island (the modern Iturup and Kunashiri considered as one) on the west. (Delisle's application, Pl. I, of the name to the strait between Yezo and State Island is unusual; this strait was generally called Canal Pieck or Pico after Vries's peak Antony on Yezo.) The exaggerated expansion eastward of Company Land and its identification with De Gama Land as the northwestern part of North America (see, above, footnotes 27, 28, and 148) made Vries Strait, therefore, according to this conception, the first open channel leading past the land barrier of America on the west. Steller often refers to it simply as "the Channel." (J)

[150] From the position of the *St. Peter* at noon on August 19 (civil time) it was not possible to see land to the north. The vessel was then in about lat. 52° 15′ N., long. 159° W. (see Vol. I, Pl. I; the latitude is calculated from the latitude by observation on August 18 as given in Khitrov's journal, *ibid.*, p. 128, which differs by 7′ from the latitude by dead reckoning given for August 19 in Yushin's journal, p. 129). The arc of visibility which extends out from the land farthest toward this position is that of Pavlov Volcano on the Alaska Peninsula in about 55½° N. and 162° W., 8900 feet high (on the calculation of arcs of visibility see, above, footnote 58). But the radius of this arc is only 108 nautical miles, while the *St. Peter* was about 215 nautical miles away. The land nearest to the *St. Peter* was the Shumagin Islands, but their highest point, a 2270-foot mountain in the center of Unga Island, is only visible 54 nautical miles, and from that peak the vessel was 195 nautical miles away. It must therefore be concluded that Steller was again misled in his belief that he had seen land. (J)

and land birds, and even by a change in the water—evidence which had already so often proved correct. But nobody except myself and a few others would believe or see it, though confirmed by the diminishing force of the wind and its change to and from land.[151] Nevertheless we steered a little more southerly, and, when on August 20 we were so far out that neither the land itself nor the above-mentioned signs of it were visible, I was asked mockingly whether I was still seeing land, although I had not laughed when these gentlemen were seeing land even on the 51st parallel or thrown in their faces the fact that they could see no farther than nature and experience permitted them.

From the 20th to the 23rd we tacked on the parallel of 53°. I saw at this time whales[152] very frequently, no longer singly but in pairs, swimming together side by side or pursuing one another, which made me think that this must be their mating time.

On the 25th a heavy storm from the west compelled us to drift.[153] The 26th was spent in tacking. On the 27th the horizon was quite clear. The weather was cold and bright, and the wind straight out of the west. In a sea council, held during the day, it was suddenly decided,[154] on account of the contrary winds and the threatened shortage of water (as only twenty-six full

[151] In the MS the clause beginning with "though confirmed" reads: "though confirmed by the diminishing wind and its change according to the well-known rule and observation of seamen, namely that near land the wind blows from shore during the day and from the sea towards the shore during the night." Possibly this misstatement of the habitus of land and sea breeze is due to a copyist's error.

[152] It is probable that by the term "Wallfische" Steller means the whalebone whales as distinguished from the dolphins and porpoises. In that case the whales he saw must have been one or more species of the five known from the North Pacific (see F. W. True: The Whalebone Whales of the Western North Atlantic Compared With Those Occurring in European Waters, With Some Observations on the Species of the North Pacific, *Smithsonian Contr. to Knowl. No. 1414*, in Vol. 33, Washington, 1904; reference on pp. 269–296). (S)

[153] In the MS the 24th is accounted for in this sentence, which there reads: "We had a heavy storm from the west on the 24th and 25th."

[154] For the text of the decision, see Vol. 1, p. 138.

casks were still on hand), to sail on a northeast course towards
the land. This would not have been necessary had we filled at
Cape St. Elias those twenty empty barrels which, without reason,
were left behind.—This sea council was barely ended, the decision made and signed, when in the afternoon the wind suddenly
shifted and with it, consequently, the plan. The ship had no
more than put about when the wind shifted once more, blowing
again from the west and, by continuing steadily, compelled us,
after all, to make a run for the land.

We kept this course towards the land on the 28th, and toward
four o'clock in the evening we saw signs of it, such as sea lions,
a species of cod[155] which lives on the banks at a depth of ninety
fathoms at the most, and a black gull (*Diomedea*).[156] Shortly
afterwards land itself was seen to the N by E, though very
indistinctly.[157] During the night, however, we made so much
headway that on August 29 in the morning we could make out
plainly five islands, beyond which the mainland appeared ten
or twelve miles distant. The weather during the day was very
pleasant and perfectly favorable for our purpose of going close
to the land in search of a harbor or shelter. About three o'clock
in the afternoon we reached the outer one of the aforementioned
islands,[158] which lay north and south, and late in the evening we
anchored alongside a rocky and bare island,[159] three versts to
the east of the first one.

In the early morning of August 30 the start was made to

[155] This is the North Pacific codfish, *Gadus macrocephalus* Tilesius, if
indeed specifically different from the Atlantic *G. morrhua* Linnaeus. (S)

[156] "(*Diomedea*)" is not in the MS and is an addition by Pallas. It
is very doubtful if Steller meant a black albatross (*Diomedea albatrus*)
as a sign of the nearness of land. More likely it was a young gull (*Larus*)
in the dark plumage. Pallas relates (Zoogr. rosso-asiat., Vol. 2, 1826,
p. 308) that Steller in his manuscript on birds refers to the albatross as
"Larus maximus niger vel albus." (S)

[157] The log book first mentions the sighting of land, which was the
Shumagin Islands, at 8 A.M., August 29 (civil time) (see Vol. 1, p. 140).

[158] Nagai Island (see Vol. 1, p. 142, footnote 84, and p. 336; also,
below, Fig. 13).

[159] Near Island (*ibid.*).

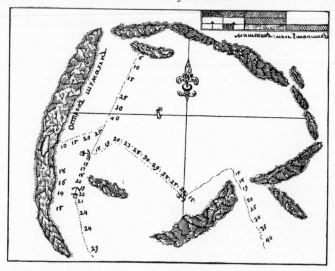

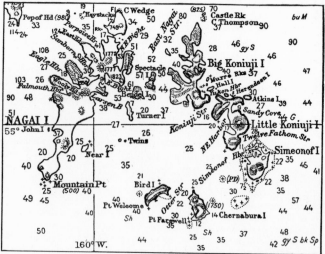

FIG. 12—Khitrov's sketch map of the Shumagin Islands from the end of the entry of September 5, 1741, in the log book kept by him (also reproduced in Vol. 1 in Fig. 11).

FIG. 13—Modern map of the Shumagin Islands (section from U. S. Coast and Geodetic Chart No. 8802). Scale, 1:1,050,000.

carry into effect a double program, viz. to look around for the nearest place where fresh water could be had and, as a fire had been seen burning in the night on the island[160] to the north of us, to send Master Khitrov with a crew to it in order to reconnoiter the place and search for people. In order that the naval officers might have the honor of the expected discovery, they asked me of their own accord if I did not wish to go ashore. Although it was easy to perceive their intention, I nevertheless accepted their offer very kindly and went ashore[161] with the water carriers in the hope that both parties might discover something useful, although there was little of that to be expected on a bare and wretched island.

No sooner had I landed than I made efforts at once to locate a watering place and found several springs which had good and wholesome water. In the meantime the sailors had chosen the first and nearest stagnant puddle and already started operations. I found fault with this water because it was stagnant and alkaline, as proven at once when boiled for tea and later on when tested with soap, and also because I observed at the beach that it fell and rose with the sea and consequently must be brackish, as it also betrayed to the taste when boiled. I therefore proposed that the springs found by me should be used for taking water and sent on board a sample of their water with an oral report, pointing out particularly that by using the [other] water the scurvy would quickly increase and that, because of its lime content, the people would become dried up and lose strength and that this water, after a short while in the vessel, would even increase in salinity from day to day and finally through standing become salt water, while on the other hand none of this had to be feared from the spring water.—But although in this matter I ought to have been listened to in my capacity of physician,[162] neverthe-

[160] Turner Island (see Fig. 13). See also log book for August 30 (Vol. I, p. 141), entry for 3 A. M. and footnote 83.

[161] On the eastern side of Nagai Island.

[162] The MS here has the additional clause "and although so much damage, even our final misfortune, resulted from it" [use of the bad water].

less my proposition, most honestly made in order to preserve the life of my fellow beings as well as my own,[163] now fallen into the power of others, was rejected from the old overbearing habit of contradicting.—The answer was: "Why, what is the matter with this water? The water is good, fill up with it!" Even though in the meantime I had found a still nearer watering place than the beloved salty puddle and proposed it in case the spring water should not please, it should and must not be so, in order that they might deny me all sense and all knowledge.

As I was already accustomed to such treatment I paid no more attention to it and began to reconnoiter the land. I observed that the island on which we were was the largest of eight lying round, about three or four German miles long and about three or four versts broad from east to west. On the north and west the mainland was visible at a distance of about ten miles from it.* Yet it remains undecided whether the island

[163] In the MS this clause reads only "in order to preserve my own life and health."

* Steller according to his once preconceived opinion thought he saw the mainland everywhere, where probably islands lying close together or behind each other caused such an impression.—P.

Steller, however, was right, for 10 [German] miles, or 40 nautical miles, back of him lay the mainland of the Alaska Peninsula. Even if this land had not literally been the mainland, in principle his observation was correct, for it was the *main mass of land*. In such matters the broader conception will prove more fruitful. For example, in this very region, Unimak Island (55° N. and 164° W.; see Pl. I) is by strict definition an island; but the fact that crustal forces have happened to cut it off from the Alaska Peninsula by a narrow and insignificant strait makes it no less a part of the land mass of the peninsula. Severance might just as well have taken place farther east, at Port Moller, or been deferred, as it were, to the major channel of Unimak Pass to the west. Indeed the Alaska Peninsula and the Aleutian Island chain together should be viewed as the submerged mountain arc that they are. From this standpoint it is futile, as has been done, to contend that the Bering expedition discovered little of the mainland of America. It remains that the expedition was the first to outline the whole unknown coast of northwestern North America throughout the great arc in which it sweeps, as mainland around the Gulf of Alaska, and as islands in the Aleutian chain, from the fiord coast of the Alaska Panhandle to the northeastern shores of Asia. (J)

did not connect towards the north with the mainland and form
a peninsula, as we could not see the end of it in that direction.
This island, as well as all the others, consists only of high solid
rocks covered with vegetation. The rock is mainly a coarse,
gray and yellowish graywacke,[164] in some places a gray sandstone; a black, thick slate occurs also. The shore is everywhere
stony and rocky; springs and small brooks [are] in abundance.
Of animals I met a black fox[165] right at the start, which, as he
barked at me like a dog and was not shy at all, I took to be a
dog at first. After close inspection, however, I realized my mistake and thought of having him shot either by Plenisner or my
huntsman, in order to take him along as a piece of evidence,
but [the plan] miscarried. Red foxes[165] were seen by us in different parts of the island; *yevrashkas*, or small marmots, *[166] were
found in great abundance. Besides these, I noticed the track of
an entirely unknown animal. The footprints, made on the
clayey beach of a small lake, resembled the track of a wolf but
by their expanse and the great size of the claws indicated that a
different and larger animal, or a very big species of wolf, must
live here.[167]

[164] The MS has only "Felsen Stein," which Pallas has changed to
"Graufels." On the probable occurrence of graywacke on Kayak Island
see, above, footnote 116.

[165] Black and red foxes: possibly, as on Kayak Island (see, above,
footnote 122), *Vulpes kenaiensis* Merriam. (S)

* *Mus Citillus.*—P.

[166] The *yevrashka* (*Mus citillus* according to Pallas' footnote) is *Citellus
nebulicola* Osgood, which was described from Nagai Island in the Shumagin group (*Proc. Biol. Soc. of Washington*, Vol. 16, 1903, p. 26). (S)

[167] The large tracks seen by Steller cannot well have been of any
other animal than those of a wolf, as of course he was familiar with bear
tracks. I am not aware that any form of wolf has been definitely recorded
from the Shumagins or from the Alaska Peninsula, so it is not possible to
say with certainty definitely what species originated the tracks. However, it is not likely to have been any of the timber wolf races, as the
region in question is destitute of forests. It is most probable, therefore,
that the species is *Canis tundrarum* Miller (*Smithsonian Misc. Colls.*,
Vol. 59, No. 15, 1912, p. 1). (S)

All sorts of water birds[168] in abundance were seen, such as swans,[169] two kinds of *urili* (*Pelecani*),[170] auks (*Torda*),[171] ducks, snipes, sandpipers, various kinds of gulls,[172] divers, among them a very remarkable and unknown species,[173] Greenland pigeons,[174] sea parrots (*Alca arctica*)[175] and *michagatkas* (*Alca cirrata*).[176]

[168] In the following enumeration of birds and fishes the Latin names are not in the MS; they have been added by Pallas. The following notes give identifications on the basis of present knowledge and in terms of current zoölogical nomenclature.

[169] The swans seen must have been *Olor columbianus* (Ord), which has been recorded by Dall from Sannak Island, about 100 statute miles farther southwest, in September (Dall, *Proc. California Acad. of Sci.*, Vol. 5, 1873–74, p. 275). (S)

[170] The two species of *urili* are the violet-green cormorant (*Phalacrocorax pelagicus robustus* Ridgway) and the white-crested cormorant (*Ph. dilophus cincinnatus* (Brandt)). (S)

[171] Of course they were not *Alca torda* Linnaeus, which does not occur in the Pacific. The nearest approach in appearance in this region are the murres (*Uria*), but Steller would probably have recorded these as *ari*, not as auks. Moreover, murres seem to be rare at the Shumagins. Dall (*Proc. California Acad. of Sci.*, Vol. 5, 1873–74, p. 34) says expressly that they were not noticed, and Bean (*Proc. U. S. Natl. Museum*, Vol. 5, 1882, pp. 174–175) does not mention them. It is most likely that Steller in the term auk included the various auklets so characteristic of the North Pacific. (S)

[172] Ducks, snipes, sandpipers, various gulls: numerous species are common in this region. (S)

[173] It is not likely that Steller by using the word "Taucher" meant to indicate a species belonging to the genera *Colymbus* (*Podiceps*) or *Gavia* (*Urinator*) but rather in general a diving bird unknown to him (see also, below, footnotes 239 and 285). In that case it is probably permissible to guess at *Cerorhinca monocerata* (Pallas) or *Ptychoramphus aleuticus* (Pallas), none of which he had seen in Kamchatka. (S)

[174] The "Greenland pigeons" are undoubtedly the pigeon guillemot (*Cepphus columba* Pallas), which Dall records as breeding on the Shumagins (*Proc. California Acad. of Sci.*, Vol. 5, 1873–74, p. 11). (S)

[175] "(*Alca arctica*)," added by Pallas, refers to the Atlantic species. The one seen by Steller is *Fratercula corniculata* (Naumann), the horned puffin. (S)

[176] *Michagatka* is the name used by the western Kamchadals for *Lunda cirrhata* Pallas, the tufted puffin. (S)

Of land birds, however, I observed only ravens, flycatchers (*Grisola*),[177] snowbirds (*Emberiza nivalis*),[178] willow ptarmigans (*Tetrao Lagopus*),[179] and no others whatever.

The fishes which we saw were the *malma* (a kind of salmon)[180] and *ramsha* (*Cottus scorpius*).[181] Of trees, not a single one was to be seen on any of the eight islands lying here together in a circumference of six German miles; [it was] otherwise on those which we saw on August 4 on the same parallel[182] and which cannot have been more than 40 miles from here. All the islands situated between here and Kamchatka, at least those which we

[177] The "flycatcher" seen by Steller on Nagai Island (Pallas by adding the word *Grisola* probably only means to conjecture that it was a gray flycatcher) was neither a muscicapine nor probably a tyrannine bird. The Old World flycatchers are not represented in the western hemisphere, and the only American flycatcher which suggests itself, viz. the western wood pewee (*Myiochanes richardsoni* (Swainson)), is not known from that part of Alaska. It is much more likely that Steller mistook the dwarf thrush (*Hylocichla guttata* (Pallas)) for a flycatcher, a not unnatural mistake, especially when we consider that Pallas, with specimens before him, described it as *Muscicapa guttata* (Zoogr. rosso-asiat., Vol. 1, 1811, p. 465). The dwarf thrush is recorded from the Shumagins by Keeler (Harriman Alaska Expedition, Vol. 2, 1910, p. 228). (S)

[178] The "snowbird" is undoubtedly the snowflake, *Plectrophenax nivalis* (Linnaeus), of which specimens from the Shumagins are in the U. S. National Museum. (S)

[179] The willow ptarmigan (*Lagopus lagopus* (Linnaeus)) is probably the form *alexandrae* Grinnell, recorded as occurring as far west as the Shumagin Islands (Check-List of North American Birds, Prepared by a Committee of the American Ornithologists' Union, 3rd edit., New York, 1910, p. 141). It was collected on Unga Island of that group by Bean (*Proc. U. S. Natl. Museum*, Vol. 5, 1882, p. 163). (S)

[180] The *malma* is a charr (*Salvelinus malma* (Walbaum)), also known in Russian as the *golets*, and common throughout the region. (S)

[181] *Ramsha* is the name by which the Russians in Kamchatka know the red sculpin (*Hemilepidotus hemilepidotus* (Tilesius)), recorded by Pallas as *Cottus scorpius* (Zoogr. rosso-asiat., Vol. 3, 1831, p. 130), which name properly belongs to the European sculpin (*Myoxocephalus scorpius* (Linnaeus)). (S)

[182] Semidi Islands. They are on the 56th parallel, the Shumagins on the 55th.

afterwards saw, were equally bare and without any woods.[183]
I have not been able to find any explanation beyond the following:

(1) These islands have a twofold position. Those from here
on towards America bear northeast and southwest, while on the
other hand, those in the Channel and nearer Kamchatka[184] trend
northwest and southeast, and I have noticed both with regard
to the large and the small rocks that they strike in the same
direction.

(2) In addition, all have the peculiarity that they are very
long and at the same time their breadth is quite out of proportion, for example: Shumagin's Island[185] is from twenty to thirty
versts long [and] two to three broad, Bering's Island is thirty
miles long and only four, or at most seven, versts broad. All the
islands, of which we noticed seven[186] between here and Bering's
Island, were quite similarly formed. From this it follows that,
as they lie exposed to the north and south and consequently
suffer the most rapid changes of heat and cold, and on account of
such a slight breadth are moreover swept freely by the exceedingly severe storms of these regions, neither tree nor shrub can
grow or get rooted.[187] Even the smallest shrubs grow so crooked
and interwoven that it is impossible to find in the entire region a

[183] It is interesting to note this observation of Steller's on the western
limit of tree growth on the offshore islands of the Alaska Peninsula and
its continuation, the Aleutian Islands. The general features of the vegetation according to present knowledge may be studied on two maps by
the late Dr. A. H. Brooks (*U. S. Geol. Survey Prof. Paper No. 45*, 1906,
Pl. 12, and *Geogr. Rev.*, Vol. 15, 1925, Pl. I, land classification map). (J)

[184] By "those in the Channel and nearer Kamchatka" Steller means
Bering and Copper Islands and the westernmost of the Aleutian Islands
proper, ending in Attu. On "the Channel" see, above, footnote 149.

[185] Now Nagai Island (see Vol. 1, p. 142, footnote 86).

[186] Possibly the following are meant according to the identifications
made in the present work: Atka, Adak, Kiska, Buldir, two of the Semichi
Islands, Copper Island. (J)

[187] Steller is probably right in his theory that the lack of shelter from
severe winds accounts for the absence of timber on narrow islands whose
axes are parallel to the prevailing high winds. (B)

straight stick two feet long. Similarly, it is observed in Kamchatka that those districts that have a sufficient breadth of land from north to south are most prolific in forests and other needful things. On the contrary, the narrower the land gradually becomes, the more obvious is the change, as for example between the Bolshaya River and [Cape] Lopatka. On the other hand, the region opposite Karaga,[188] where the land is still narrower and the latitude, in addition, six degrees farther north, is conditioned quite differently. With regard to the islands situated in the Channel[189] the explanation is even more obvious.[190] The fact that the eastern islands, though similarly situated and narrow, were found to be forested has its demonstrable explanation in the circumstance that they lie close under the mainland and thereby are protected,[191] while a hypothetical explanation is my conjecture that the corner of America projecting towards Asia decreases in width towards the west and is of the same nature on its northwestern coast as Kamchatka on its northeastern.[192]

[188] The narrow neck of the Kamchatka Peninsula in 59° N. (see Vol. I, Pl. I).

[189] See footnote 184.

[190] The MS here has the additional clause: "as on their narrow end they are exposed without protection to all the violent winds originating between northeast and southwest."

[191] It is interesting to compare this explanation of Steller's with the similar reflection of modern naturalists visiting the same region. I quote the following from Osgood (North Amer. Fauna No. 24, 1904, pp. 23–24). "Just what are all the causes determining the non-existence of coniferous trees on the greater part of the [Alaska] peninsula can hardly be ascertained until more work is done. Possibly one of the most effective checks to the extension of timber southward is the prevalence of wind and storm regardless of temperature. The topography and situation of the peninsula are most favorable for stormy weather. Being long and narrow, with a ridge of high mountains extending throughout its length, and situated as it is between Bering Sea and the North Pacific Ocean, it must necessarily receive at nearly all seasons the force of many atmospheric disturbances. In the fall it is swept by fierce winds, whether the temperature be moderate or not. Such conditions would restrict arborescent vegetation in almost any latitude." (S)

[192] The MS here has the following sentence concluding the argument: "For these reasons, then, the islands situated to the east are wooded on

Of the plants which grow on these islands other than the willow bushes, which are barely two ells high, a separate list has been given.[193] Upon the whole, I only remark that the greater number of the rare and rock-inhabiting American plants described at Cape St. Elias were still met with here and, in addition, a few already which were seen on Bering's Island in 1742 and, later on in the fall, in similar localities in Kamchatka. However, as far as concerns those plants which grow in the valleys and in the low and damp places, they are, with a few exceptions, the same as those in Europe, Asia, and America in the same latitude. Aside from the red whortleberries and the black crowberry, or *shiksha* (*Empetrum*), which are found here in the greatest abundance, the products of the vegetable kingdom of greatest use to us were the glorious antiscorbutic herbs, such as *Cochlearia*, *Lapathum folio cubitali*,* *Gentiana* and other cresslike herbs,[194] which I

---

account of the better protection and the breadth of the land toward the north, and the westerly ones bare on account of the opposite conditions, whether they are nearer to Asia, such as the first, second, and third Kurile Islands and the two islands we saw on October 30 [Semichi Islands], or nearer to America, like all those we observed in September and October."

[193] The MS reads: "has been given at the end." Among the five manuscript botanical documents mentioned above in footnote 119 there is no plant list specifically devoted to the Shumagin Islands. The "Catalogus plantarum . . . iuxta promontorium Eliae observatarum" there referred to contains throughout references to plants observed "on the island on September 1" and one reference to Shumagin Island. It is therefore probable that this is the separate list here referred to or else its embodiment.

* *Rheum palmatum*, which Steller used to designate thus in his manuscripts.—P. [See next footnote, third paragraph.]

[194] The red whortleberries are *Vaccinium vitis idaea* L., and the *Empetrum* is *E. nigrum* L.

The *Cochlearia* occurring in this region is now known as *C. oblongifolia* D. C. It is probably identical with the water cress occurring on Bering Island and variously recorded as *C. oblongifolia* and *C. officinalis*.

By *Lapathum folio cubitali*, dock with leaves a cubit long, Steller probably meant *Rumex occidentalis* S. Wats., which is credited to Alaska. Pallas' reference in the footnote to *Rheum palmatum* is quite unintelligi-

gathered solely for my use and that of the Captain Commander. For although I had made representations that our medicine chest, from the very beginning, had been miserably supplied, inasmuch as it was mostly filled with plasters, ointments, oils, and other surgical remedies enough for four to five hundred men in case of a battle but had none whatever of the medicines most needed on sea voyages and serviceable against scurvy and asthma, our commonest cases; and although I had therefore requested the detail of several men for the purpose of collecting such quantity of antiscorbutic herbs as would be enough for all, nevertheless even this proposition, so valuable to all and for which I merited gratitude besides, was spurned. Later, however, there were regrets enough, and when we had scarcely more than four able-bodied men left on the vessel, I was tearfully begged to help and assist, which then, though with empty hands, I did to the utmost of my strength and means, although it was not my office and my services had always been scorned before the disaster. It[195] must also at last have caused even the coarsest and

---

ble, as no true rhubarb is known to occur in any of the regions in which Steller collected. The confusion may be due to the fact that some of the species of *Rumex* have been used as substitutes for rhubarb and were known under various names, as monk's rhubarb, false rhubarb, etc. *R. occidentalis* has been collected on the Shumagins both by J. Kincaid and by Dr. F. A. Golder (specimen in the U. S. National Herbarium).

Of *Gentiana* several species are known from the Shumagins. The one referred to by Steller is probably *G. acuta* Michx. or *G. frigida*, of which specimens collected by Dr. Golder in the Shumagins are in the U. S. National Herbarium.

In this connection it is interesting to read the following explanation of the name *Herba britannica* for *Rumex aquaticus*, also known as water rhubarb, as given in "Allgemeines Polyglotten-Lexicon der Natur-geschichte," Vol. 2, Hamburg, 1794, col. 1184: "The name *Britannica*, according to Munting, is said not to be derived from the island of that name, but to be compounded from the Frisian *brit*, to make fast; *tan*, a tooth; *ica* or *hica*, ejection, and consequently to denote the power of the plant to make loose or rickety teeth fast again." (S)

[195] Instead of "It" the MS has: "My services to them, under the Divine blessing."

most ungrateful persons to take notice when the Captain Commander, who from scurvy and confinement had entirely lost the use of his limbs, was restored by me to such an extent simply by his partaking of the fresh spoonwort that within eight days he could get out of bed and on deck again and felt as well as at the beginning of the voyage, and also when the use of *Lapathum* for only three days, according to my direction, made the teeth of most of the sailors firm again.

Because of the rain which began towards evening I had already built myself a hut and intended to spend the night on the island; I decided nevertheless finally to return to the vessel in order once more to present emphatically and with the greatest respect my opinion on the bad water and on the collecting of the herbs. However, when I saw my opinion concerning the water again spurned and coarsely contradicted and had to hear myself, like a surgeon's apprentice belonging to the command, ordered to gather the herbs, and that this important work, which affected the health and lives of all, was not considered worth the labor of a few sailors, I repented of my good intentions and resolved that in the future I would only look after the preservation of my own self without wasting another word. With this in mind, I went ashore again on the morning of August 31, continued my work, and together with Mr. Plenisner explored the land. However, towards evening, we were hurriedly called on board by a *sluzhiv* [servant] with the announcement that because of an apprehended storm, of which, however, we had not the slightest signs on land, all the men were being assembled on board so as to be ready to go to sea in case the anchors did not hold in the rising gale, as the place where we were standing was highly dangerous, although previously, in spite of all protests, it was pronounced protected on all sides.—Immediately we all ran as fast as we could to the eastern shore of the island, a distance of over a mile, and discovered everything there as we had been told. We also found that the confusion on shore, on account of the sick who had been brought here the day before and who now could be dragged into the boat only with difficulty because of the high surf on the beach, was so great that we decided to wade waist deep to the boat through the *burun* (the breakers) and, trusting to luck, to let ourselves be ferried over in it. On this day we buried the first of our crew, the sailor Shumagin, who had died on the previous day almost as soon as he got ashore. The island is since called Shumagin's Island after him.[196]

When after some anxiety we arrived on board there was the greatest lamentation because Master Khitrov and his men were not yet at hand and it might be necessary to leave them on shore. I now thanked God that through the cunning plots of the naval men I had been kept away from his company. However, soon after our arrival a big fire was observed not far from the spot where we had been taken into the boat, and, judging from the position, I concluded that Master Khitrov and his men must be stopping at the lake where I had the second time advised that water should be taken.—In the meantime the gale increased, and it was our great good luck that, although the wind began in the northeast, it suddenly shifted to the west, then to the south and again back to west, but finally became northwest,[197] from which quarter we were sheltered by the land and in no great danger. It was very lucky for us that during the first storm, at midnight, the Captain Commander did not permit the anchor [cable] to be needlessly cut in order to drop another, supposed to be better, in its place, as otherwise, in such a dark night and with the usual confusion, we surely should have drifted on the rocks and been wrecked.—This same evening I learned that the officers, although too late, had changed their mind and from fear of death sent ashore a few barrels to be filled, for their own consumption, with spring water from the place I had indicated. But Fate would not let them benefit by it, for, in the great hurry

196 The name Shumagin is now given to the whole group; as already mentioned in footnote 185, the Shumagin Island of Steller is now called Nagai (see also Vol. 1, p. 142, footnote 86). (G)

197 The MS reads more plausibly as follows: "although the wind began in the northeast, the wind suddenly shifted, and changed to southwest, then west, and then northwest."

and because the boat had to be loaded with the sick, the barrels were left behind on shore.

On September 1 the wind was still very strong and with steady rain. The day was spent in anxious deliberations as to how the Master was to be brought back to the vessel and how to get away from the land. If he had not gone at all or if, on not meeting anybody, he had returned betimes and thereby had not delayed the watering by depriving us of the yawl, we could have gotten out with the fair gale and been more than a hundred miles farther on our course. But on his account we all had thus to remain in danger near land without being able to take advantage of the fair wind, which continued for five days after. Everyone grumbled because whatever that man had touched, from Okhotsk on until the return voyage, had gone wrong and had brought misfortune. Similarly, at Cape St. Elias, by his long and fruitless absence, he was also the cause of so many casks having to remain empty because of the lack of the yawl for carrying the water, thereby making it necessary to approach land a second time, which step he also was the first to counsel. On the whole, he was observed to be very anxious to give daring advice[198] but when facing disaster to be without decision and wits and to complain and try to hide himself.*

On September 2 we got a southeast wind, and the large boat with eight men was sent ashore to bring Master Khitrov and his party on board, as of necessity the yawl had to be left behind. In the meantime we weighed anchor and with the southeast wind moved up along land farther towards the north, in order to pick up the oncoming boat more easily, and there came to anchor. It rained and blew very hard all day, so that for the sake of greater safety the other anchor was also thrown over. But, as towards evening there suddenly blew up from the south-

[198] The MS here has in addition: "leaving the execution to others."

* How does this agree with what Steller says about him above and with the character attributed to this man in the "Sammlung Russ. Gesch."?—P. [The work referred to is the account of the expedition by G. F. Müller cited in the bibliography in Vol. 1, p. 359, second item.]

east a violent squall, the third anchor was also kept ready in case one of the other two [cables] should break. But, God be thanked, the wind shortly afterwards shifted to the southwest, from which quarter we lay sheltered, and became more quiet, but the boat remained ashore over night.

During the entire day on September 3 the weather was uncommonly pleasant and quiet. The wind continued southwesterly. In addition to this we had towards morning the further satisfaction of getting the boat with Master Khitrov and all the rest of our men aboard again without losing a man. The little yawl, however, was left on the island on purpose; a hawser[199] out of forgetfulness, besides a few other objects as souvenirs;[200] however, constable Roselius brought back with him all the guns, powder, and lead entrusted to him.

We immediately weighed both anchors and with a southwest wind turned around the rock[201] as far as the outermost island[202] situated to the southeast, because we could not get out of the bay into the sea in a southerly direction. Master Khitrov,[203] who had become uncommonly happy because of his deliverance and jolly over his welcome, took the lead in hand and at the first attempt left it on the bottom of the sea, which incident the common sailors interpreted as an evil omen and called to mind

[199] The printed German text has here the word "Pierleine." It does not occur in the MS. There is no such word in the German language. It is evidently a direct rendering of the Russian *perlin*, which means "hawser, warp, towline, small cable, or cablet," again a foreign word borrowed from the Danish *pertline*. Many of the naval officers of Peter the Great, Bering among them, were Danes. (S)

[200] The sentence up to this point in the MS reads: "The little yawl as well as a few needed objects were without any necessity left behind on land as souvenirs." The rest of the sentence as given in the printed text does not occur in the MS.

[201] i.e. rocky islet (see, in the journal, the description to which footnote 159, above, refers), namely Near Island.

[202] Bird Island. For the track of the *St. Peter* see Khitrov's sketch map (Fig. 12), adjusting the relations to the correct outlines as shown on the modern map (Fig. 13).

[203] The MS reads: "who, with the rest, had become" etc.

that just a year ago today the provisions were lost at the mouth of the Okhota through this same man's cleverness. At two o'clock in the afternoon we came to anchor behind this outermost island two versts from shore.

On September 4, likewise with quiet weather, we attempted to get out to sea by going round the western side of this island, but as it could not be done on account of the west wind we found ourselves compelled to turn back east to our former position, which we finally reached[204] and dropped anchor. Through this event it came about that without expectation or search we chanced to meet with Americans. We had scarcely dropped the anchor when we heard a loud shout from the rock to the south of us, which at first, not expecting any human beings on this miserable island twenty miles away from the mainland, we held to be the roar of a sea lion. A little later, however, we saw two small boats paddling toward our vessel from shore. We all waited for them with the greatest eagerness and full of wonder in order, on the arrival of these islanders, to pay special attention to their appearance and characteristics.—When yet about half a verst distant from us both men in their boats began, while still paddling, simultaneously to make an uninterrupted, long speech in a loud voice of which none of our interpreters could understand a word. We construed it therefore as either a formula of prayer or incantation, or a ceremony of welcoming us as friends,[205] since both customs are in use in Kamchatka and the Kurile

[204] The MS has in addition: "at four o'clock in the afternoon." This tallies with the entry in the log book for 4 P.M., September 5 (i.e. September 4, civil date); see Vol. 1, p. 147.

[205] In order to secure the viewpoint of modern ethnology on this and other matters, the whole passage describing the meeting with the Aleuts was submitted for comment to Mr. F. W. Hodge of the Museum of the American Indian, Heye Foundation, New York. Footnotes 207 (partly), 211, and 216 (partly) are based on the information kindly supplied by Mr. Hodge.

With regard to the "uninterrupted long speech in a loud voice" Mr. Hodge knows of no explanation other than the second here suggested by Steller, which is also given by Captain Cook (see Vol. 1, p. 148, footnote 92). (J)

Islands.[206] As they now came gradually nearer constantly shouting while paddling, they began to talk to us intermittently, but,
as nobody could understand their language, we only beckoned
with our hands, that they might come nearer without being
afraid of anything. They, in turn, however, pointed with the
hand towards the land that we should come to them there,
besides pointing with their fingers to the mouth and scooping up
sea water with their hands as if to indicate that we could have
food and water with them. We beckoned them again over to us,
and, as we shouted to them the word "nichi," which occurs in
Baron Lahontan's description of North America and means
water,[207] they repeated it many times and pointed again to the

[206] The MS here adds: "as may be seen in detail in my historical
description of the Kuriles." The reference is presumably to one of the
numerous manuscript reports which Steller prepared, which are hard to
trace at the present day. This report is not in the list by Krasheninnikov
of those of Steller's papers that were delivered to the Academy of Sciences by Berckhan, painter of the expedition, as published in Pekarski's
life of Steller (Historiya Akademii Nauk, Vol. 1, St. Petersburg, 1870),
pp. 613–616.

[207] Mr. Hodge comments: "Lahontan (Nouveaux Voyages dans
l'Amérique Septentrionale, 2 vols., The Hague, 1703; reference in Vol.
2, p. 204; English edit., London, 1703, Vol. 2, p. 297) correctly gives *nibi*
or *nipi* (not *nichi*) as the Algonquian term for water (Natick, *nippe*;
Chippewa, *nebbi, neebi, nipi*, according to the vagaries of orthography;
Abnaki, *nebi*, etc.). In addressing the Aleut, however, Bering's men
might as well have used a Greek or a Zulu word, as it would not have
been less intelligible."

Müller had already perceived the incongruity of this assumption.
On this point he says (Sammlung Russischer Geschichte, Vol. 3, 1758,
p. 220; Jefferys' translation, p. 48): "What might be farther added here
is only this, that a certain person maintains that he made himself understood, in some measure by these people by the list of words, which *La
Hontan* has subjoined to his description of *North America*. For having
pronounced according to the said list, the words *water*, or *wood*, the people
had pointed to such parts where these things are found; but, I think, this
they may have done by chance, or the gestures, which accompanied the
words, may have contributed to render them intelligible; for *La Hontan*
is not to be placed among the conscientious and credible writers of
travels. But, setting aside this, the distance between the countries is two

shore as if they wanted to call attention to it.[208] Nevertheless one of them came very near to us, but, before approaching quite close, he reached into his bosom, pulled out some iron- or lead-colored shiny earth, and with this he painted himself from the wings of the nose across the cheeks in the form of two pears, stuffed the nostrils full of grass (the nose wings on each side, however, were pierced with fine pieces of bone), and then took from the sticks lying behind him on the skin boat one which was like a billiard cue, about three ells long, of spruce wood and painted red, placed two falcon wings on it and tied them fast with whalebone, showed it to us, and then with a laugh threw it towards our vessel into the water. I can not tell whether it was meant as a sacrifice or a sign of good friendship. On our part we tied two Chinese tobacco pipes and some glass beads to a piece of board and tossed it to him. He picked it up, looked at it a little, and then brought it over to his companion, who placed it on top of his boat. After this he became somewhat more courageous, approached still nearer to us, though with the greatest caution, tied an eviscerated entire falcon to another stick and passed it up to our Koryak interpreter in order to receive from us a piece of Chinese silk and a mirror. It was not at all his intention that we should keep the bird but that we should place the piece of silk between the claws so that it would not become wet. However, as the interpreter held the stick fast and by it pulled the American, who held the other end in his hand, together with his boat toward our vessel, the latter let go the stick, became frightened, and paddled a little to one side, and would not come so near again. Therefore the mirror and silk were thrown to him, with which they both paddled towards

[sic] great for one and the same language to be spoken in them; not to maintain, that an *European*, particularly a *Frenchman*, will hardly conceive and write the words of such a language in such a manner as to be intelligible to another nation, that speaks nearly the same language." (J)

[208] That the "it" of the published version refers to water is evident from the clearer wording of the MS, which reads after "shore": "doubtless in order to call attention that water was to be had there."

shore and beckoned us to follow in order that they might give us to eat and drink. All the time while these two islanders stayed around the vessel their companions on land called continually and shouted loudly without our being able to make out their purpose.

After a short consultation the boat was let down, in which I, besides Lieutenant Waxel, the Koryak interpreter, and nine sailors and soldiers decided to pull ashore. We provided ourselves with lances, sabers, and guns but covered all with canvas so as not to arouse suspicion. In addition we took along biscuits, brandy, and other trifles, in order to be able to make presents to the islanders. The greatest misfortune was that we were not able to make a landing, because the beach was very rocky, the tide rapidly rising; wind and waves were likewise so high that with the greatest difficulty we kept the boat from being dashed to pieces. From the place on the beach where their boats and also our presents were lying scattered about unappreciated, both men and women, who because of the uniformity of the dress could hardly be distinguished from each other, all came to meet us at our approach, full of wonder and friendliness and continually beckoning with their hands towards land. As we saw that we ourselves had no hope of getting ashore, we let our interpreter and two other persons undress and go through the water to them, in order that they might observe a thing or two. The islanders received the interpreter and the others in a very friendly way and led them by the arms, quite deferentially as if they were very great personages, to the place where they had been seated, presented them there with a piece of whale blubber, talked a bit with them, though nobody understood the other, and pointed at the same time frequently over the mountain, perhaps to indicate that they had come here on our account only but that they had their dwellings on the other side of the mountain, as, indeed, [later] in going to sea towards the east around the island we got sight of a few huts from a distance. A part of the islanders remained standing on the beach abreast of us, gazing at us without taking their eyes away, and frequently inviting us to them by beckoning. However, as we gave them to understand with various signs why that was impossible for us, one of them got into his boat, which he had lifted with one hand and carried under his arm to the water, and came paddling up to us. He was made welcome with a cup of brandy, which, following our example, he emptied quickly, but also immediately spit out again, and acted strangely, as if he did not seem to be any too well pleased with this fancied deception. Although I advised against such things as tobacco and pipes, our gentlemen opined nevertheless that the Americans had the stomachs of sailors and consequently, intending to neutralize the first displeasure with a new one, gave the stranger a lighted pipe of tobacco, which he accepted indeed, though paddling away quite disgusted. The smartest European would have done just the same if he had been treated to fly mushroom or rotten fish soup and willow bark, which the Kamchadals, however, consider such delicacies.—As in the meantime the surf and wind were increasing more and more, our people were called back to the boat. The kind islanders, on the other hand, wanted their company still further and would not at all let them off to the vessel. They manifested especially great inclination towards our Koryak interpreter, who quite resembled them in manner of speech and in facial appearance. At first they presented them with more whale blubber and iron-colored paint; but, as they would not let themselves be influenced by gifts, they tried to hold on to them by violence, seized them by the arms, and kept them from the boat by force. Another party took hold of the painter with which our boat was made fast and intended, perhaps not with evil design but from sheer thoughtlessness, not realizing our danger, to haul the boat with its occupants ashore, where it would have been wrecked on the rocks. As in this confusion and danger there was no time to be lost and as the islanders could not be dissuaded from their purpose by sign language, shots were fired simultaneously over their heads at the rocks from three muskets loaded with balls, by which unheard-of occurrence they became so frightened that they all fell down on the ground as if hit by thunder, letting go of everything in their hands. Our men ran at once through the water and got safely into the boat. Laughable as was the consternation to behold, it was nevertheless even more funny how they at once rose up again, scolded us because we had rewarded their good intentions so badly, and waved their hands to us to be off quickly as they did not want us any longer. Some of them in getting up picked up stones and held them in their hands; we, however, were obliged hurriedly to cut the rope of the boat anchor, which held fast to a rock, and returned to the ship rather dissatisfied, as we had not been able to observe what we had intended but on the other hand had met what we had not expected. Soon, however, we had reason for thanking God that we were on the vessel and that this was so well sheltered, for immediately there arose a heavy storm from the south, and shortly after rain also began to fall, which lasted all through the night. Our Americans, however, had lighted a fire on shore and kept us pondering on what had happened.

I must here mention a few circumstances which I observed in the course of the quarter of an hour we were at the shore. The American boats[209] are about two fathoms long, two feet high, and two feet wide on the deck, pointed towards the nose but truncate and smooth in the rear. To judge by appearances, the frame is of sticks fastened together at both ends and spread apart by crosspieces inside. On the outside this frame is covered with skins, perhaps of seals, and colored a dark brown. With these skins the boat is [covered] flat above but sloping towards the keel on the sides; underneath there seems to be affixed a shoe or keel which at the bow is connected with the bow by a vertical piece of wood or bone representing a stem piece, so that the upper surface rests on it. About two arshins [210] from the rear on top is a circular hole, around the whole of which is sewn

[209] Cf. the illustrations, Vol. 1, Fig. 12, upper and lower. The upper drawing, by Waxel, represents one of the two Aleuts who approached the *St. Peter* He is seen holding the stick with the falcon feathers mentioned above in the journal. p. 92.

[210] Less than five feet (1 arshin = 28 inches).

[a strip made of] whale guts having a hollow hem with a leather string running through it, by means of which it may be tightened or loosened like a purse. When the American has sat down in his boat and stretched out his legs under the deck, he draws this hem together around his body and fastens it with a bowknot in order to prevent any water from getting in. Behind the paddler on the boat there lie ten or more red-painted sticks, pointed at one end, all made in the same way as the one we secured but for what purpose[211] I cannot imagine, unless perhaps they serve to repair the boat in case the frame should break. The American puts his right hand into the hole of the boat and, holding the paddle in the other hand, carries it thus because of its lightness on to the land anywhere he wants to and back from the land into the water.[212] The paddle consists of a stick a fathom long, at each end provided with a shovel, a hand wide. With this he beats alternately to the right and to the left into the water and thereby propels his boat with great adroitness even among large waves. On the whole, this kind of boat is very little different, if at all, from those used by the Samoyeds and by the Americans in New Denmark.[213]

As far as the personal appearance of the islanders is concerned, of whom I counted on the beach nine, mostly young or middle-aged people, they are of medium stature, strong and stocky, yet fairly well proportioned, and with very fleshy arms and legs. The hair of the head is glossy black and hangs straight down all around the head. The face is brownish, a little flat and concave. The nose is also flattened, though not particularly broad or large. The eyes are as black as coals, the lips prominent and turned up. In addition they have short necks, broad shoulders, and their body is plump though not big-bellied. All had on whale-gut

[211] Dr. W. Jochelson, the authority on the tribes of northeastern Siberia and on the Aleuts, whom Mr. Hodge kindly consulted on this point, stated that he can offer no explanation of the purpose of the red sticks other than the one suggested by Steller. (J)

[212] The MS reads instead: "carries it . . . from the land to the water, seats himself in it, and fastens himself in."

[213] i. e. the Eskimos of Greenland.

shirts with sleeves, very neatly sewed together, which reach to
the calf of the leg. Some had the shirts tied below the navel with
a string, but others wore them loose. Two of them had on boots
and trousers which seemed to be made after the fashion of the
Kamchadals out of seal leather and dyed brownish-red with
alder bark. Two had hanging on their belt, like the Russian
peasants, a long iron knife in a sheath of very poor workmanship,
which may have been their own and not a foreign [214] invention.
Although I asked that one of these knives might be obtained in
exchange by offering [215] three or more of ours, of which our stores
had plenty, because it was very important and perhaps marks
might be found on them from which it might be possible to
conclude with what nation these islanders had communication,
nevertheless this also was not done. From the distance I observed
the nature of this knife very carefully as one of the Americans
unsheathed it and cut a bladder in two with it. It was easy to
see that it was of iron and, besides, that it was not like any European product. From this, then, might be concluded that the
Americans not only have iron ore, of which thus far few or no
traces at all have been discovered in Kamchatka, but that they
also know how to smelt and work it. And it would seem indisputable from the smooth workmanship observed, [both] on the
arrows found at Cape St. Elias and on the hut there, that the
savages must have knives,[216] whether they be of iron or of

[214] MS: "European."

[215] The MS from here on has slightly different expressions, as follows:
"by offering two, three, or more of ours, as it was very important, because, in case it was not their own work, it might be possible to ascertain
from some mark stamped on it with what European nation they were in
communication, nevertheless this was not done, although there were
several hundred [knives] among the gifts in our stores."

[216] It is more than probable that Steller did see iron knives. A party
of Russian hunters who spent the years 1759 to 1763 among the Aleuts
of Unimak and Unalaska reported that the inhabitants "made knives
out of iron, which iron they obtain from the islands to the eastward,
which islands are wooded, in exchange for furs and clothing." In 1767
the officers of the Krenitsin and Levashev expedition saw and sketched
these knives. It is not likely that the natives to the eastward knew how

copper.[217] On the other hand I know from quite reliable information that the Chukchis traded from the second Chukchi island [218] with America and that, although for some years this commerce was interrupted because a misunderstanding arose, this trade is still carried on by the inhabitants of the islands; the principal articles are knives, axes, lances, and iron arrow points,[219] which the Chukchis acquire at a very high price from the Russians at Anadyrsk and exchange with the Americans at a many

---

to smelt iron. They probably obtained this metal in some indirect way either from the white men or from wrecked vessels. In a report of a Russian hunter (about 1765) a statement is made that the Aleuts told him a large ship had been driven ashore to the eastward. (G)

Independently of this note by Dr. Golder, Mr. Hodge supplies the following comment: "No American aborigines smelted iron ore; indeed, iron ore was unknown until introduced by trade or found with wreckage that had been cast ashore. Copper, however, was used in prehistoric times." On the use of copper see also, above, footnote 99 by Dr. Brooks.

The reader will notice that, in the journal as originally written, Steller himself advances two arguments against the likelihood of the natives' knowing how to smelt iron: (1) the obvious dullness of the tools with which the trees on Kayak Island had been felled (see the next footnote); (2) the high price which the natives of Alaska were reported to be willing to pay for Russian knives secured through trade with the Chukchis. (J)

[217] In the MS this sentence is replaced by the following: "Yet the following reasons seemed to oppose this opinion: (1) If they can forge knives, why should they be ignorant of how to make an ax or some similar instrument for cutting down trees? However, at Cape St. Elias the felled trees, hacked to pieces with many dull cuts, demonstrated to me that the Americans used axes of stone or bone like the Kamchadals, though at the same time their smoothly worked arrows and also the well-built hut made a different impression, namely that at least they must have knives, be they iron or copper." In the MS then follows as point (2) the sentence beginning "on the other hand," just as in the published text.

[218] The text reads literally "the other Chukchi island." Probably by this is meant Little Diomede Island, the smaller and more easterly of the two Diomede Islands, which lie midway between East Cape, Siberia, and Cape Prince of Wales, Alaska, i.e. the narrowest part of Bering Strait. (J)

[219] The words "lances, and iron arrow points" do not occur in the MS.

times higher price for sea otters, martens, and foxes,[220] some of which are brought to Russia by way of Anadyrsk. Therefore, if the Americans themselves could smelt iron and make said articles, why should they buy them at a high price from others? At the same time, it is remarkable that the cossacks on the Anadyr River traded with the Americans before the Kamchatka Expedition had obtained any knowledge of the country itself. For this a two-fold reason may be advanced as regards the cossacks: (1) selfishness and perjury of the commanders, (2) fear, because usually the one who in these remote places suggests anything new for the benefit of the Empire is compelled to carry it out himself and in place of [receiving] thanks loses all his goods and property.—On the other hand, the officers are too haughty to engage in conversation with common people and too negligent and incredulous even when anything is reported to them. Upon my arrival in Kamchatka in the year 1740, I eagerly took pains to obtain such information, questioning all newcomers, traders, cossacks with the greatest friendliness, and, in case I got nothing out of them with fair means, brought them to confession with brandy, as the most pleasant torture. But when I had acquired so much information of that kind that I could prove with more than twenty conclusive reasons where the land is nearest[221]

[220] Pallas has: "Seebiber, Marder und Füchse." The MS has: "Seebiber, Iltiss und Füchse." The "Marder," marten (*Martes*), is undoubtedly substituted by Pallas because no "Iltiss," polecat (*Putorius*), was known from America at that time. (S)

[221] Namely opposite the Chukchi Peninsula, according to Krasheninnikov's rendering of Steller's views (Histoire et description du Kamtchatka, 2 vols., Amsterdam, 1770; reference in Vol. 1, pp. 398–399). According to this view Steller, while believing that the two continents approach most closely there, thought that they are near to each other throughout the whole extent from latitude 52° to 60° N., in which he believed the American coast to trend southwest-northeast practically parallel to the coast of Kamchatka. It is this conception that is reflected in the great southwest-projecting land mass shown in the St. Petersburg Academy of Sciences map mentioned, below, in footnote 223, third paragraph (our Fig. 14). This nearness of the two continents led Steller to believe, according to Krasheninnikov, that they were formerly connected,

and in what direction the voyage ought to be undertaken, and
brought all this before the Captain Commander, my numerous
efforts were considered unworthy even of being laid before the
other officers in council, the whole supreme judgment amounting to this: "People talk much; who would believe a cossack?
I place no confidence whatever in it."—Now, however, this information is corroborated by these gentlemen's own journals
and charts, and many have even died and are buried in consequence [of this disregard]. One might perhaps even get the
notion that the chart of the First Expedition is still less trust-
worthy, since it has forgotten the islands along Kamchatka
opposite Olyutora, likewise the fine harbors at the Avacha,
before Avacha at the Uka and Olyutora,[222] and since according
to its indication no land was found within thirty miles of Kamchatka, although Bering's Island is distant only twenty miles
directly to the east of it.[223]

---

for which Steller adduces four reasons: (1) the outline of the Kamchatkan and American coasts, which indicate violent separation; (2) the numerous capes which project as much as 30 to 60 versts into the sea; (3) the
numerous islands in the sea between Kamchatka and America; (4) the
situation of the islands and the small extent of this sea.   (G)

[222] Although this passage is obscure, possibly owing to repetition of
words and other errors by the copyist, the meaning may be that the chart
of the first expedition (Vol. 1, Fig. 5) failed to show the harbors on the
Avacha and Uka coasts (in the sense defined by Krasheninnikov, *op. cit.*,
Vol. 1, pp. 238-239, of the coasts around Avacha Bay and north of the
Kamchatka River, respectively).   The reference to islands opposite the
Olyutora coast is not clear, as there are none in this location.   (J)

[223] The MS has in addition: "and the mainland forty miles."   The
reference is to the attempt Bering made in the summer of 1729 to find
land east of Kamchatka, the year after his main voyage to Bering Strait
(see Vol. 1, p. 20, and map, Fig. 6).   Bering sailed from the mouth of the
Kamchatka River on June 5 and, according to Berkh's abstract of the
midshipman Peter Chaplin's log book (Berkh, pp. 72-73, Dall's translation, p. 769; for references see bibliography in Vol. 1, pp. 363-364 and 366-
367 respectively), sailed 114 nautical miles on an E by S course before
abandoning the search on June 9.   This distance and the position in latitude and longitude by reckoning as given in Chaplin's log book would
place the vessel not far from the northern end of Bering Island.   It is one
of the ironies of fate that Bering did not see the island, as a knowledge of

Fig. 14.—Map of the North Pacific region by the St. Petersburg Academy of Sciences, 1758, incorporating the results of Bering's two expeditions and illustrating the conception of the time (reduced section from redraft in Jefferys' "Voyages from Asia to America," London, 1761, translated from G. F. Müller). According to this conception, which was also held by Steller, the mainland of North America extended close to Asia in the form of a wide projecting land mass.

The map also illustrates the conception of Chukchi Promontory as a great protuberance to the north of and beyond East Cape (see, above, footnote 11).

On September 5 it rained very hard during the forenoon. In
the afternoon it seemed several times as if it might clear, but

---

its relation to Kamchatka might have proved of incalculable value to him,
possibly even preventing his death on its very shores twelve years later.
Steller's reference to no land having been found within 30 miles of
of Kamchatka tallies with the above distance of 114 nautical miles inasmuch as he means German miles and 30 German miles are equal to 120
nautical miles. So does Bering's statement of the distance (Vol. 1, p. 20)
as 200 versts.

Steller's figure of 20 German miles for the distance from Bering Island
to Kamchatka is somewhat low, as even from the nearest land, Cape
Kamchatka, the island is 100 nautical, or 25 German miles away (see
Vol. 1, Pl. I).

The statement, omitted by Pallas, that the mainland is in this region
only 40 miles from Kamchatka tallies with Steller's conception as expressed later in the journal (see, below, footnote 418). According to this
passage he considered the land alleged to have been seen to the east from
Bering Island to be the westward extension of the American mainland.
This is in conformity with the view entertained by the members of the
expedition in general that what we now know as the Aleutian Islands
was, taken as a whole, the mainland coast of America (see, below, footnotes 260 and 418). Steller's conception is illustrated by the map incorporating the results of Bering's two expeditions published by the St.
Petersburg Academy of Sciences, a redraft of which accompanies Jefferys' translation, London, 1761, of Müller's account of these expeditions
in Sammlung Russischer Geschichte, Vol. 3, St. Petersburg, 1758 (section
reproduced in our Fig. 14) and the compilation of which is discussed in
the same works, viz. Müller, pp. 279-302, Jefferys, pp. 67-75. This
map (of which Bellin's map of 1766, reproduced in Teleki's "Atlas zur
Geschichte der Kartographie der Japanischen Inseln," 1909, Pl. 15, is
essentially a copy) shows an immense projection of land extending southwest from the northwestern corner of North America. The coast limiting
it on its southeastern side consists of the landfalls of Bering's second expedition, with the islands which the expedition recognized as such indicated
as offshore islands. The southwestern end of the projection approaches to
within the same distance of Bering Island that Bering Island is from
Kamchatka—thus corresponding, relatively, to Steller's figures, although,
absolutely, the distances shown on the map are more than his 20 and 40
miles.

Incidentally, Pallas' omission of Steller's statement that the American
mainland was only 40 miles from Kamchatka is in keeping with his

clouded over again each time. We could not[224] stay longer in this place, as the wind had now veered to the southwest; we therefore weighed anchor about two o'clock in the afternoon and just then saw two Americans in their boats paddling towards shore. We tried to reach a place where we could again stay protected on the west by the island, and a place such as we wanted was found about five o'clock, and we anchored once more.[225] About half an hour later we again saw nine Americans in their boats paddling in single file towards the ship, with similar shouts and ceremonies as the first time. However, only two of them came near to our vessel and once more made us presents of sticks with falcon feathers and of iron-colored face paint. On their heads they had hats made of the bark of trees, colored green and red, that resembled in shape the eye shades that are usually worn around the head; the crown was uncovered, and these hats appeared to have been invented only for the purpose of shading the eyes from the sun.[226] Between the hat and the forehead some had placed a few variegated falcon feathers, others tufts of grass,[227] in the same manner as the Americans on the east side, about Brazil, decorate themselves with feather tufts. From these hats an argument might again be derived for the supposition that the Americans came from Asia, because the

---

direct reversal of Steller's corresponding statement later in the journal (footnote 418). By the time Pallas published Steller's journal (1793) the geography of the northwestern part of the continent was known in its broad outlines, mainly through the work of Captain Cook, and Pallas therefore used his editorial prerogative in this case to adjust his author's views to the known facts, although elsewhere (e.g. note between footnotes 163 and 164, above) he supplies necessary corrections in the form of footnotes. The present instance, however, illustrates the value of having the MS of the journal at hand to supplement the published version. (J)

[224] In the printed text the word "leicht," easily, is a misprint for "nicht," not, as correctly given in the MS.

[225] Off Bird Island (see Vol. 1, p. 337, and, above, Figs. 12 and 13).

[226] For a representation of one of these hats, see Vol. 1, Fig. 12, lower.

[227] The published text has "buschigt Grass"; the MS, *gramen paniculatum*.

Kamchadals and the Koryaks are in the habit of wearing exactly similar hats, several kinds of which have been purchased for the Art and Natural History Cabinet.—By much gesticulation we gave the Americans to understand that we desired one of their hats, and they handed us two. On one of these there was fastened a small carved image, or sitting idol, of bone, with a feather sticking out from behind, intended no doubt to represent the tail. In return we presented them with a rusty iron kettle, five sewing needles, and some thread. After having considered the exchange and consulted with each other, they paddled towards the shore without any further ado, built a big fire, and shouted very loudly for a while. It grew dark soon after, and after that we did not see them again.

I noticed on this occasion once more that these people regard it as a special ornament to pierce holes anywhere in their faces, as we do in the lobes of the ear, and to insert in them various stones and bones. One of these fellows had stuck a slate pencil, about 2½ inches long and exactly like those with which we write on ciphering slates, through the nasal septum. Another had a piece of bone three inches[228] long stuck through crosswise above the chin just under the lower lip. Still another had a bone like it fastened in the forehead, and another, finally, had a similar one in each of the wings of the nose. From this it may be seen how thoughtlessly I had been contradicted in the year 1741, before the departure from Avacha, when among other things I announced that I held the Chukchis to be Americans or at any rate believed that Americans lived among them, inasmuch as I had heard from more than ten different persons that there were among them people who wore pieces of walrus teeth inserted in the nose and cheeks, such as all those who live on the mainland opposite are said to wear as ornaments, according to the reports of the Russians who have had indirect communication with the Chukchis.[229]

[228] The MS has "1 inch."
[229] Instead of the clause "such as all those . . . Chukchis" the MS has: "and when the Russians asked the meaning of it they were told

Finally, I observed also on all these Americans that they had a very scant beard, but most of them none at all, in which respect they again agree with the inhabitants of Kamchatka and with other East Siberian peoples.[230]

In spite of all this there still remains to be discussed the question whether these Americans may be inhabitants of the mainland or only of the islands. I hold that these people do not live constantly on the islands but are there only during the summer and spend the winter on the mainland.[231] These people may in part be attracted hither by the large numbers of birds and birds' eggs, which the Kamchadals, at the greatest peril, likewise gather among the cliffs, although every year some of them break their necks in the attempt;[232] in part they may perhaps go after whales cast up on the off-lying islands and after the seals which are more numerous there, the blubber of which is preferred also by the Kamchadals to all other delicacies. Their return in winter to the mainland, however, is the more probable

---

that everybody on the mainland opposite made use of similar ornaments, facts which I have now verified with my own eyes to be as I had noted them down a year before in the historical account of Chukotski Nos'' [Chukchi Cape]. (S)

The historical account of the Chukchi Cape region was never published, and there is no record that it ever reached the Academy. (G)

[230] The MS does not have: "and with other East Siberian peoples."

[231] Steller was mistaken; the natives did have their homes on these islands. (G)

[232] The MS from this point to the end of the paragraph reads as follows: "It is likewise generally known concerning Kamchatka that no food is preferred to the whale and seal blubber as being more delicious; now, since the seals are most numerous about these islands and since also the dead whales thrown out by the sea cannot be brought to the mainland because of the islands lying in the way but become stranded on them, it is quite credible that they [the natives], because of this circumstance alone, repair hither in summer but go to the mainland in winter. The less possible it is to winter here, because of lack of wood for building and fuel, the more reason there is for believing that the island on which we watered is continuous in the north with America, from which all the others are not very distant."

the less possible it is to winter here * on account of lack of wood for building and for fuel and, moreover, because the island on which we watered seems to be continuous with the mainland in the north,[233] while none of the others seem to be very distant from it.

Even though the weather on September 6 was cloudy throughout the day, yet because the wind was SW by S and serviceable for our getting away, we went around the eastern side of the island [234] out to sea between two islands.[235] The Americans on shore raised their voices once more as a farewell, and it seemed to us as if we saw people and huts on the near-by low island lying opposite to the east.[236] When we were out to sea about half a mile, we were especially astonished at the untold numbers of sea birds which we saw on the northern side of the island. I noted here, besides the *urili* (*Pelecani*), auks, sea parrots, gulls, *glupyshi*[237] (*Procellaria glacialis*), and Greenland sea pigeons, an entirely black snipe, with red bill and feet, which constantly moved the head like Ray's redshank;[238] further a very beautiful

* Steller did not know the underground huts of the islanders and their cold-defying hardiness like that of the Greenlanders; nor did he consider that almost everywhere on the islands they can have a sufficient supply of driftwood, about which more may be read hereafter.—P.

[233] Nagai Island is, of course, not continuous with the mainland.

[234] Bird Island.

[235] Bird Island and Chernabura Island (see Vol. 1, p. 337, and, above, Figs. 12 and 13).

[236] As Chernabura Island is "high and mountainous" (United States Coast Pilot, Alaska: Part II, Yakutat Bay to Arctic Ocean, U. S. Coast and Geodetic Survey, Washington, 1916, p. 168) it is not clear which Steller means by "the near-by low island" although Chernabura otherwise fits the location indicated. Possibly the "rocky islet" which "lies off its northern end" (Coast Pilot, p. 168) is meant.

[237] From a Russian word meaning fool, stupid fellow, etc., used by the Russians in Kamchatka for the fulmar, the Pacific form of *Fulmarus glacialis* (Linnaeus). See Stejneger, *U. S. Natl. Museum Bull. 29*, 1885, p. 91. On the birds in this list not here identified, see, above, p. 80. (S)

[238] This bird was *Haematopus bachmani* (Audubon), originally described as a snipe (black snipe, Thomas Pennant: Arctic Zoölogy, Vol. 2, London, 1785, p. 469, *Scolopax nigra* Gmelin). It occurs from

black-and-white pied diver, never before seen;[239] not to speak of other wonderful and hitherto unknown birds. As for the rest, the wind was so favorable that we lost sight of the mainland and islands towards two o'clock in the afternoon. However, the many whales which we met, one of which rose straight upright in the water for more than half its length, gave us nevertheless to understand that a storm was at hand.

On September 7 the wind and the weather were as on the day before. Toward twelve o'clock noon we were already over twenty miles away from the last island. In the afternoon the wind increased in force, and the rising sea compelled us to shorten sail. It stormed very hard all night through, so that we ran with the spanker only. Under these conditions, the late autumnal season and the great distance from Avacha, the courage of our sailors and officers dropped all of a sudden. The unwholesome water lessened the number of healthy men from day to day, and very many were heard to complain of hitherto unwonted disorders. For that reason some began to be doubtful about getting home and to discuss the question of whether we ought

---

Kiska, Aleutian Islands, to Lower California. Dall found a nest with eggs on Range Island, between Popof and Unga Islands (160½° W.) on June 23, 1872 (*Proc. California Acad. of Sci.*, Vol. 5, 1873–74, p. 28). The true redshanks, *Totanus totanus* (Linnaeus) and *Totanus fuscus* (Linnaeus), are west palearctic in their distribution and are not found in eastern Siberia or Alaska. Pallas (Zoogr. rosso-asiat., Vol. 2, 1826, p. 187) referred Steller's observation to the latter species, but erroneously. (S)

[239] The beautiful black-and-white diver which Steller had never seen before may well have been the *Synthliboramphus antiquus* (Gmelin), the *starik* of the Russians (see the journal at footnote 285, where, as well as here, this bird is referred to as a "Taucher" in the German text). The generic term *Mergus* used in the MS recalls Pallas' quotation (Zoogr. rosso-asiat., Vol. 2, 1826, p. 237) of Steller's description of the bird: "Mergulus marinus niger, ventre albo, plumis angustis albis auritus." It should be noted that in this diagnosis the bird is also described as black-and-white, and seen at a distance it may well have given this impression. Steller apparently did not secure any specimens. This species breeds from Kodiak westwards. (S)

to winter in Japan or America, although there was no particular desire for either.

On September 8 the weather was thick all day. The wind, however, decreased and shifted so that in the forenoon it blew west by north and in the afternoon west by south, for which reason we gradually worked south with both winds and by evening found ourselves on the parallel of Avacha, latitude 53°. During the night the wind died down completely.

Towards morning on September 9 we got a light wind from the east, by the aid of which we made progress of a knot and a half to two knots until eight o'clock. Thereafter it increased so that towards ten o'clock we were driven forward at the rate of four knots, or a mile an hour. During the morning it rained, and the sky was overcast; in the afternoon, however, the horizon became very clear, though without sunshine. According to the reckoning kept it was believed that at 12 o'clock we were still 312 Dutch miles distant from Avacha.[240]

On September 10 it rained in the morning, the sky being overcast. Nevertheless, towards noon the sun showed itself a little, and later it cleared gradually on the horizon. The wind was at first SSW, then SW by S. At noon the reckoning was 298 from Avacha.[241] It is marvelous that after such protracted and oft-repeated experiences it was not yet understood that these

[240] The log book (Vol. 1, p. 152) gives 316¾ German (= Dutch) miles. From this and other references it is clear that Steller uses the astronomical day for the unit of calculation of the day's run, as he naturally would inasmuch as he could only get these figures from the officers' records, who kept them in this manner. For his own record of happenings, Steller, however, adhered to the civil day, as we have seen (footnote 131).

The slight discrepancy often occurring between Steller's figure for a given day's distance from Avacha and that in the log book seems to indicate that he secured these data from some one other than Yushin, whose version of the log book is followed for the greater part in Volume 1 of the present work. However, even in one case in which he cites Yushin as the source of his figures (p. 121) they do not tally with Yushin's figures as given in the log book (footnote 274).

[241] The log book (Vol. 1, p. 153) gives 301½ miles.

changes of wind were again due to the nearness of land[242] and
that consequently we ought to turn more to the south without
paying attention to the parallel, inasmuch as the land extended
farther south and infallibly was to be expected farther south.[243]
This was further corroborated by our noticing sea parrots [and]
the John of Ghent [John of Gaunt] (*Pelecan. Bassanus*) and other
gulls[244] flying constantly from north and west to the south,

[242] See, above, footnote 144, last paragraph.

[243] Instead of "and infallibly was to be expected farther south" the
MS has: "and doubtless was to be expected on the 54th degree." See
also, above, footnote 144, first two paragraphs.

[244] Instead of "sea parrots . . . other gulls" the MS has: "anates
arcticas Clasii, Larum Joh. v. Rent [*sic*] dictum, Laros Wayel [*sic*]
Anglis dictos." By *Anas arctica* the pre-Linnean writers generally understood the Atlantic puffin, *Fratercula arctica* (Linnaeus), and John Ray
(Synopsis methodica avium et piscium, London, 1713, p. 120) describes
it as *Anas arcticus* Clus. The "Clasii" in the MS is undoubtedly a lapsus
for "Clusii." Pallas correctly renders it "Seepapageien." The Pacific
representative, which Steller saw, is *Fratercula corniculata* (Naumann).

"Larum Joh. v. Rent dictum," the gull called John of Ghent, of the
MS is hard to interpret. Pallas in the printed text suggests the gannet,
Pelecanus bassanus (= *Sula bassana* (Linnaeus)), and in his "Zoographia
rosso-asiatica" (Vol. 2, 1826, p. 307) he specifically states that Steller
during his American voyage saw it rather frequently flying among the
petrels. However, a few pages later, under *Catarractes skua*, with which
he synonymizes Ray's "Cornish gannet" (Ray, Synopsis, p. 128) and
Clusius' "*Skua hojeri*," he says that this was undoubtedly the bird which
Steller on various occasions had taken for an albatross. It is to be noted,
however, that neither the gannet nor the skua occur in the North Pacific.
While it is true that the Dutch by "Jan van Ghent" mean the *Sula
bassana* it is highly probable that Steller did not know this bird except
from description, and as there is no reference to the name Jan van Ghent
in Ray's "Synopsis," the book on birds we know Steller had with him, it
is permissible to suggest that he confused this name with that of "*Skua
hoieri*" and "*Sula hoieri*" of Clusius as quoted by Ray (Synopsis, pp.
128 and 123). The former is the true skua (*Megalestri skua* (Bruennich)),
but Ray says he "believes it to be the gannet of the Cornish," while the
former he refers, though somewhat doubtfully, to his *Anser bassanus*,
the true gannet. It is consequently not possible even to say whether the
birds seen by Steller were white or black, though more probably the latter, since the only light-colored bird in the North Pacific which even

while already some seaweeds came floating by, as happens when
land is approached.

On September 11 the wind and weather were as on the previous day. In the twenty-four hours we sailed twenty miles and
at noon calculated we were still 278 miles from Avacha.[245] Signs
of land were seen today as yesterday.

On September 12 the weather was cloudy and dark throughout
the day, and calm besides; the signs of birds and floating objects
were the same as before. Instead of the favorable wind expected
towards the evening, we encountered a wind directly from the
west with rain and progressed only two miles[246] during these
twenty-four hours.

The 13th of September was a bright day. In the morning a
NW by W wind arose, held on until two o'clock in the afternoon,
and then died down.[247] Moreover, many whales were seen at
play, and we expected nothing good.

On the 14th it stormed very hard all day and night from the
northwest, and we found ourselves compelled at noon to

---

remotely corresponds to the gannet in color is Rodger's fulmar (*Fulmarus
rodgersi*), while there are several dusky species.

Steller's "Laros Wayel Anglis dictos," gulls called Wayel by the English, causes no special difficulty. Ray (Synopsis, p. 130) mentions "the
great gray gull" to which he refers the "*Wagellus cornubiensium*," the
Wagel of the Cornishmen. Whether Newton be right that this is meant
for the skua (Alfred Newton: A Dictionary of Birds, London, 1893-96,
p. 1017) or, as others believe, for a young *Larus marinus* Linnaeus, there
can be little doubt that the birds observed by Steller were the young of
the glaucous-winged gull (*Larus glaucescens* Naumann), which is very
common in the region. (S)

[245] The log book (Vol. 1, p. 154) gives nearly 21 German miles (83.7
knots) for the 24-hour run and 283¼ miles for the distance from Avacha.

[246] The log book (Vol. 1, p. 155) gives nearly 8 miles (31½ knots).

[247] This hardly tallies with the log book, which indicates (Vol. 1, p.
156, entries for 7 and 9 A. M.) a light S to S by E wind in the morning
veering to a stronger SSW and WSW wind in the evening (p. 157, entries
for 7 and 8 P. M., September 14, astronomical day, i. e. September 13,
civil day).

drift, at which hour we calculated we were 258 miles from Avacha.[248]

*On the 15th we enjoyed a pleasant day. Towards noon the long-wished-for sun appeared again.[249] The unusual chilliness gave hope of a northerly wind, with the aid of which we might gradually get back on our old course. This might perhaps also have happened thus if we had been farther west in the Channel[250] or a couple of degrees farther south. As it was, however, we were too near land, so that towards evening even an owl[251]

[248] The MS reads "288 miles." This is clearly an error, as the MS itself reads farther up that on September 11 the vessel was only 278 miles from Avacha. The figure in the printed version agrees exactly with that given in the log book (Vol. 1, p. 157).

*Since one half of a leaf in the German original was greatly damaged all matter concerning September 15th and 16th, as well as concerning September 19th to 21st and the 24th had to be supplemented from the [Russian] translation.—P. [See also Pallas' footnote, between footnotes 132 and 133, above, and the Preface, p. viii, above.]

[249] From here to the end of the paragraph the MS reads: "Towards evening the unusual chilliness increased our hope for a north wind, as with a NW wind since five o'clock in the morning we had again been able gradually to get back on our course, which perhaps also might have happened thus if we had been 40 [or this might be the figure 10 corrected into 20] miles farther west in the Channel, in which they erroneously tried to persuade themselves to be, [and] a couple of degrees farther south. As it was, however, we were close to and behind the land, which nobody, however, would believe, although towards evening an owl, *sych*, which came from land, appeared for half an hour about our vessel. Many river gulls also [showed themselves], and more than two *svinki* were seen to rush about, carrying on their play for a quarter of an hour and thus causing us to reflect doubly: first, that we were near land and, second, that once more a storm was to be apprehended, because these animals in particular indicate changes at sea and are, as is well known, thereby incited to such play."

[250] See, above, footnote 149.

[251] As just indicated, Steller in the MS adds the Russian word *sych*. This name Pallas assigns in his "Zoographia rosso-asiatica" specifically to the pearly owl (*Cryptoglaux tengmalmi* (Gmelin) = *Stryx passerina* Pallas, Zoogr. rosso-asiat., Vol. 2, 1826, p. 323, but not of Linnaeus), which is a bird of the wooded interior and does not occur in the region visited by Steller. On the other hand the same name is used by the na-

appeared about the vessel. River gulls[252] also showed themselves, and about six *svinki*,[253] or storm fishes, gamboled around us, from which we could plainly enough presage the coming storm.

On September 16, soon after midnight, there came up a southeast wind which lasted until nine o'clock, when it suddenly jumped from south to west and from there to north, then went back to west again, and became south-southwest towards three o'clock in the afternoon, when it began to rain. However, during the forenoon we had progressed so far that at twelve o'clock we figured we were yet 240 miles from Avacha.[254] This was the first contest with the southeast wind, which we afterwards met so often and became so well acquainted with, that we really knew its shifts beforehand.—In the afternoon we saw a very large quantity of seaweed drifting towards our vessel from the north, also the same kind of large bundles as on August 2 and the days following, when we were among and between the American islands.[255]

---

tives of Bering Island for the snowy owl (*Nyctea nyctea* (Linnaeus), Stejneger, *U. S. Natl. Museum Bull. 29*, 1885, p. 223), but it is not likely that the bird seen by Steller belonged to this conspicuous species, and he does not definitely identify it as such. It is more probable that by *sych* he meant to indicate one of the smaller species, in this case undoubtedly the short-eared owl (*Asio flammeus* (Pontoppidan) = *A. accipitrinus* (Pallas), which occurs throughout the Aleutian chain, specific reports being had from Attu, Atka, and Unalaska, etc.   (S)

[252] No true river gulls live in the Aleutian Islands.   It is therefore probable that Steller mistook some other small gull for river gulls.   It is then permissible to conjecture that the species seen by him was the red-legged kittiwake, *Rissa brevirostris* (Bruch), which has bright red feet, like the river gulls, and inhabits the Aleutian Islands from Bering Island to Sannak (163° W.).   (S)

[253] *Svinka* (understood *morskaya*) means little sea pig and, like that and the German "Sturmfisch," is a general term for the common porpoise (see also, above, footnote 135).

[254] The log book (Vol. 1, p. 159) gives 241¼ miles.

[255] Steller under date of August 2 and the following days has nothing about drifting bundles of any description.   Perhaps he meant to refer to the reed grass, *Calamagrostis*, mentioned by him in the journal (see, above, p. 29 and footnote 55) without there assigning a date.   (S)

On September 17 we had a violent and, in addition, very changeable wind though mostly from NW by W. At noon we reckoned ourselves to be 234 miles from Avacha.[256] During the entire day birds were seen flying from the north to the west.

On September 18 we had showers; the wind was SW by W. At noon we were 229 miles from Avacha.[257] At sunset I observed large flocks of small snipes and other land birds flying from north to west.

On September 19 the weather was clear but rather cold. The wind was NW by W. At noon we were 226 miles from Avacha,[258] and saw sea otters repeatedly. On the 20th wind and weather were as on the day before, and in the night there was a complete calm.

The 21st brought very pleasant weather with sunshine. The sea was quieter than we had seen it for two months. Towards evening a southeast wind came up, but about two o'clock[259] after midnight the wind shifted to NW by W.—The 22nd was very pleasant, the wind NW by N.—On the 23rd it stormed all day and night, and we sailed northerly with a southwest wind. This evening the second man on our vessel died, the grenadier Tretyakov.

On the 24th of September the weather was gloomy almost the whole day. Towards evening to our great dismay we saw land ahead of us in latitude 51°, and many islands seemed to lie only three or four miles from us.[260] We took the bearings of the land,

256 The log book (Vol. i, p. 160) gives practically the same distance, 233¼ miles.

257 The log book (Vol. i, p. 161) gives 227½ miles.

258 The log book (Vol. i, p. 162) gives 224¾ miles.

259 The MS has "one o'clock." The log book (Vol. i, p. 165) records a N by W wind at 1 A. M. and a NNW wind at 3 A. M.

260 Instead of "and many islands . . . from us" the MS reads: "The mainland and the high, snow-covered mountains we saw at a distance of 6 to 8, the many islands, however, only 3 to 4 miles from us." The land seen was probably Adak and Atka Islands with the intervening islands. One of the high snow-covered mountains seen was probably the volcano on Great Sitkin Island (on these identifications see Vol. i, p. 168, footnotes 100 and 101, and p. 338). The conception of the members

but, because we were too near and too far north and also because with the southwest wind we were going straight towards land without being able to pass to the south of it, we turned hurriedly towards the east back to sea. This would not have been necessary if we had let ourselves be warned by the signs of land, known so long and so often called to mind, and gone farther south. But even this very morning Khitrov's unlucky proposition to go still farther north, because he thought that the land extended straight west in latitude 56°, and imagined that he was already in the Channel,[261] came near being approved.—It was most fortunate that we caught sight of the land while yet day and before the storm came up which did shortly afterwards, for otherwise we should certainly have run onto it in the night, or else, in spite of ourselves and without any means of escape, should have been driven by the southeast wind and been wrecked on it. In the excitement it was incidentally hinted at among the officers that this was surely the place where we had parted from Captain

---

of the expedition was that they were still skirting the mainland of America and that the islands which they recognized as such were offshore islands. This conception is reflected in two maps by the officers themselves showing the results of the expedition, one showing Bering's and Chirikov's tracks according to their own calculations, published by Sokolov in *Zapiski Hydrogr. Depart.*, Vol. 9, St. Petersburg, 1851 (copied by Lauridsen in his "Vitus Bering"), and the other by Lieutenant Waxel, published by Dall as Pl. 70 in Appendix No. 19, *U. S. Coast and Geodetic Survey Rept. for 1890* (for references see bibliography in Vol. 1, pp. 365, 366, and 366–367; see also, below, title of Fig. 29). On both maps the mainland is shown to extend west about as far as this point (see also, above, Fig. 14).

Although, as stated in Vol. 1, p. 338, no name is recorded in the log book to have been given to this land, Müller (Sammlung Russischer Geschichte, Vol. 3, 1758, p. 223) says that one of the highest mountains was named Mt. St. John as it was the church day of the conception of John the Baptist. Davidson (Tracks and Landfalls of Bering and Chirikof, 1901, p. 40) repeats this statement and seems, on his accompanying map and in the text, to identify Korovin Volcano, 4852 feet high, as Mt. St. John (Great Sitkin volcano is 5033 feet). The name, in the form of "The Mountain of St. John", also occurs on the map by Waxel just referred to. (J)

[261] See, above, footnote 149.

Chirikov.[262] And it is quite true that on that occasion, when we went south after having weathered the storm, we were told by the men that land had been seen to the north, which at the time we would not believe, and thus missed the right way. Captain Chirikov has without doubt touched land here,[263] a circumstance of which I have already made mention in the beginning of this account.*

On September 25 with an increasing and continuous storm we scudded until noon under the lower sails, spanker, and fore-course (just as on the night before) in order to get away from the land in a southeasterly direction, being in constant danger of losing spars and masts because of the very violent wind. In the

[262] On this point see, above, footnote 42, last two paragraphs.

[263] Chirikov did touch land in this region, anchoring off Adak Island on September 9 (see Vol. 1, pp. 302–306, 319–320, 346–347). Steller knew that Chirikov had struck land on that date, for, although Steller reached Petropavlosk after Chirikov had left for Okhotsk (see Vol. 1, pp. 280 and 329), copies of Chirikov's journal and report were doubtless available to him, either there or at Bolsheretsk, right across the peninsula, where he prepared the present journal during the winter of 1742–1743 (see below, p. 190, footnote 1). However, from that information he must have assumed that the landfall of the St. Peter on September 24 was about $2\frac{1}{4}°$ in longitude to the *west* of the landing place of the St. Paul on September 9 (longitude of the former vessel from Vaua, 20°45', according to the log book, Vol. 1, p. 167; longitude of the latter, about 23°, according to the implication of the corrected distance in Chirikov's report, Vol. 1, p. 320; see also map in Zapiski Hydrogr. Depart., Vol. 9, 1851, mentioned in footnote 260; see Vol. 1, Pl. I) while it really was about $1\frac{1}{4}°$ to the *east*.

By his previous reference to Chirikov to which Steller alludes in the next clause, he probably means his mention, on pp. 24–25, above, of the land alleged to have been seen to the north at the time the two ships parted company. (J)

* The location of the land here mentioned and noticed during Bering's outward voyage and on the return on the 51st parallel agrees fairly well with the now well-known Aleutian Islands, and the actual difference is doubtless attributable to the chances of a stormy navigation.—P. [That this land could not have been noticed on Bering's outward voyage has already been dealt with in footnote 42, last paragraph. This does not, of course, affect the correctness of Pallas' identification of the landfall of September 24. (J)]

afternoon we began to run only under the spanker, because we were already tolerably far from land and, on account of the west wind, need not fear being driven on the land.

On September 26, although the west wind died down somewhat, the sea remained turbulent, and we were now already three days retreating towards the southeast.

On September 27 we again had a very violent storm from the southeast, which, however, after an hour veered to the west and continued with extreme violence. Every now and then we could hear the wind rush as if out of a narrow passage, with such terrible whistling, raging, and blustering that we were every minute in danger of losing masts or rudder or else of seeing the vessel itself damaged by the force of the waves, which pounded it as when cannons are fired, so that we were expecting every moment the last stroke and death. Even the old and experienced pilot, Andreas Hesselberg,[264] could not recall among the experiences of his fifty years at sea having passed through a storm which even resembled it.

On the 28th of September the storm continued with even greater violence, together with hail, lightning, and rain. We were now for the fifth day being continuously driven back towards the southeast.

On the 29th it seemed throughout the day as if it might abate. Towards 10 o'clock at night, however, the wind, suddenly shifting to the southeast, once more heralded a most terrific storm, then shifted again to west, and continued as before.

On the 30th, about five o'clock in the morning, we encountered a storm from the southwest of such redoubled violence as we never have experienced before or since; we could not imagine that it could be greater or that we should be able to stand it out. Every moment we expected the destruction of our vessel, and no one could lie down, sit up, or stand. Nobody was able to remain at his post; we were drifting under the might of God whither the angry heavens willed to send us. Half of our crew lay sick and weak, the other half were of necessity able-bodied

[264] On the spelling of this name, see above, footnote 33, last paragraph.

but quite crazed and maddened from the terrifying motion of the sea and ship. There was much praying, to be sure, but the curses piled up during ten years in Siberia prevented any response. Beyond the ship we could not see a fathom out into the ocean because we continuously lay buried among the cruel waves. Furthermore, we could neither cook nor have anything cold to eat except half-burnt biscuits, which were already beginning to run short. Under such conditions no one any longer possessed either courage or counsel. They began too late to regret that matters had not been managed right and that various things had been overlooked.—Let no one imagine that our situation is here represented as too dangerous, let him rather believe that the most eloquent pen would have found itself too weak to describe our misery.

During October 1 this terrible southwestern storm continued with equal violence. Now for the first time the officers began to consider that, if God would help in weathering the storm, they should seek a harbor in America, in consideration of the fact that the weather thus late in the fall is too severe and unsettled, that we had already been driven back too far east, and that most of the men were sick and weak. For to go a couple of degrees farther south was too much out of the way for them. But even now I could not believe that they were earnest in their decision, as every one of them had his goods and their caretaker (*prikash-chik*) in Kamchatka.—Today, and before as early as September 24, I observed two phenomena that I had never seen before in my life, namely, the *ignes lambentes*, or Castor and Pollux, which the sailors call St. Elmo's fire, and then the terribly rapid flight of the clouds which, during the storm with incredible swiftness shot like arrows past our eyes and even met and crossed each other with equal rapidity, often from opposite directions.

On October 2 it began at last to moderate, which, however, it took the sea more than twenty-four hours to do. Nevertheless, the wind remained southwest and the sky was dark. Since September 24 we had been driven back towards the east over fifty miles. We had twenty-four men sick and two dead.—As I had supposed, so it also came to pass: there was again talk of Kamchatka, which, however, God was not willing we should reach this year.—But the joy did not last long, for towards ten o'clock at night we again encountered a southeast wind with the usual violent gusts and storm, so that the minds of all again became as shaky as were their teeth already from the scurvy.

On October 3, because of the excessively violent storm, we scudded under the spanker. For the first time the weather was very clear and unusually cold.—On the 4th it began to moderate a little; the air continued clear and very cold, although we had sunshine for a few hours; we also used the lower sails. However, this luck did not last long but was suddenly interrupted by a southeast wind with rain, followed by a violent storm from the southwest. But we had by this time become quite accustomed to the storms as well as to the daily deaths.—Also on October 5 we still scudded under the spanker. With the violence of the gale the weather was very clear and unusually cold.

On October 6 we scudded likewise under the spanker; for, although the storm had gone down somewhat, the sea was still running too high. During the greater part of the day the sun was visible; at times, however, hail and snow squalls occurred, and, shortly after, we saw rainbows twice; at the same time it was very cold. Towards evening many sharks (*Canes Galeos*)[265] were seen for the first time on this voyage, swimming about our ship. During the night the wind died down. This day our ship's brandy gave out.

On October 7 the air was cold and clear. At seven o'clock in the morning we began again to make use of the lower sails but with poor success on account of the high sea. The wind was SW by W.

On October 8 the wind and the weather during the day were as on the day before, but towards evening, about three o'clock, the unlucky southeaster suddenly started in with greatest force. Two hours later with a westerly wind we again encountered a very severe gale with mixed rain and hail. It seemed now as if it would finally be decided to go to America, since, with the lower

[265] See, above, footnote 121. (S)

sails set even in this gale, we were running toward the north-east.

On October 9 the storm became even more violent, conse-quently we scudded northeast the whole day. However, we had sunshine today and a very clear night. During the 10th the storm continued with equal violence. Lieutenant Waxel very eagerly made it his business to persuade the Captain Com-mander, who, because of too much inactivity, was laid up very badly with the scurvy, to agree that we should approach the mainland of America in order to winter there, as the impossi-bility [of reaching Kamchatka] was obvious and as within a few days we should no longer be able to handle the sails and the ship with so many sick persons, when it would seem that one and all, with the whole equipment, must be irretrievably lost. But the Commander, who had been imposed upon so often, placed now as little faith in the one as in the other and encompassed his un-qualified opinion in the command that a vow might be made for the purpose of collecting money, by the Russians for the church of the expedition in Avacha but by the Lutherans for the church at Viborg.[266]

On the 11th of October we got very beautiful bright weather and sunshine. The wind was WNW, and with it we sailed south-west. Towards night the wind died down completely, and it became as calm as on September 21. However, about one o'clock after midnight a strong south wind began to blow, with which we scurried westward at such a rate that we made more than one and three-quarter miles an hour. On the 12th we ran with this wind W by N; but towards noon the wind shifted to south-west, and about six o'clock in the evening we again got a fierce storm with snow, rain, and hail. A rainbow was also seen.

On October 13 the storm moderated. Owing to the contrary

[266] In the MS the last clause reads: "a vow might be made and money collected, one half to be given to the Russians for the church of the expe-dition at Avacha, but the other half to the Lutherans for the church in Viborg." Doubtless Viborg, Finland, not Denmark, is meant, inasmuch as Bering lived at the former place.

westerly wind we tacked between south and northwest. During the forenoon the sun was seen frequently, but in the afternoon it began alternately raining and hailing, and towards evening a rainbow was again seen. On the 14th the sea quieted down completely; the air at the same time was clear, the sun shone, but it was rather cold nevertheless. On this day the talk of America was again started.[267] On the 15th we had sunshine all day, moderate northwest winds, and a quiet sea.

On October 16 the weather was very pleasant and warm and the sea still. Towards evening, about six o'clock, God sent us a strong south wind with which at first we sailed [at the hourly rate of] three, and soon after four knots. During the night the wind shifted to the east, so that we made five, six, and six and a half [knots]. At the break of day it veered to the northeast and became so strong that we dared to run only under the lower sails.

On October 17 it rained the whole day. For the first time we now sailed twenty-four hours with a steady northeast wind, though it was altogether too strong. After we had advanced 24 miles in twenty hours, the wind increased to such a degree that from four o'clock in the evening we had to lay to. At night it stormed rather hard, but in the morning it began to moderate.

On the 18th of October the weather was by turns bright and dark, though very cold, the sea rather quiet, and the wind NW by N. We sailed all day SW by W [at the rate of] two and two and a half knots. By this time we had thirty-two sick persons. However, both the sick and those who of necessity were up were extremely depressed because of the changeable wind. During the 19th the wind, course, and weather were as on the day preceding. Grenadier Kiselev[268] died.—On the 20th the wind,

[267] In the MS there here follows this sentence: "But as our officers constantly prate only about what gets into their heads, I am not going to heed their talk until they shall reflect beforehand upon what they intend to say, since up to this time I credit them with no brain work, as they only think, do, and talk according to and to the extent of what they see with their eyes."

[268] Spelled "Kisselow" in the Pallas text, which in English transliteration would be Kisselov.

course, and weather were the same as on the day before, though it
stormed in the night. The *sluzhiv* [servant] Kharitonov died.—
There was no change in the wind and the course on the 21st;
towards the evening, however, we encountered a storm, and the
soldier Luka Zaviakov[269] died.

On October 22 we had bright weather, sunshine, heavy frost,
and westerly wind, and the course was set N by E straight for
the mainland, a decision taken suddenly, since it was reported to
Lieutenant Waxel that there were only fifteen casks of water on
hand,[270] of which three[271] had become damaged and were almost
empty. Because of the many other heavy expenses nobody had
been willing to be responsible for iron hoops on the barrels,
although on board wooden hoops decay during such a long
voyage.[272]

On the 23rd of October the wind changed and, with the wind,
the eagerness of the officers to go to America. During the forenoon, therefore, we ran with southeast wind and in the afternoon
and night with east wind at such a rate,[273] in spite of the bad
weather and hail showers, that in twenty-four hours we made 31
miles, and thus, with thirteen casks of water, we pushed on close
to America with the intention of either reaching Kamchatka or
stopping at the earliest opportunity at the nearest convenient
island. This was proclaimed openly in order to discourage the
sick still more.

On October 24 the wind and the weather were as on the day
before; in the evening, however, the wind became northerly.
We had progressed with it so far that, according to Mr. Waxel's
reckoning, we were believed to be 134 and, according to second

[269] Spelled "Sawialow" in the Pallas text, which in English transliteration would be Savialov or Zavialov.

[270] On this decision see the log book for October 23 (Vol. 1, p. 196),
1 P. M. and footnote 108.

[271] The MS has "two," which tallies with the statement in the next
paragraph.

[272] In the MS this sentence differs considerably but is too obscure to
admit of translation. (S)

[273] The MS has in addition: "toward the west."

mate Yushin's, 122 miles from Avacha.[274] We were gradually nearing the parallel of 53° because it was believed that there was no more land in the way, and the decision was made to keep steadily on 52°, so that, in case of eventual extreme lack of water, we might be in a position to make use of any wind blowing along the land of Kamchatka. If the wind should become northerly, we would run between the first and second Kurile Islands and anchor there; however, if the wind should come from the south we could make the port of Avacha with even less difficulty; besides, easterly winds would be advantageous in all events. This project, brought upon the tapis by Lieutenant Waxel, was indeed the most reasonable, in case they wanted to go to Avacha without letting themselves be turned away by something else. But time will tell how constant they were in this matter and why, likewise at whose instigation, five days later, without any reason whatsoever they wickedly deviated from it, which might have been the destruction of many [men] and of the vessel, nay of us all, if God, manifestly by a miracle, had not preserved us, wherein the officers had as little part as their own understanding and conscience probably has persuaded them that they have.— Moreover, misery and death suddenly got the upper hand on our ship to such an extent that not only did the sick die off, but those who according to their own assertion were well, on being relieved at their posts, dropped dead from exhaustion. The small allowance of water, the lack of biscuits and brandy, the cold, dampness, nakedness, vermin, fright, and terror were not the least important causes.

On October 25 we had very clear weather with sunshine. Still, there were occasional hailstorms in the afternoon. In the morning we discovered to our astonishment to the north of us, on the 51st parallel, a large and high island[275] which on the

---

[274] For the day's run to noon of October 24 the log book as published in Vol. 1 (p. 197), which is the one kept by Yushin, records a distance of 142¾ miles.

[275] Probably Kiska Island. As to the basis for this identification, see Vol. 1, p. 199, footnotes 111 and 110.

outward voyage we had forty miles to the east of us.[276] At noon we were in 50° 35' north latitude.[277]

On the 26th of October the sea was very quiet, the air gloomy, frosty, and frequently alternating snow and hail. At noon the reckoning was yet 103 miles from Avacha.[278]

On October 27 after one o'clock in the night we got a SSW wind with which we sailed northwest throughout that night and day in order to make the latitude of 52° as agreed upon. The calculation at noon gave still 90 miles from Avacha.[279] In the afternoon the wind changed to a gale; however, now that the men have become bolder and have learned to know the vessel and our masts better, the topsails were kept standing all day. It was now quite evident that we were in the Channel,[280] because the waves, even when a storm arose, were not so high and the winds were not subject to such sudden changes. I also observed now that the waves, with winds of the same force, did not rage so furiously as in September, probably because now the air was heavier and stronger[281] and consequently exercised a greater

[276] It is not readily evident how Steller derived this incorrect estimate. According to his own statement the island lies on the 51st parallel; on the outward voyage it was on June 7, at noon, that the *St. Peter* crossed this parallel (see log book, Vol. 1, p. 52). The log book gives the longitude from Vaua of that position as 5° 05' while that of October 25 is given (Vol. 1, p. 198) as 13° 09'. The difference, representing the distance between the two points on an east-west line, would be about 8°, or, in this latitude, 303 nautical miles. As compared with this, 40 [German] miles are 160 nautical miles. Even 8° is too little, owing to the error in longitude accumulated during the voyage (see Vol. 1, p. 210, footnote 124); the real difference in longitude between the two points is about 14° (see Vol. 1, Pl. I), or 530 nautical miles. (J)

[277] The log book (Vol. 1, p. 198) gives 50° 40' by dead reckoning and 50° 50' by observation. On a matter bearing on the true latitude of the vessel at this time see, however, Vol. 1, p. 199, footnote 110.

[278] The MS reads 108 miles. The log book (Vol. 1, p. 199) gives 111½ miles.

[279] The log book (Vol. 1, p. 200) gives 100¼ miles.

[280] See, above, footnote 149.

[281] Instead of "stronger" the MS has "colder."

pressure on the surface of the sea.[282] The same reason will also explain the fact that now the air is clear and brighter, while on the other hand nothing but fog and thick and dark atmosphere prevail in spring and summer, inasmuch as the west, southwest, and south winds, which mostly blow steadily through the spring and summer, fill the atmosphere with vapors which are only driven hither and thither, but not dispersed, by the occasional north winds. However, through the coldness of the air these vapors are condensed in the form of hail and snow and consequently are precipitated, so that the air becomes clearer after each squall; whereupon it remains calm for a while, until new vapor has gathered at the same place.[283]

On the 28th of October, in the morning, we were surprised again by something new: When the day broke we observed a great change in the water, from which it was not difficult to conclude that we must be near land. When the lead was heaved we found ourselves in fourteen fathoms. A little later the atmosphere cleared and we saw an island ahead of us, straight on our

[282] In the MS the following passage, of which the first sentence may be considered parenthetical, here intervenes: "In this I saw an explanation of the phenomenon that the waves, with a wind of the same force in both cases, reach the shores twice as high in autumn and winter as they do in spring and summer, because the pressure is from the center towards the periphery and the shores offer resistance. Also [continuing the argument on the less turbulent sea], the air is cleared in autumn by the frequent falls of hail and snow, and these, in falling, deaden the motion of the waves by their pressure."

[283] If Pallas' text be read in conjunction with the MS, of which the only essential variant has been quoted in footnote 282, Steller's thought in this passage may possibly be rendered as follows: The heavy and cold air of autumn and winter has, as compared with the conditions existing in spring and summer, a deadening effect on wave formation in the open sea, both by exerting greater pressure on the surface of the water and by the blanket of hail and snow which results from the condensation of moisture in this form at this season of the year. On the other hand, because this pressure is from the center outwards and because this pressure is greater in autumn and winter than in spring and summer, it causes higher waves to strike the shore in the former seasonal half of the year than it does in the latter half.

course, only about a mile distant.[284]   It lay NE and SW in
relation to the mainland of America and did not seem to be very
high, but rather low, with flat and sandy beaches. For the second
time we had here occasion to see plainly God's gracious help,
as we should have been done for without fail if we had come into
this situation a couple of hours sooner and in the dark of night,
or if God, even now, had not driven the fog away. We might
well conclude that, in addition to the islands seen, there must
have been many others here and there along our course, which
we may have sailed past at night and in foggy weather, indicated,
it is true, by the seaweed constantly drifting from land towards
us. Similarly, about this time a small species of diver, known as
starik,[285] flew aboard our vessel during the night; these birds
habitually pass the night on the rocks and fly against everything

[284] Buldir Island (see Vol. 1, p. 201, footnote 114, and p. 339). As to a
different identification, namely as Kiska Island, see Vol. 1, p. 199, footnote 111. Steller's immediately following statement, that the island
trends NE–SW, to a certain extent fits Kiska better, although it might
apply to the transverse southeastern portion of Buldir, but the specific
statement in Khitrov's journal (Vol. 1, p. 201, footnote 115) that the
island sighted on October 28 trended WNW–ESE, which is precisely
the trend of the longitudinal, or main, portion of Buldir (U. S. Coast
Chart No. 9102), would seem to confirm the identification as Buldir.
Steller's description of the island as not very high (see, however, Yushin's
log book 7 A.M. entry "sighted high land," Vol. 1, p. 201) would apply
equally to Buldir and to the southern part of Kiska, both of which do
not exceed 1200–1500 feet in height (the northern part of Kiska, consisting of a volcanic cone of 4050 feet altitude, may even have been
thought by the officers of the *St. Peter* to be a separate island; see Vol.
1, p. 199, footnote 112); but Steller's statement that the island's beaches
were flat and sandy could only apply to Buldir, as Kiska's shores are
described as "hilly and rocky" (U. S. Coast Pilot, Part II: Yakutat Bay
to Arctic Ocean, U. S. Coast and Geodetic Survey, Washington, 1916,
p. 222). If to these criteria be added the probable position of the *St. Peter*
at the time of sighting the islands in this region, as discussed in Vol. 1,
p. 199, footnote 111, the identification as Buldir seems highly probable.
(J)

[285] *Starik* (a Russian word meaning old man; so called probably from
the white hairlike feathers on the head; hence Gmelin's name *Alca
antiquus* and Pallas' *Uria senicula*) is the "ancient murrelet" (*Synthli-*

that they see only dimly near at hand, like owls in the daytime.[286]
Because of this, large numbers of them around Avacha are caught
alive with the hands* by merely sitting down near them covered with a mantle or *kuklanka* (a fur coat of the Kamchadals),
under which they then gather as if in a ready nest.—Under the
circumstances it was our luck that Master Khitrov's unfortunate
proposition was not accepted: he would that we should anchor
here out in the open sea and lower the boat in order to fetch water
from shore, regardless of the fact that only ten feeble persons
were left, who, though able to lend a hand, were yet in no condition to hoist the anchor again from the bottom; so that in the
storm which ensued three hours later we should assuredly all
together have found our grave in the waves.

On October 29 we continued our course with the same wind.
At intervals it rained throughout the day. On the 30th, likewise
in the morning, we saw in latitude 50° and some minutes two
islands,[287] lying close to one another, which were separated from

---

boramphus antiquus (Gmelin)), which is a common breeding bird in the
region where Steller observed it (records: Commander Islands, Attu,
Agattu, Semichi, Atka, Unalaska, etc.). The suggestion in Pallas' next
footnote that this bird was probably one of the small auks mentioned in
his "Spicilegia" is not correct, as admitted later on by Pallas himself
(Zoogr. rosso-asiat., Vol. 2, 1826, p. 368). In the latter work he quotes
Steller's account of how the Kamchadals catch these birds, knowledge
of which Steller evidently first obtained after his return to Kamchatka
in 1742. See also, above, footnote 239. (S)

[286] Thus reads the MS, which seems a more reasonable statement
than that of the published version, which reads: "and, like owls, in the
daytime fly against everything that they see only dimly in the darkness."

* This seems to have reference to that rare species of Alca which is
described and figured in Pallas' *Spicil. Zool.*—P. ["Spicilegia zoologica,"
Berlin, 1767.]

[287] The Semichi Islands (see Vol. 1, p. 202, footnote 117). They consist
of three islands, but possibly only two were seen, or, if the whole group
was taken for two islands, this may have been due to the fact "the two
eastern ones are low and the western one higher" (U. S. Coast Pilot,
Part II: Yakutat Bay to Arctic Ocean, U. S. Coast and Geodetic Survey,
Washington, 1916, p. 223).

According to the log book (Vol. 1, p. 202) the islands were first sighted

each other by a narrow channel. These were taken for the first two Kurile Islands, especially on the statements of and the landmarks indicated by the Kamchatkan natives who were on board the vessel. But as no one would venture to assert it positively, the officers disregarded it recklessly, nor would they listen to those who thought they saw the mainland beyond. And yet four other reasons might be advanced for this, viz.: (1) the many sea otters which now appeared about our ship and never before during the voyage had come in sight so frequently, while at the Kurile Islands they really are so numerous;[288] (2) the west wind, which we encountered here suddenly, as an indication that

---

at 10 A. M., October 29 (both civil and astronomical date)—not on October 30.

The latitude of "50° and some minutes," which was partly responsible for the fallacious identification of the Semichi Islands as the "first" (i. e. northernmost) two Kurile Islands, is, of course, incorrect. The Semichi Islands lie in 52° 45′ N. How this large error, for latitude, came about is not quite clear. The log book for October 29 (Vol. 1, p. 202) records a latitude of 52° 31′ at noon, two hours after sighting the islands, which, although probably a little short, was much closer to the truth. There is evidence in the other records of the expedition of uncertainty in the determination of latitude at this time. The log book records the latitude of 50° 50′ by observation for noon of October 25 (Vol. 1, p. 198), while Khitrov's journal gives 51° 11′ as the latitude of the vessel's probably slightly more southerly position four hours earlier (Vol. 1, p. 199, footnote 110), which seems to be much nearer the truth. Likewise, Waxel in his report records (Vol. 1, p. 276) that, from the later more accurately determined latitude of the landing place of the expedition on Bering Island, it was evident that the ship's reckoning was out by about one degree of latitude when they passed Copper Island on November 4 (see also Vol. 1, p. 208, last entry in log book under November 4). In addition to the unrealized effect of currents and tidal rips these errors may possibly legitimately be ascribed to the scurvy-stricken condition of the officers and crew (J).

[288] What Steller says here about the sea otter being so numerous on the Kurile Islands does not conflict with his previous statement (p. 31, above). Steller only knew of their occurrence at the first two Kuriles (see also footnote 57, above). (S)

we were near land;[289] (3) the observed latitude,* which corre-
sponded to that of the first Kurile Islands;[290] (4) the heavy fog
which in the west seemed to hide the land, while on the contrary
it was clear in the east. Likewise, if the position of Lopatka and
the first Kurile Islands be compared with the five days' course
kept from there directly north and the distance run then west
by south until we came to Bering Island—the position of which,
as we learned later, is twenty miles straight east of the mouth of
the Kamchatka River—it will be seen that without any doubt
we have been at the first two Kurile Islands,[291] though the officers,

[289] See, above, footnote 144, last paragraph.

* If this single reason had not been against it, I would much rather
regard it as certain that the two islands in question were the westernmost
of the nearer, properly so-called Aleutian Islands; at least, this conjecture is a very probable one.—P.

[290] The latitude of "50° and some minutes" does correspond to that of
the "first," or northernmost, Kurile Island but not to that of the Semichi
Islands, as we have just seen in footnote 287, nor to that of "this westernmost of the nearer Aleutian Islands," as Pallas in his footnote nearly
correctly identifies the islands sighted on October 29. (J)

[291] This deduction does not seem permissible even on the basis of
Steller's own statements. For the meaning of this passage would seem to
be: "If our route be plotted from the point where we sighted the two
islands (= 'from there') as it led northwards for five days (see, below,
p. 129, and footnote 296) and then W by S until we came to Bering Island
and if this route be considered in relation to the now known position of
Bering Island as 20 [German] miles due east of the mouth of the Kamchatka River, then the initial point of this route at the two islands will be
seen to coincide with the known position in latitude of the first Kurile
island in 50° and some minutes." These relations can be visualized better
in the form of a right-angled triangle (see Vol. 1, Pl. I) in which the
southern apex is represented by the point at which the Semichi Islands
were sighted, the right angle by the point at which the course changed
from northward to westward, and the northwestern apex by the mouth of
the Kamchatka River, the two included sides of the right angle being
represented respectively by the northward course and by the westward
course with its extension to the mouth of the Kamchatka River. This
leaves the third side of the triangle, with its northwest-southeast trend,
to represent the eastern coast of Kamchatka. Steller's argument would
thus be understandable if he thought that this coast trended northwest-
southeast. But a few pages below (p. 134) he tells us precisely that it

to this hour, will neither admit nor believe it. Besides, to the question, why they went as far north as 56°, consequently deviating from their own decision not to go beyond 52°, thereby causing our non-arrival and the final ruin of the ship, they will not in all eternity be able to return an answer.

Accordingly, against all reason we sailed northward because, as Master Khitrov told Lieutenant Waxel, otherwise our dead reckoning would not come out even,[292] since it indicated still over sixty miles from Avacha. They would rather jeopardize the welfare of us all than appear to have made a mistake, whereby, in addition, the whole chart, as well as the reckoning, would be incorrect and uncertain, if the error were only covered up and not pointed out, especially since, in view of the long voyage, the many storms gone through, the unknown currents,[293] the beating to windward, etc., and also in view of the fact that the method used in determining the longitude (though the best, in default of a better one) is nevertheless subject to very many inaccuracies, an error of thirty to forty miles would not be considered bad, while on the contrary a too precise exactness must to intelligent people appear either a miracle or humbug.

Apart from this baseless excuse, there seems, judging from many circumstances, to have been hidden behind it quite a secret motive which had egotistical designs for its object. Namely, they preferred to go north in order to be able to use the dire necessity as a pretext why they would have to enter the mouth of the Kamchatka River and not Avacha [Bay]. This we under-

---

trends northeast-southwest. The only basis for his deduction is thereby removed, and it remains unclear how he arrived at it.

In this connection it should be remarked that Bering Island is not due east of the mouth of the Kamchatka River, that point being in latitude about 56⅓°, while Bering Island is bisected by the 55th parallel. (J)

[292] On the error in longitude in the ship's reckoning see Vol. I, p. 210, footnote 124, and pp. 276 and 332.

[293] The printed text has "bei . . . nicht bemerkten Strömungen," strictly "in view of currents that were not noticed"; the MS has "bey so vielen . . . observirten Ströhmen," "in view of the many currents whose presence was observed."

stood well enough, partly from the bad terms they were on with the Captain Commander and partly from the jealousy between Lieutenant Waxel and Master Khitrov.[294]

On October 31, as well as on November 1, 2, and 3, nothing unusual occurred except that our patients were dying off very rapidly[295] and many at a time, so that it was scarcely possible to manage the ship or make any change in the sails. At God's mercy, under two leaders, betrayed and sold, we proceeded northward, through the 51st, 52nd, 53rd, 54th, 55th, and as far as the 56th parallel. On November 4, in the middle of the night, we started to run W by S with a suitable wind.[296] On the 5th in the morning the order was given to shorten sail so as not to run on the land. Everybody stood on deck and looked about for the land, as the thing was announced with very great mathematical certainty. To our great astonishment it chanced that towards nine o'clock land was seen.[297] It is impossible to describe how great and extraordinary was the joy of everybody at this sight. The half-dead crawled up to see it, and all thanked God heartily for this great mercy. The Captain Commander, who was a very sick man, became not a little aroused, and all talked of how,

[294] In the MS the sentence is here completed with the clause: "and our subsequent ruin is therefore attributable more to artificial than to natural winds."

[295] The log book (Vol. 1, pp. 204, 206, 208) and Waxel's report (*ibid.*, p. 281) record the death of four persons in these four days (civil dates).

[296] Thus, according to Steller, the course was northward from the morning of October 30 (see, above, p. 125 combined with p. 127)— equivalent in his chronology to the time of sighting the two islands—to the middle of the night of November 4 (p. 129), agreeing with his previous reference (p. 127) to the "five days' course . . . directly north." This does not agree with the log book. According to this record the northward course lasted 3¼ days—from the time of sighting the two islands (actually, on the morning of October 29) to 5 P. M. of November 1 (civil date, or November 2, astronomical date; see Vol. 1, p. 206). It was on that date, and not on November 4, according to the log book, that the course was changed to westward (see also Vol. 1, Pl. I). (J)

[297] Copper Island (Medni Island); see Vol. 1, p. 208, footnote 120. According to the log book it was the morning of November 4 (both civil and astronomical date).

after having suffered such terrible misery, they were going to care for their health and take a rest. Little cups of brandy concealed here and there made their appearance in order to keep up the joy. These cool words were heard trumpeted forth with the voice of a herald: "Even if there had been a thousand navigators, they could not have hit it off to a hair like this in their reckoning; we are not a half mile off."—The sketches of Avacha were pro-

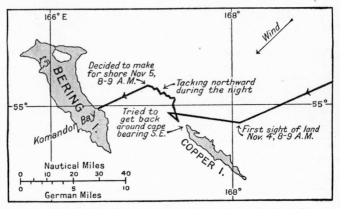

Fig. 15—Track of the *St. Peter* on approaching Bering Island, November 4–5, 1741, as reconstructed by L. Stejneger. Scale, 1:2,560,000. (This should replace the representation in Vol. 1, Pl. I.)

duced and the land was found to agree exactly with them; Isopa [Cape], Cape Shipunski, the mouth of the harbor, and the *mayak* [lighthouse] were pointed out.[298] Although it might have been known from the dead reckoning that we were at the very least on the 55th parallel, while Avacha is two degrees farther south, yet, because a headland was seen which was taken to be Shipunski, our course was set northerly. When we had doubled the sup-

[298] Isopa Cape is the modern Cape Povorotni south of Avacha Bay; Cape Shipunski is north of the bay. The lighthouse was on the headland on the northern side of the entrance to the bay. (For locations see Vol. 1, Pl. I, inset, also p. 49, footnote 5.)

posed Isopa, which was, however, the extreme point of the first island,[299] and already were in the arm of the sea between the first and the second island,[300] though before the channel [between them] could be seen or their nature as islands ascertained, it happened that the noon sun permitted an observation to be taken, according to which we were between the 55th and 56th degrees of north latitude, and we consequently began to doubt, quite naturally, that this was the region about Avacha. We attempted to get back around the first island's end, which lay to the southeast[300a] and had been taken for Isopa, but in vain, though

[299] Copper Island.

[300] Bering Island.

[300a] A careful study of the movements of the *St. Peter* as related by Steller possibly affords a surer clue to the track of the vessel on approaching Bering Island than the log book alone. For this reason the following analysis is here offered as affording possibly a more satisfactory reconstruction of her track in these waters than shown on Pl. I in Vol. 1. In the otherwise admirable plotting of the track by the late Captain Bertholf on that map he used Steller's journal as well as the log book (see Vol. 1, p. 330, footnote 1). But in the translation of the journal available to him at that time the words at this point, "das nach Südosten gelegne Ende der ersten Insul" were rendered by "the southeastern end of the first island" instead of "the first island's end, which lay to the southeast." The log book is not explicit enough alone to counteract the resulting misconception; but its details, when applied to the interpretation here given, will, it is thought, be found to fit well. This interpretation, which is illustrated on Fig. 15, is as follows:

During the night of November 4 (astronomical; we accept the chronology of the log book in preference to that of Steller) the *St. Peter* was approaching the Commander Islands on a WSW course. On the following morning towards nine o'clock (Steller; log book) land was sighted SW by S, 4 German miles away (log book, Yushin's version). This bearing, which need not be taken too literally, however, would indicate the higher parts of south-central Copper Island. As more land gradually came into view the northwestern cape of Copper Island covered the southern end of Bering Island to such an extent that the two islands appeared as one continuous land with a deep embayment beyond the northwestern cape of Copper Island. This was the situation which led to identification with the Avacha Bay region. The northwestern cape of Copper Island was taken for Isopa Cape (the modern Povorotni; see Vol. 1, Pl. I), some headland on the eastern shore of Bering Island for

we tried to do so by tacking until evening.—Towards evening we turned northward, in order to get away from land, because a storm was expected, that actually broke out in the night. The shrouds of the mainmast broke from the violent force of the wind and [the weight of] the sails, since the topsails and courses remained set as they had stood during the day without being reefed and since it was impossible for the feeble remnant of the crew to take them in during the middle of the night in the growing storm; so that in the morning, after the turbulent and stormy night had changed into a most pleasant day and weather, we did not dare carry all the sail we could and should have carried. On November 6,[301] Master Khitrov, who had already won Lieutenant Waxel over to his side and also brought around the petty officers and the crew, therefore proposed that, in view of the late autumn

---

Cape Shipunski, and the reëntrant between them for the embayment at the head of which lies Avacha Bay. When the vessel had passed beyond the northwestern cape of Copper Island and the noon observation of the sun had shown that they were not in the latitude of Avacha, they tried to get back around (Steller: "um das Ende zurücke herumzukommen") the point which was then to the southeast of them, viz. the northwestern cape of Copper Island. This they had difficulty in doing, and in order not to be driven on a lee shore during the night (a northeaster was blowing), they changed to a N/E and N course by tacking. On thus changing their course at 5 P. M. the northwestern cape of Copper Island bore SE ½ E (Khitrov's version of the log book: Vol. 1, p. 210, footnote 122; for thus his "S point" may reasonably be interpreted inasmuch as to them it was Isopa, the point limiting the embayment on the south). All during that night in their enfeebled condition they fought against that northeasterly gale. While not able to keep a straight northerly course, they had succeeded in keeping far enough away from Bering Island so that in the morning they were still at an estimated distance of six German miles (Steller) to the east of it. The "S point" recorded by Yushin as bearing SE ½ E 3 German miles at 5 A. M. may again be taken to refer to the northwestern cape of Copper Island sighted over the stern. At 8 A. M. the decision was made to steer straight for the shore in sight, and accordingly the course was changed to WSW, which led the vessel to Komandor Bay on Bering Island. (S)

[301] On November 5 (civil and astronomical), according to the log book (Vol. 1, p. 209, 8 A. M. entry, and p. 210, footnote 123).

season, the bad weather,[302] the unserviceable mast, as well as the
distance from Avacha, and the small number of sailors and soldiers, feeble and sick, the Captain Commander should call a
council, in which it should be decided to land in the bay to the
west of us, where, at an estimated distance of six miles, a harbor
was suspected. And this was accomplished in the following
manner:—The Captain Commander, it is true, insisted that since
we had already risked and endured worse and could still use the
foremast and since we had yet six casks of water, an attempt
should be made to reach the port [Avacha]. However, both
officers opposed his proposition, insisted on a landing in the bay,
and persuaded all the petty officers and crew, who likewise
assented but nevertheless were only willing to sign on condition
that, as non-experts, they could be assured that this land was
Kamchatka; if it was not, they would be prepared still to risk
the utmost and work to the last. As Master Khitrov now assured
them that, if this were not Kamchatka, he would let his head be
cut off, the outcome depended upon a few only, some of whom,
however, by smooth as well as hard words were compelled to
sign against their will.—The Captain Commander thereupon
ordered the adjutant, at that time reduced to the rank of sailor,
at present the Lieutenant Ovtsin, to express his opinion.[303] But
as he concurred in the opinion of the Captain Commander, the
order of both the officers was: "Get out, shut up,[304] scoundrel,

[302] The MS has as an additional reason: "the broken shrouds."

[303] Lieutenant Dimitri Ovtsin, on the expedition subsidiary to Bering's the purpose of which was to explore the Arctic coast of Siberia (see,
above, footnote 18), was detailed in 1734 to survey the coast from the Ob
to the Yenisei, which he did in 1737. But because of friendly relations
with the exiled Prince Dolgoruki, Ovtsin was reduced to the rank of
sailor and was sent to Okhotsk to join Bering. Bering, apparently, used
him as an adjutant, or assistant. See also his later counter-statement on
the condition of the *St. Peter* after the landing on Bering Island (Vol. 1,
pp. 231–232). (G)

[304] Both in the printed version and the MS these two expressions are
given in German transliteration of the Russian, which, in English transliteration, would be: *von*, get out; *malshi* (in the printed version, *mashi*),
i. e. *molchi*, hold your tongue.

rascal!" and so he had to leave the council. At last, according to the favorite[305] order of precedence, my turn came also; but warned by the example of Ovtsin I answered: "I have never been consulted in anything from the beginning, nor will my advice be taken if it does not agree with what is wanted; besides, the gentlemen themselves say that I am not a sailor; therefore I would rather not say anything."—I was next asked if I, as a person worthy of belief (being now for the first time so considered) would not at least add a written certificate regarding the sickness and the miserable condition of the crew.—This I thereupon undertook to do, in accord with my conscience.—And thus it was decided to enter the bay and to land there but to send from there to Lower Kamchatka Post for *podvods* (posthorses) to transport the men.

Although the situation contradicted the opinion that this was Kamchatka, because the mainland of Kamchatka from Chukotski Nos to Lopatka lies NE-SW, while the island before us, afterwards called Bering's Island, lay NW-SE, yet the hope remained that it might be a *nos* (headland) of Kamchatka, most of which have such a position. On the other hand, the land seemed too large to be a *nos* of Kamchatka, as no headland in Kamchatka is known that equals the fifteen-mile-long Shipunski, while by eye measure the island before us was at least twenty-five miles long[305a] and, besides, other projections extended from it very far out to sea, so that by good rights it might have been considered a separate land rather than a promontory. In the end, therefore, the conclusion would probably have to be drawn that it could be neither the mainland of Kamchatka nor a promontory of it, which [promontory, if it were a promontory], moreover, no one on our vessel professed to know. However, the erroneous

---

[305] "favorite" does not occur in the MS.

[305a] This probably refers to the whole stretch of land as it lay before them, from the southeastern cape of Copper Island to the northeastern cape of Bering Island. For this distance 25 German miles is a reasonable approximation. Cape Shipunski may be considered 15 German miles long if measured from its tip to midway of the embayment constituting the Gulf of Kronotski (see Vol. 1, Pl. I). (J)

idea originating from Bering's first expedition was too deeply
rooted, that there could exist no island so near Kamchatka,
especially in this latitude where the sea was said to have been
explored for fifty miles from land.[306]

Accordingly they went, without further concern, straight
towards the land into the bay. When towards four o'clock in the
evening we were so near land that it appeared to be scarcely a
mile away from us, and for three hours no officer had shown
himself on deck, as was usual on all dangerous occasions, and all
were gently and sweetly sleeping, I went to the Captain Commander and begged that he might order that at least one of the
officers should remain at his watch,[307] since it looked as though
they were intending to run ashore without further precaution.
Both officers were indeed ordered on deck, but they evinced no
further concern than to order the course to be held straight for
land. When towards sundown we had arrived within two versts
of shore, they began to heave the lead and advanced about
another verst, where at last they anchored in nine fathoms. It
was now already night but very light on account of the moon,
and after the lapse of half an hour such a heavy surf, or *burun*,
began to run at this place that the ship was tossed about like a
ball and threatened to strike against the bottom. It also snapped
the anchor cable, so that we expected nothing short of being
wrecked. The confusion became still greater by the constant
breaking of the waves, the shouting and the wailing, so that no
one any longer knew who should give or who should take orders.
All that the officers, terrified and seized with the fear of death,
did was to shout that the [cable of the] second anchor be cut
and a new [anchor] thrown over into the *burun*. When they had

[306] Instead of "from land" the MS reads "to the east." On this sally,
made during the first expedition, see, above, footnote 223. In the earlier
passage of the journal (p. 100) it was said that no land was found within
thirty miles of Kamchatka. Possibly these somewhat divergent figures
may be due to a misreading by the copyist of the figure 30 as 50.

[307] In the MS the following clause is here inserted: "in order to decide
on the place to anchor."

thus lost two anchors in half a quarter of an hour, the present Lieutenant Ovtsin and the boatswain came forward at last and forbade the throwing over of any more anchors, because it was to no purpose so long as we were tossed about among the waves on the reef; they advised on the contrary to let the vessel drift. —When we had thus passed inside the bar and the surf, these men, who alone had retained their reason, let the last anchor drop, because we now lay between the *burun* and the shore as in a placid lake, all at once quiet and delivered of all fear of stranding.—The wise sayings which were uttered while we were in imminent peril of death, and about which one could scarcely keep himself from laughing[308] even in the midst of the danger, can be judged, among other things, by the fact that someone asked whether the water was very salty, as if death in fresh water would be more delightful.—Another, for the better encouragement of the panic-stricken men shouted: "Oh, God! It is all over with us! Oh, God, our ship! A disaster has befallen our ship!" God now laid bare the resoluteness of the hearts which ordinarily were bursting with courage. He who until now had been the greatest talker and advice-giver[309] kept himself concealed, until others, with God's help, had found a way out, whereupon he began valiantly to preach courage to the men, though he himself from high-heartedness was as pale as a corpse. —In the midst of this hubbub another ridiculous performance took place. For several days we had been carrying with us the dead trumpeter and a soldier[310] in order to bury them ashore,

[308] A somewhat different aspect is furnished by this passage as given in the MS. It there reads: "How strange the behavior and the wise sayings uttered at this time were, can be judged by the fact that some, in spite of the imminent peril of death, could not refrain from laughing, and that someone asked whether the water was very salty," etc.

[309] Probably Khitrov is meant.

[310] Instead of "the dead trumpeter and a soldier" the MS reads "the bodies of several soldiers and of the trumpeter." The entries in the log book would seem to confirm the published version as edited by Pallas, as, of all who died between October 31 and November 5, the bodies of all but two (the grenadiers Alexei Popov and Ivan Nebaranov; Vol. 1,

but now they were thrown without ceremony neck and heels into the sea, because some superstitious fellows, at the beginning of the terror, regarded the dead bodies as the cause of the commotion.

The night was otherwise very pleasant and light. On November 7[311] we had again a very pleasant day and a northeast wind. I spent the morning in packing so much of my baggage as I could get hold of near by. Because I could see plainly that our vessel could not hold together longer than till the first violent storm, when it must either be driven out to sea or dashed to pieces against the beach, I, with Mr. Plenisner, my cossack, and several of the sick men went ashore first.

We had not yet reached the beach when a strange and disquieting[312] sight greeted us, inasmuch as from the land a number of sea otters came towards us in the sea, which from a distance some of us took for bears, others for wolverines, but later on we learned to know, unfortunately, only too well.—As soon as we had landed, Mr. Plenisner went to hunt with the gun, while I investigated the natural conditions of the surroundings. After having made various observations, I returned towards evening to the sick men, and there I also found Lieutenant Waxel, who was very weak and faint. We refreshed ourselves with tea. Among other things I remarked: "God knows whether this is Kamchatka!"—receiving, however, from him [Waxel] the reply: "What else can it be? We shall soon send for *podvods* (horses); the ship, however, we shall cause to be taken to the mouth of the Kamchatka River by cossacks, the anchors can be had any time, the most important thing now is to save the men."—In the

---

pp. 208 and 209) are mentioned as having been cast into the sea. Also, there is no mention of a trumpeter among the dead prior to landing on Bering Island; subsequent to that date, however, on November 11 (astronomical; November 10, civil) is recorded (*ibid.*, p. 215) the death of the trumpeter Mikhail Toroptsov.

[311] According to the log book, on November 6, as far as events can be correlated from the brief record in that document.

[312] The words "and disquieting" are not in the MS.

meantime Mr. Plenisner also came back, told what he had seen, and brought half a dozen ptarmigans,[313] which he sent on board to the Captain Commander with the Lieutenant, in order to revive him by means of the fresh food. I, however, sent him some nasturtium-like herbs[314] for a salad.—Later two cossacks and a cannoneer arrived, who had killed two sea otters and two seals, news which appeared quite remarkable to us. When we reproached them for[315] not bringing the meat in for our refreshment, they fetched us a seal, which seemed to them preferable to the sea otter for eating. As evening came I made a soup from a couple of ptarmigans and ate this dish with Mr. Plenisner, young Waxel, and my cossack. In the meanwhile Mr. Plenisner made a hut out of driftwood and an old sail, and under it we slept that night alongside the sick.

On November 8[316] we again enjoyed pleasant weather. This morning Mr. Plenisner made the agreement with me that he should shoot birds, while I should look for other kinds of food, and that we should meet again towards noon in this place. With my cossack I went at first along the beach to the eastward, gathered various natural curiosities, and also chased a sea otter;

[313] The ptarmigan of the Commander Islands is a distinct species peculiar to those islands (*Lagopus ridgwayi* Stejneger). A full account of the natural history of this bird has been given by me in *U. S. Natl. Museum Bull. 29*, 1885, pp. 194-202, and a colored plate has been published in *Zeitschr. für die Gesammte Ornithologie*, Vol. 1, 1884, Budapest, Pl. 5. (S)

[314] The MS reads: "Nasturcische Kräuter und Bach Brung." The nasturtiums were undoubtedly *Cardamine pratensis* L. and *C. hirsuta* L. (*C. umbellata* Green), probably also *Cochlearia officinalis* L., all of which are common on Bering Island. "Bach Brung" is a lapsus for Bachbung (*Veronica americana* Schwein.), the American brooklime. The European *Veronica beccabunga* L. and the above crucifers are used extensively as salads in Northern Europe and are credited with antiscorbutic properties. (S)

[315] To render the wording of the MS, insert here, between "for" and "not" the words "having taken the skins and."

[316] Judging by the later reference to anchoring the vessel more securely, this day was November 7 (civil date) according to the log book (Vol. 1, p. 212).

my cossack, however, shot eight blue foxes,[317] the number and fatness of which as well as the fact that they were not shy astonished me exceedingly. Moreover, since I saw the many manati[318]

[317] In the MS: "blue *pesci.*" The blue fox, or Arctic fox (*Alopex lagopus* (Linnaeus)) of the Commander Islands has been described by Merriam as a separate form under the name *Vulpes beringensis* (*Proc. Biol. Soc. of Washington*, Vol. 15, 1902, p. 171). The *pesets*, as it is called by the Russians (*pestsi* in the plural, whence *pesci*, the German form of transliteration in the MS), is still common on the island and is of considerable economic importance (see Stejneger, *Proc. U. S. Natl. Museum*, Vol. 6, 1883, pp. 87–88; *idem*, Asiatic Fur-Seal Islands, 1898, pp. 30, 42–44). (S)

[318] i. e. sea cows. The sea cow (*Hydrodamalis gigas*, also known as *Rhytina gigas* or *stelleri*) possesses great interest on account of its early extermination by man, which took place in 1768, twenty-seven years after its discovery by Steller. He gave a very full description of this animal in his famous treatise "De bestiis marinis" (*Novi Commentarii Acad. Sci. Imp. Petropol.*, Vol. 2, 1751). Skeletons and parts of skeletons are preserved in various museums, such as Petrograd, Helsingfors, Stockholm, etc. The U. S. National Museum in Washington possesses one whole and several partial skeletons together with an unequaled series of skulls from Bering Island. Most of this material was secured by L. Stejneger in 1882–1883.

The sea cow was an herbivorous animal, anteriorly shaped somewhat like a seal, but with a large caudal fin like that of a whale and without hind legs. It belongs to the mammalian order Sirenia, which represents an "aquatic modification of the Ungulate type." The Sirenians are therefore not related to the seals and whales but more probably to the elephants. The members of this once numerous group are nowadays represented only by the true manatees and the dugong, which inhabit only the tropical waters of both hemispheres. The only northern form known is Steller's sea cow. There is no indisputable evidence of its having ever inhabited other coasts than those of the Commander Islands, as the find of a rib on Attu, the westernmost of the Aleutian Islands proper, does not necessarily prove that the animal once lived there, though that is not improbable. The history of this animal, imperfectly known as it is, fills volumes, and all we can do in the present connection is to refer to some of the more recent literature, viz. Stejneger: On the Extermination of the Great Northern Sea-Cow (Rytina), *Bull. Amer. Geogr. Soc.*, Vol. 18, 1886, pp. 317–328; *idem*, How the Great Northern Sea-Cow (Rytina) Became Exterminated, *Amer. Naturalist*, Vol. 21, 1887, pp. 1047–1054; *idem*, Investigations Relating to the Date of the Extermination of Steller's Sea-Cow, *Proc. U. S. Natl. Museum*, Vol. 7, 1884, pp. 181–189. (S)

near shore in the water, [animals] which I had never before seen and even now could not well make out as they lay all the time half in the water, but concerning which my cossack asserted that they were known nowhere in Kamchatka,[319] and likewise since nowhere any tree or shrubbery was to be seen, I began to doubt that this was Kamchatka, especially as the sea sky over in the south indicated sufficiently that we were on an island surrounded by the sea.[320]

Toward noon I returned to the hut and after dinner decided to go with Mr. Plenisner and our cossack westward along the beach in order to search for forests or small timber; we found nothing whatever, but saw a few sea otters and killed various

[319] The MS is somewhat differently worded regarding the manati: "and moreover, since I saw the many manati near shore, which I had never seen before nor could know what kind of sea animal it was because I saw one half all the time under water, and as my cossack, to the question whether this were not the *plebun* or the *makoai* of the Kamchadals, about which I had only gathered verbal information, replied that this animal occurs nowhere in Kamchatka," etc.

Plevun, according to Pallas (Zoogr. rosso-asiat., Vol. 1, 1811, p. 287), is the Russian name for the sperm whale. In the form "*pla-un*" it is used by the present inhabitants of the Commander Islands for one of the ziphoid whales (*Berardius bairdii* Stejneger; see *Proc. U. S. Natl. Museum*, Vol. 6, 1883, p. 76). Steller, in his "Beschreibung von dem Lande Kamtschatka," 1774, p. 105, has this to say on the *plevun*: "Man hat noch ein grosses Seethier, so einem Wallfisch gleichet, aber kleiner und in der *circumferenze* nach Proportion viel dinner ist, dieses nennen die Russen *Morskox Woik* [*morskoi volk*], einen Seewolf; die Itälmen [natives of Kamchatka] *Plebun*." (There is another large marine animal, which is like a whale, but smaller and proportionately much less in girth. The Russians call it *morskoi volk*, a sea wolf; the Itaelmens, *plebun*.)

Makoai, also according to Pallas (*op. cit.*, Vol. 3, 1831, p. 63), is the Kamchadal name for the large shark occurring in the waters off the east coast between Capes Kronotski and Lopatka. This may be the *Somniosus microcephalus* (Bloch), which is said to occur in Bering Sea, or *Lamna cornubica* (Gmelin), which has been taken in Avacha Bay. (S)

[320] After the words "that this was Kamchatka" the MS reads: "[and to think] rather that it might be an island, wherein the sea-sky over in the south confirmed me still more [in my conviction] that the land was not wide and therefore was an island everywhere surrounded by water."

blue foxes and ptarmigans. On the way back we sat down at a small stream, regaled ourselves with tea, and thanked God heartily that once more we had good water and under us solid ground, at the same time recalling how wonderfully we had fared and remembering the unjust conduct of various people.

During the day an effort was made by the disposition of the anchors, large and small, as many as we had, to make the ship secure to the land[321] in the best possible manner, and for that reason the boat did not come ashore. In the evening, as we were sitting around the camp fire after having eaten our meal, a blue fox came up and took away two ptarmigans right before our eyes. This was the first sample of the many tricks and thefts which those animals practiced on us later.—I had to encourage my sick and feeble cossack, who regarded me as the cause of his misfortune and reproached me for my curiosity which had led me into this misery, [thus] making the first step to our future companionship. "Be of good cheer," I said, "God will help. Even if this is not our country, we have still hope of getting there; you will not starve; if you cannot work and wait on me, I will do it for you; I know your upright nature and what you have done for me; all that I have belongs to you also; only ask and I will divide with you equally until God helps."—But he said: "Good enough; I will gladly serve Your Majesty, but you have brought me into this misery. Who compelled you to go with these people? Could you not have enjoyed the good times on the Bolshaya River?"—I laughed heartily at his frankness and said: "God be praised, we are both alive! If I have dragged you into this misery, you have in me, with God's help, a lifelong friend and benefactor. My intentions were good, Thoma, so let yours

[321] In the MS the words "to the land" do not occur. Also, the word at the beginning of the sentence here translated by "disposition" reads "Anbringung" in the published text, but "Ausbringung" in the MS. In the MS the meaning of the passage would rather seem to be that the vessel was anchored more securely where she lay, but not secured to the land—a construction which seems more in keeping with the description of this measure as given in the log book (1 P. M. entry, November 8, astronomical, in Vol. 1, p. 212).

be good also; moreover, you do not know what might have happened to you at home."

In the meantime I took this as a cue to consider how we could protect ourselves against the winter by building a hut, in case it turned out that we were not in Kamchatka but on an island. That evening, therefore, I started to confer with Mr. Plenisner about building a hut for all eventualities and assisting each other with word and deed as good friends, no matter how the circumstances might shape themselves. Although for appearance's sake, in order not to discourage me, he did not assent to my opinion that this was an island,[322] nevertheless he accepted my plan in regard to the hut.

On November 9 the wind was from the east and the weather rather bearable. In the morning we went out to look for a site and to collect wood and selected during the day the spot where we built later on and where the whole command also set up their huts and wintered.—However, we were far too busy killing blue foxes, of which I and Mr. Plenisner in one day got sixty, partly knocking them down with the axe and partly stabbing them with a Yakut *palma*.[323]—Towards evening we returned to our old hut, where again some of the sick had been brought ashore.

On the 10th of November the wind was from the east; in the forenoon it was clear, in the afternoon cloudy, and during the night the wind whirled much snow about. We carried all our baggage a verst away to the place which we had selected the day before for the building of a dwelling. In the meantime more sick were brought ashore, among them also the Captain Commander,[324] who spent the evening and night in a tent. I, with

[322] The published version has "keine Insel," which is a misprint. The MS has "eine Insel."

[323] The published version has *pama*, instead of *palma* as correctly rendered previously (p. 47). On this type of knife see, above, footnote 85.

[324] According to the log book (Vol. I, p. 213) this took place at 2 P. M. on November 9, astronomical time, or November 8, civil time (which is the time used by Steller in this journal). Waxel's report (*ibid.*, p. 277) gives the date as November 8, presumably astronomical time, as in other

others, was with him and wondered at his composure and singular contentment. He asked what my idea was about this land.— I answered that it did not look to me like Kamchatka; the great number and tame assurance of the animals of itself clearly indicated that it must be sparsely inhabited or not at all; but nevertheless it could not be far from Kamchatka, as the land plants observed here occur in the same number, proportion, and size as in Kamchatka, while on the other hand the peculiar plants discovered in America are not found in the corresponding localities. Besides, I had found on the beach a poplar-wood window shutter, with cross moldings, that some years ago the high water had washed ashore and covered with sand near the place where we later built our huts; I showed it and pointed out that it was unquestionably of Russian workmanship and probably from the *ambars* which stood at the mouth of the Kamchatka River. The most likely place for which this land might be taken[325] would be Cape Kronotski. Nevertheless, I did not fail to make known my doubts as to this, based on the following experience: I showed, namely, a piece of a fox trap that I had found on the beach during the first day; on this the teeth, instead of being of iron, consisted of so-called Entale,[326] of the

---

instances the unit used in the report is the same as that used in the log book. For 2 P. M. this would correspond to the civil date of November 7. If, however, the 2 P. M. entry is not exact and Bering's removal from the ship took place a few hours earlier, both the astronomical and the civil date would be November 8.

[325] In the MS the following words are here inserted: "in default of reliable information." The meaning of course is: If this is Kamchatka— which is not probable—the most likely place is the Cape Kronotski region.

[326] The MS reads: "consisted of a shell, the Entale of authors." The shell alluded to is the well-known toothshell, or tuskshell (genus *Dentalium*, from which systematic name the common name, "Entale," was derived), so called because of its shape, which resembles a walrus or elephant tusk. No *Dentalium*, as far as I have been able to ascertain, has been found in Kamchatka, and in that respect Steller's argument seems to be sound. A species (*D. rectius* Carpenter) occurs in Alaska and the eastern part of Bering Sea, but it is very brittle, entirely unsuited to serve

occurrence of which in Kamchatka I have no information and regarding which it consequently is to be supposed that the sea must have washed this token over from America, where, in default of iron, this invention may well have been made use of, while in Kamchatka, where iron already is plentiful through trade, it would be superfluous. I mentioned at the same time the unknown sea animal, manati, which I had seen, and the character of the water sky opposite in the south.—To all this I got the reply: "The vessel can probably not be saved, may God at least spare our longboat."

In the evening after having eaten in company with the Commander the ptarmigans which Mr. Plenisner shot during the day, I told Betge, the assistant surgeon, that he might live with us if he liked, for which he gave thanks; and thus our company now consisted of four. We therefore walked over to the place of our new quarters, sat by the camp fire, and discussed, over a cup of tea, how we would put our plan into execution. I built near by a small hut which I covered with my two overcoats and an old blanket; the openings on the sides were stopped up with dead foxes which we had killed during the day and were lying about in heaps, and then we retired to rest, but Mr. Betge returned to the Commander.

Towards midnight a strong wind arose, which was accompanied by much snow, tore off our roof, and drove the three of us from our quarters. We ran up and down the beach in the dark gathering driftwood, carried it to a pit dug like a grave for two

---

as teeth in a fox trap. Nor is it known to have been utilized by the inhabitants of those regions for any sort of implements. It is, or was, extensively used, however, for ornamental purposes, and it seems possible that the object found by Steller may have been not a trap, but a fragment of some wooden article to which the *Dentalium* had been fastened as an ornament, for instance, a wooden hat or mask. However, there is in the anthropological collection of the U. S. National Museum a part of a trap made of bone (No. 260,155), from Kotzebue Sound, which has inserted in it a pointed tooth of walrus ivory suggesting in size and shape a *Dentalium*. Is it possible that the one picked up by Steller can have been a child's plaything made in imitation of one like this?   (S)

persons, and decided to pass the night there. We laid the wood crosswise over it and covered the top with our clothes, overcoats, and blankets, made a fire to warm ourselves, went to sleep again, and thus, God be thanked, passed a very good night.

On the following day (November 11) I went down to the sea and fetched a seal, the fat of which I cooked with peas and ate in company with my three comrades, who in the meantime had made two shovels and begun to enlarge our pit.—In the afternoon the Captain Commander was brought to us on a stretcher and had a tent, made of a sail, put upon the spot that we had originally chosen for our dwelling place. We entertained him, as well as the other officers who had come to our pit, with tea.— Towards evening both officers returned to the ship. Master Khitrov even proposed to Lieutenant Waxel that they should winter on board the vessel in the open sea, because, according to his idea, more warmth and comfort could be had there than on land, where, for lack of wood, one would have to endure the winter in a tent. This proposition was now approved as very sensible, yet three days later[327] the Master, on his own accord, came ashore and could not be brought back on board the vessel by any orders when later he was to haul it up on the beach.— However, we continued to enlarge our underground home by digging and collected everywhere on the beach wood for a roof and inside coating.—This evening[328] we fixed up a light roof and in the person of assistant constable Roselius obtained the fifth member of our party.[329] In the same manner a few others, who still had strength left, began also to dig a four-cornered pit

[327] This does not seem to tally with the log book. Khitrov is himself the author of the entries as published in Volume 1 covering this period, and there are references which imply he was still on board the *St. Peter* as late as November 21 (astronomical; *ibid.*, p. 225). By November 26 (*ibid.*, p. 229) there is a statement implying that he was then on shore.

[328] The MS reads "every evening."

[329] A November 21 entry in the log book (Vol. 1, p. 225) would seem to imply that Roselius was still on board the vessel at that date. There is a reference, however (*ibid.*, p. 214), to his being ashore on November 9 (civil date), which is probably equivalent to Steller's November 11.

in the frozen sand and covered it over the next day with double sails in order to shelter the sick.

On November 12[330] we worked with the greatest industry on our habitation, observed also that others, following our example, dug for themselves in the same manner a third habitation which received its name from its founder, the boatswain Alexei Ivanov. —During the day many of the sick were brought from the vessel, some of whom expired as soon as they came into the air, as was the case with the cannoneer; others in the boat on the way over, as the soldier Savin Stepanov; some right on the beach, as the sailor Sylvester.[331]—Everywhere on the shore there was nothing but pitiful and terrifying sights. The dead, before they could be interred, were mutilated by the foxes, who even dared to attack the living and helpless sick, who lay about on the beach without cover, and sniffed at them like dogs. Some of the sick cried because they were cold, others because hungry and thirsty, since the mouths of many were so miserably affected by the scurvy that they could not eat anything because of the great pain, as the gums were swollen like a sponge, brown black, grown over the teeth and covering them.

The blue foxes (*Lagopus*),[331a] which by now had gathered about us in countless numbers, became, contrary to habit and nature, at the sight of man more and more tame, mischievous, and to such a degree malicious that they pulled all the baggage about, chewed up the leather soles,[332] scattered the provisions, stole and carried off from one his boots, from another his socks, trousers, gloves, coats, etc., all of which were lying under the open sky and could not be guarded because of the lack of well persons.

---

[330] According to the date indicated in the log book (Vol. I, p. 215) for Ivanov's activities, this would be November 10 (civil date).

[331] In the log book (Vol. I, pp. 219–220) and Waxel's report (*ibid.*, p. 281) the deaths are stated to have taken place on the following dates: the cannoneer (Ilya Dergachev) and the sailor Seliverst (= Sylvester) Tarakanov on November 15 (astronomical), the soldier Savin Stepanov on November 16 (astronomical). The last is stated to have died on board.

[331a] See, above, footnote 317, and, below, pp. 211–216.

[332] The MS reads "leather bags."

Even objects made of iron, and other kinds which they could not eat, were nevertheless sniffed at and stolen. It even seemed as if these miserable animals were to plague and chastise us more and more in the future, as actually happened, perhaps in order that we, like the Philistines,[333] might also be punished by the foxes for our eagerness for the precious Kamchatkan fox skins. It even seemed that the more of them we killed and tortured for revenge most cruelly before the eyes of the others, letting them run away half-skinned, without eyes, ears, tails, half roasted, etc., the more malevolent and audacious became the others, so that they also broke into our habitations and dragged out of them whatever they could get hold of, though occasionally, in spite of our misery, they moved us to laughter by their cunning and funny monkey tricks.[334]

November 14.[335] This afternoon, with Mr. Plenisner and Mr. Betge, I went hunting for the first time, or, as we afterwards used to say in the Siberian way, went on the *promysl*. We clubbed four sea otters, half of which we threw into a creek, which therefrom afterwards retained the name Bobrovaya Ryechka [Sea Otter Creek] and the place where we killed them Bobrovoe Pole [Sea Otter Field],[336] but the best meat, together with the skins

[333] The allusion is to Judges xv, 4 and 5.

[334] In the MS the whole passage beginning with the words "Everywhere on the shore" in the middle of the preceding paragraph, down to this point, ending with "monkey tricks," follows after the words "from Lyesnaya Ryechka (Wood Creek), thus named by us," on page 150 below. What led Pallas to make this transposition, other than a more orderly presentation of topics, is not clear, as it leads him into creating a confusion in the sequence of events (see the next footnote) as given in the MS.

[335] The MS has no date here, the account continuing as under date of November 13 follow, both in the printed text (see, below, p. 150) and in the preceding footnote. It should be noted that the happenings of November 13 follow, both in the printed text (see, below, p. 150) and in the MS; also that in both November 15 follows the 13th. Hence the sequence in the MS is Nov. 12, 13, 15; in the printed text Nov. 12, 14, 13, 15.

[336] As Steller does not say whether they went east or west from their camp, it is not possible to locate his Bobrovaya Ryechka and Bobrovoe Pole with certainty. The nearest creek to the east is Chigachiganakh,

and the entrails, we carried home, where we did not arrive until night. From the liver, kidneys, heart, and the meat of these animals we made several palatable dishes and ate them gratefully and with the wish that Providence would not deprive us of this food in the future or put us in the necessity of eating the stinking, disgusting, and hated foxes, which nevertheless, out of prudence, we did not want to exterminate but only to frighten. The precious skins of the sea otters we regarded already as a burden which had lost its value to us, and, as we had no leisure to dry and prepare them, they were thrown about from one day to another until finally they spoiled, together with many others, and were chewed to pieces by the foxes. On the other hand, we now began to regard many things as treasures to which formerly we had paid little or no attention, such as axes, knives, awls, needles, thread, shoe twine, shoes, shirts, socks, sticks, strings, and similar things which in former days many of us would not have stooped to pick up. We all realized that rank, learning, and other distinctions would be of no advantage here in the future or suffice as a means of sustenance; therefore, before being driven to it by shame and necessity, we ourselves decided to work with what strength we had still left, so as not to be laughed at afterward or wait until we were ordered. Thus we five[337] introduced among ourselves a community of goods with regard to the victuals we still had left and arranged our housekeeping in such a manner that at the end there might be no want. The others of our party, three cossacks, and the two servants of the Captain Commander,[338] whom we later took over, we man-

---

about 3 miles to the east (see map, Pl. II). To the northwest there are several small creeks much nearer, the first one about $\frac{2}{3}$ mile, the third one a little more than $1\frac{1}{2}$ mile distant. One of these is probably meant. (S)

[337] The MS reads "we five Germans." The following persons are meant: Steller, Betge, Plenisner, Roselius, and Boris Sänd, the addition of the last-named to the group, if it be he, being mentioned below under November 15 (p. 151; see also, below, footnote 348). (G)

[338] This is obviously the meaning, although strictly the published version reads: "The other three cossacks of our party and the two servants."

aged, though not exactly as before, yet in such a way that they had to obey when we decided anything jointly, since they received all household goods[339] from us. Nevertheless, we began in the meantime to address everybody somewhat more politely by their patronymics and given name, so as to win them over and be able to rely more on their fidelity[340] in case of misfortune later on; and we soon learned that Peter Maximovich was more ready to serve than Petrusha * was formerly. This evening we talked over how we would arrange our household affairs in the future, prepare beforehand against all unexpected mishaps, and, as far as possible, try to keep alive the hope of returning to Asia;[341] we also discussed the unfortunate circumstances in which we had been placed in such a short time that, setting aside the decencies of life to which everyone was entitled, we now were obliged to work in this unaccustomed way simply to sustain a miserable existence. Nevertheless, we encouraged one another not to lose heart but with the greatest possible cheerfulness and earnestness

---

etc. (Die übrigen drey Kosaken unsrer Gesellschaft und die . . . zwey Bedienten). The MS lacks the words "unsrer Gesellschaft"; if a comma be inserted between "übrigen" and "drey," the original meaning appears. That this comma is omitted in the MS is not surprising in view of its general lack of punctuation.

Steller has already mentioned his own cossack; and it is likely that two other members, probably Plenisner and Betge, each had a cossack as a body servant. The names of the two servants of the Captain Commander were Ivan Maltsan and Maffei Kukushkin (see list, Vol. 1, p. 235).

[339] The MS here has in addition: "and other necessaries."

[340] The MS here has in addition: "and in order to be one move ahead," i. e. prepared for eventualities.

* According to Russian custom only an equal or a person of higher rank is addressed, in addition to his Christian name, by the name of his father, to which is appended the syllable *vich*, which may be said to be the equivalent to the Irish prefix *Fitz* and the Scotch *Mac*. Less polite is the bare Christian name, especially when made into a diminutive.—P.

[341] The MS seems rather to read: "how we would arrange our household affairs in the future, in case this or that misfortune should occur, inasmuch as the hope of returning to Asia, so far as we were concerned, had not been completely given up."

to work for our own benefit as well as for the welfare of the others and by our exertions to support loyally their strength and undertakings.

Today[342] I brought the Captain Commander a young, still suckling sea otter and counseled him in every way and manner to let it be prepared for himself in default of other fresh food, but he showed a very great disgust at it and wondered at my taste, which adapted itself to circumstances.[343] He much preferred to regale himself with ptarmigans as long as possible, of which he received from our company more than he could eat.

On November 13 the building of dwellings was continued. We divided ourselves into three parties; the first went on the vessel to work in order to bring the sick and the provisions ashore; the others dragged home great logs a distance of four versts from Lyesnaya Ryechka[344] (Wood Creek), thus named by us; I, however, and a sick cannoneer[345] remained at home, I attending to the kitchen and the other making a sled for hauling wood and other supplies. While thus taking upon myself the office of cook

[342] Owing to the transposition mentioned in footnote 334 this episode in the MS still falls under November 12.

[343] An educated Englishman, the late Captain H. J. Snow, than whom no white man had more experience with the sea otter, has this to say on the same subject: "Steller, in speaking of the flesh of the otter, describes it as savory and delicious. There is no accounting for taste, of course. I have tried it on many occasions cooked in various ways, but a more disagreeable, ranker-tasting meat I have yet to find. Not a hunting season would pass without someone trying it. The sailors, both Chinese and Japanese, whom I had at different times, ate crow, shag, gull, fox, whale, and, of course, seal, fur-seal and sea-lion, but they always gave otter-flesh the go-by" (In Forbidden Seas, London, 1910, p. 279). (S)

[344] This is the stream debouching at "Polovina" on the map of Bering Island (Pl. II); its valley forms part of a transverse depression across the island terminating on the other side in Gladkovskaya Bay. (S)

[345] Probably Michael Chechuev, mentioned as cannoneer in the list in Vol. 1, p. 235. The only other cannoneer of the expedition, Ilya Dergachev, does not come into consideration, as, according to Steller, he had already died or, according to the log book, was to die in two days (see, above, footnote 331).

I also assumed a twofold minor function, namely, to visit the Captain Commander off and on and to assist him in various ways, as he could now expect but little service from his two attendants.[346] Furthermore, as we were the first to set up housekeeping, it also became my duty to succor some of the weak and sick and to bring them warm soups, continuing this until they had recovered somewhat and were able to take care of themselves.

This day the "Barracks" were completed, and during the afternoon many of the sick were carried in but on account of the narrowness of the space were lying everywhere about on the ground covered with rags and clothing. No one was able to care for another, and nothing was heard but wailing and lamenting, the men times out of number calling down God's judgment for revenge on the authors of their misfortune. And, truly, the sight was so pitiful that even the bravest might lose courage thereat.

On November 15,[347] at last, all of the sick had been brought ashore. We took one of them, by name Boris Sänd,[348] to be cared for in our dwelling, whom God withal helped back to health within three months. Master Khitrov also implored us for God's sake to take him into our company and give him a corner, because he could not possibly longer remain among the crew, who day and night let him hear reproaches and threats for past doings,[349] but as our dwelling was already filled up and as nobody was allowed to undertake anything without the assent of the others, all of us objected, as all were equally insulted by

[346] The MS here has in addition: "who often were not present when he asked for a drink of water."

[347] In the MS there is no entry for November 14. See, above, footnote 335.

[348] No such name appears in the list of survivors in Waxel's report (Vol. 1, p. 235). It is possible, however, that it is identical with that of midshipman Ivan Sint in that list.

[349] The MS reads: "who day and night reproached him for all kinds of past doings, accused him of all kinds of ill-treatment, and made all sorts of threats, so that he could not stand it any longer, and he would otherwise have to die under the open sky."

him, and refused him absolutely, especially because he was mostly sick from laziness and was the chief author of our misfortune.

During the days that followed our misery and work grew apace. Finally[350] Waxel himself was also brought ashore. He was so badly ravaged by the scurvy that we abandoned all hope for his life, but nevertheless we did not fail to come to his help with both food and medicine, without a thought of former treatment. We were all the more anxious for his recovery, as it was to be feared that, after his decease, when the supreme command would fall to Khitrov, the universal hatred would destroy all discipline and delay, or even prevent, the enterprises necessary for our deliverance. We also induced our men to build a separate hut for him and a few other patients,[351] but until it was erected he had to stand it in the Barracks.

In these days we also received the news, which depressed everybody still more, that our men sent out to scout had not found any indication in the west[352] of a connection of this land with Kamchatka or even the slightest trace of human inhabitants. Besides, we were in daily fear that our vessel, in view of the constant storms, might be driven out to sea and that with it we should lose at one stroke all our provisions and our hope of deliverance. Because of the high waves we were often unable for several days to reach the vessel in the boat for the purpose of landing as many of the supplies as possible.[353] In addition ten or

[350] In the MS this sentence is preceded by: "All the sick had been landed and."

[351] In the MS this clause is represented by the following fuller statement: "In spite of his urgent entreaty we could not take him into our hut, but we promised to assist so that a separate one could be built for him and a few other patients, which we induced our men to do."

[352] In the MS the passage up to this point reads: "On this day we also received the disheartening news from three of the men who had been sent out, which depressed the rank and file still more and made them less tractable, that no indication had been found in the west," etc.

The three men were Roselius and two men from Kamchatka (see Yushin's journal, Vol. 1, p. 229, footnote 126, last paragraph).

[353] Instead of this sentence, the MS has: "as because of the high waves

twelve men were likewise taken sick who until now had worked
steadily and beyond their strength and who until the end of the
month often stood in the cold sea water to their armpits.[354]
Altogether, want, nakedness, cold, dampness, exhaustion, illness, impatience, and despair were the daily guests.[355]

By a stroke of good luck the vessel, towards the end of November, was finally thrown up on the beach in a storm in a better
way than perhaps might ever have been done by human effort.[356]
As thereby the hope of preserving the food on hand, scant as it
was, as well as materials had been greatly raised, while at the
same time the task of wading through the water to the vessel
was rendered unnecessary, we began after a few days to give up
all work for the present and to recover. Only the necessary
household tasks[357] were continued. Three men[358] were again

we were unable for the next three or four days to reach the vessel in the
boat; moreover, on account of Master Khitrov, although he had already
been ordered a long while ago to beach the vessel, too many difficulties
occurred."

[854] In the MS this sentence reads: "In addition ten or twelve men who
until now had worked beyond their strength and without being relieved
and until the end of the month had often been obliged to wade in the cold
sea water up to their armpits, were so exhausted that complete cessation
of work was in prospect."

[355] The MS has this sentence in addition: "Even what little rest [we
had] was taken on the implied condition of gaining strength thereby for
still harder and more unceasing tasks, as far as could be foreseen."

[356] In the MS the following sentences are here inserted: "I consider it
unnecessary after this to note down everything that happened to us from
day to day in the order of my diary, as from this time on scarcely anything particular presented itself, except the weather, which I am going
to treat of separately, and the everyday tasks. Nevertheless, extraordinary happenings will not be omitted in the proper place with notation
of time." Steller's separate discussion of the weather and climate of
Bering Island forms part of the description of that island which in the
MS follows immediately after the narrative of the voyage. Pallas published this description in *Neue Nordische Beyträge*, Vol. 2, 1781, pp.
255–301 (discussion of weather, pp. 269–272), twelve years prior to his
publication of the journal in the same serial. This section appears in
Appendix A, below on pp. 205–207.

[357] The MS here has: "which, however, were very heavy."

[358] Anchiugov and two men from Kamchatka (see Khitrov's journal

sent out to go into the country eastward and gather information.
For all hope had not yet been abandoned that this might be
Kamchatka and, since an error in the latitude might have been
made, perhaps the region about Olyutora,[359] the large number of
foxes there also apparently lending probability to this view.
Others believed this to be Cape Kronotski, and, although the
error was easy to see, they loved to lull themselves into pleasant
dreams with such hopes.

A number of persons died ashore at the very beginning. Among
them we were particularly grieved over the old and experienced
mate, Andreas Hesselberg,[360] who had served at sea for more
than fifty years and at the age of seventy was discharging his
duties always in such a way that he carried to his grave the
reputation of a preëminently useful man, whose disregarded
advice might perhaps have saved us earlier.[361] Besides him
there died two grenadiers, one cannoneer, the master's servant,
one sailor, and finally, on December 8, Captain Commander
Bering passed away, from whom this island was afterwards
named. Two days after him his former adjutant, the master's

---

under Dec. 1 in Vol. 1, p. 230, and Yushin's journal, *ibid.*, footnote 127,
last paragraph).

[359] About 60½° N. on the east coast of Kamchatka (see Vol. 1, Pl. I;
there spelled "Olyutorsk"). Cape Kronotski is in about 55° N. The
seemingly divergent directions in which this reconnaissance is stated to
have been undertaken—east by Steller and south by Yushin—do not
conflict, nor do the directions of the previous trip—west according to
Steller, and north according to Yushin—inasmuch as the shore of Bering
Island at the point where the *St. Peter* had stranded has a local trend of
east-west as compared with the predominant north-northwest trend of the
coast north of this point and the south trend south of it (see Pl. II). (J)

[360] Hesselberg died on November 22. On the spelling of his name see,
above, footnote 33, last paragraph.

[361] The passage "discharging . . . saved us earlier" in the published
version is much briefer than the original in the MS, which reads: "discharging his duties as befits a faithful servant. Although he left behind
many upright people in the fleet who knew his worth and who had also
in part profited by it, he had nevertheless to suffer the misfortune now
to be treated as a silly child and idiot by men scarcely half his age and

mate Khotyaintsov, died, and on January 8 the ensign Lagunov, the thirtieth in the sequence and the last one of our number [to die].[362]

Inasmuch as the tragic end of the late Captain Commander has made different impressions on different people, I cannot but pause here awhile to make a few remarks regarding his past.

Vitus Bering was by birth a Dane, a righteous and devout Christian, whose conduct was that of a man of good manners, kind, quiet, and universally liked by the whole command, both high and low. After two voyages to the Indies he entered the service of the Russian navy in 1704 as a lieutenant and served in it with the utmost fidelity until his end in 1741, having worked his way up to the rank of Captain Commander. He was employed in the execution of various undertakings, of which the two Kamchatka expeditions are the most noteworthy. Fairminded persons cannot but admit[363] that to the best of his

---

one-third his skill, who had also learned lately from him part of what they knew, and to see himself scorned to such an extent that one had to wonder at his fate with particular pity that so miserable and ignominious an end could follow such long and honorable service and good behavior. This came to pass solely and alone because the Captain Commander, as well as the others, in their foolish conceit and pride took no more notice of his remonstrances than of the opinion of anybody else who did not agree with them and as a consequence did everything alone that they wanted to, with the result of what afterwards happened."

[362] Compare this enumeration of those who died after Hesselberg with the corresponding portion of the list appended to Waxel's report (Vol. 1, p. 282). The "marine grenadier" and "marine soldier" there named may be the same as Steller's "two grenadiers." Steller's "master's servant" may be included in the "Personal servants of the officers, two men" of that list, his "sailor" may be the "admiralty calker." According to the log book (*ibid.*, p. 230) and that list Khotyaintsov died the day after Bering died, and the wording in the MS is to that effect. As to the total number of members of the expedition to die, it seems to have been 32 (see Vol. 1, p. 282, and footnote 6 on that page).

[363] In the MS this sentence is preceded by the clause "Although there are various sources from which to arrive at a judgment as to his conduct on this second, important, and, on account of our many sufferings, trying expedition."

strength and ability he tried at all times to carry out the task imposed on him, though he himself confessed and often lamented that his strength was no longer equal to so difficult an expedition, that it had been made larger and more extensive than he had proposed, and likewise that at his age he could have wished to have the whole task taken out of his hands and put into those of a young and active man[364] of the Russian[365] nation.—As is well known, the late lamented was not born to quick decisions and swift action; however, in view of his fidelity, dispassionate temper, and circumspect deliberateness, the question remains whether another with more fire and heat would have overcome equally well the innumerable difficulties of and obstacles to his task without entirely laying waste these remote regions, when a commander such as he was, free from all self-interest, could scarcely keep his subordinates sufficiently under control in this matter.[366]—The only blame which can be laid against this excellent man is that by his too lenient command he did as much harm[367] as his subordinates by their too impetuous and often

[364] In the MS this phrase reads: "a young, active, and resolute man."

[365] This qualifying adjective appears only in the MS, and the thought is there amplified by this clause following the word "nation": "who in many cases could act more fearlessly and more successfully than an old man and a foreigner."

[366] The passage "would have overcome . . . in this matter" in the MS reads as follows: "would not, in view of the innumerable disagreements and difficulties, have delayed the work more or by too despotic action entirely ruined the regions hereabout, when this careful man, free from all private interest, was unable, because of the size of the command and the divergent inclinations of the subordinates, to prevent that, while he was busy putting out a fire [i. e. putting down trouble] in one place, another started up somewhere else." By the reference to laying waste or ruining these regions is probably meant that a more impetuous man would have favored a policy of exploiting and abusing the natives— a condition which Steller at the beginning of this journal (p. 13) says actually obtained during the first expedition, although this was probably not with the approval of Bering himself.

[367] The MS reads "half as much harm." This sentence in the MS differs in other respects, all unessential, from the published version.

thoughtless action.[368] He also had a somewhat too high esteem for his officers and too good an opinion of their intelligence and experience, and as a result they finally became too conceited, looked with contempt on all those near them and finally on the commander himself, and forgot their subordination, without thought of gratitude.[369]

While the departed often used to recall, with thanks to God, how from his youth up everything had come his way and how only two months before he had been in happy circumstances, the more is his sad and miserable end to be pitied. He would undoubtedly have remained alive if he had reached Kamchatka and had only had the benefit of a warm room and fresh food.

[368] In the MS there here follows this sentence: "Examples of both are at hand."

[369] The MS here has a long, highly sarcastic, and partly enigmatical harangue of the officers and defense of Bering, which Pallas has omitted in the printed text. As far as it is intelligible it may be translated as follows: "They demonstrated all too plainly that they were much too narrow-minded for this high opinion, which, very conscious of their own strength, they regarded as a result of fear and poor judgment. It therefore came to pass that when he promoted a [certain] mate, they were completely convinced that it happened according to natural and international law. Their unenlightened intellect wandered about in all parts of the world's wisdom, according to their own opinion, like the magnetic needle at the pole. It could therefore not turn out otherwise than that their measures deviated as widely from the goal in view as the reasons for their enterprises from rational practice itself [?]. However, as a result of all this the reward he finally received as thanks consisted in this, that, because in the slimy environs of Okhotsk and Kamchatka he tried to lift out and up everybody who had fallen into the mire, they leaned so heavily on him that he himself must sink. As he took with him to his grave everyone's receipted bill, he undeservedly received this funeral text [?; word not clearly decipherable]: that he was buried like the godless [because in unconsecrated ground?] and died like a rich man. The explanation will be understood by those who know that he took with him on the voyage a man whose most outstanding crimes he intended to justify in Kamchatka and, after a lucky termination of the voyage, to free from all blame by sending him to St. Petersburg, [the same man] who afterwards contradicted him in everything, became the author of our misfortune, and after his [Bering's] death his greatest accuser."

As it was, he perished almost from hunger, thirst, cold, hardship, and grief. The edematous swelling of the feet, which he had already had a long time from a suppressed tertian fever, was increased by the cold and forced into the abdomen and chest, and finally his life was ended by the inflammation in the lower abdomen on December 8, two hours before daybreak.[370] As deplorable as his death appeared to his friends,[371] so admirable

[370] In the MS this sentence reads: "As it was, he perished rather from hunger, cold, thirst, vermin, and grief than from any disease. The fluid which already [had formed] a long time before in a swelling of the feet originating from a prematurely suppressed tertian fever, retarded by *constrictiones artuum atonia* [atonic constriction of the joints] of the internal and external parts caused by the cold, entered the abdomen. At the same time a *fistula ani* appeared, which, however, as soon as it opened, displayed *ichor lividus* [dark discharge] as a sign of internal *gangraena* [gangrene], followed shortly after by *sphacelus* [mortification of the tissues] and death itself on December 8, two hours before daybreak." In the MS the word here rendered *gangraena* reads *gangrava*. This is probably an error due to the copyists' unfamiliarity with medical Latin. In the original the word may have been written *gangräna*.

This passage was submitted to Dr. James T. Pilcher of Brooklyn, N. Y., for comment from the viewpoint of modern medicine. Dr. Pilcher kindly writes: "The account of Bering's last illness does not give a very satisfactory clinical picture. He may have had a nephritox, which caused the edema of the legs and subsequent extension of the edema into the abdomen. The extension being accounted for by a prematurely suppressed tertian fever has no basis in real etiological pathology.

"The final sentence, however, relative to a *fistula ani* from which developed a gangrene, is extremely interesting. This is a very rare record, there having been but three reports of such cases in the present-day literature. Bering's case was undoubtedly one of gas gangrene which developed from the infection of the anal fistula by what we now know as the *bacillus Welchii*. This is an infection wherein gas is formed in the affected tissues, hence the name. To infection with *bacillus Welchii* are to be ascribed the numerous cases of gas gangrene resulting from gunshot wounds during the World War." The three cases in present-day medical literature referred to by Dr. Pilcher were described by Thibaut and Schulmann, *Bull. et Mém. Soc. Méd. des Hôpitaux de Paris*, Vol. 63, 1919, Jan. 31, p. 70; by Berkow and Tolk, *Journ. Amer. Med. Assoc.*, Vol. 80, 1923, June 9, p. 1689; and by himself, *Annals of Surgery*, Jan., 1925, pp. 208–212. (J)

[371] "to the world" in the MS.

FIG. 16—Site at Komandor Bay, Bering Island, where the shipwrecked expedition wintered. The cross to the right on the hillside is on the spot where Bering is supposed to have been buried. Farther to the left is the site of the summer huts which were built after the dugouts by the side of the stream were flooded. The tent is near where the relics shown in Fig. 17 were dug up. (Photo by Col. Voloshinov, 1885.)

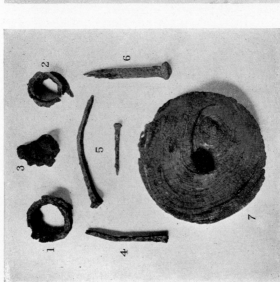

Fig. 17—Relics of Bering's second expedition recovered by L. Stejneger, August 30, 1882, from the site on Bering Island where the new vessel was built or the magazine stood in which the material was stored that had to be left behind (now in the historical collections of the U. S. National Museum).

Left: Relics from the *St. Peter*. 1, 2, iron eyelets; 4, 5, 6, iron nails and spikes; 7, wooden sheave from a pulley block.

Right: Fragments of a thin brass shield with embossed figures showing the Russian coat of arms (restored), surmised to have formed the front piece of a grenadier's cap. The edges are perforated with remnants of thread still attached with which the shield was stitched on.

was his calmness and earnest preparation for the parting, which
came while [he was] in full possession of his reason and speech.
He himself was convinced that we had been cast away upon an
unknown land, yet he did not want to dishearten the others by
saying so but on the contrary cheered them on to hope and
activity in every way.[372]—On the day following we buried his
lifeless body according to the rites of the Protestant church[373]
near our dwelling, where he lies between his adjutant, a com-
misary, and two grenadiers.[374] At our departure we placed a
wooden cross[375] on the grave as a monument, which would likewise serve as a sign of our having taken possession of the country.[376]

After the death of our leader we had made so much progress
that the entire command found itself in five underground
dwellings secure against the severity of the winter. They were
all located alongside one another on the site that had been first
selected for quarters and were named as follows: the Barracks,
the Lieutenant's *yurt* [hut], mine, Alexei Ivanov's, and Luka

[372] This sentence is an abridgment of a longer passage in the MS which
reads: "Although he was fully aware that he had discovered an unknown
land for his burial place yet he did not want to lessen their courage still
more by announcing it inopportunely. It could also easily be seen that he
was only concerned for the welfare of his command, without care for his
own life, and that he had no more heartfelt wish than our deliverance
from this country and his own complete [deliverance] from his misery.
He could hardly have found a better place to prepare for the long eternity than this deathbed under the open sky."

[373] The MS reads: "with rites similar to those of our church."

[374] By the "adjutant" may be meant Khotyaintsov, who is mentioned
in that capacity by Steller a few pages above (p. 154). According to
Steller (*loc. cit.*) he died two days after Bering, or, according to the log
book (Vol. i, pp. 230 and 282), he died the day after Bering. The "two
grenadiers" might be Alexei Popov and Ivan Nebaranov (see footnote
310), who died on November 4 and 5 respectively (Vol. i, pp. 208, 209,
and 281). As to the "commissary" no identification can be suggested.

[375] See Fig. 16 (the cross shown was erected in 1880: Suvorov, Komandorskie Ostrova, 1912, Fig. i and p. 83).

[376] In the MS this clause reads: "which, according to the custom of the
Russians in Siberia, is likewise the sign of a new country which has been
subjected to the Russian Empire."

Alexeiev's *yurts*. In front of each dwelling stood several barrels which served instead of a storehouse for keeping our supply of meat from the foxes. We had also erected scaffolds upon which to hang all kinds of clothing and effects. By holy Christmas Day most of the men had been restored to health alone by means of the excellent water and the fresh meat of various sea animals,[377] and we were only concerned with gathering more and more strength so as to be able by spring to start the work for our delivery more vigorously. Our efforts to this end were divided into three main tasks. [The] first [was], because of lack of sufficient supplies, to kill sea animals in order to provide the greater part of our food, reserving bread only as a delicacy. From the middle of November to the beginning of the month of May each man received monthly thirty pounds of flour; in July and August even that ceased, so that we had to be satisfied with meat alone, since, with the consent of all, twenty-five poods of flour were set aside for our voyage to Kamchatka. Nevertheless, everybody was so economical with his provisions that few were without bread even during the last months[378] and every hut could still make biscuits for the voyage, half of which, besides 20 poods of flour, were taken to the port [Avacha]. We were only unfortunate in that the flour had been lying pressed hard into leather sacks for two or three years and, at the stranding of the ship, had been impregnated with substances dissolved in the salt water in the hold, particularly gunpowder, to such a degree that in eating it one did not dare consult one's taste. Until we got used to it, our bodies became distended like drums from flatulence. Because no real bread could be baked, as we had no oven,[379] small cakes (*oladi*)[380] were fried from this [flour] in the Russian manner

[377] The MS adds: "and as a result of rest."

[378] In the MS this clause reads: "that on no day from beginning to end did we entirely lack bread."

[379] The MS adds: "nor did we want to because of the *ménage*."

[380] The published version has *aladi*. The word, however, is *oladya*, sing., *oladi*, plur. Steller apparently always renders the initial accented "o" with "a," as pronounced. The MS has: "Siberian *calatsches* [*kalaches*], or cakes, were baked fresh every day."

in seal fat or whale oil, but towards the end in manati [sea cow] fat, and distributed among the men one by one. Not until nearly twelve months after, when just before our departure we succeeded in putting up two ovens, did we experience the luxury of once more eating bread.[381] Game we could have had plentifully without much effort had not our men, by raging among the animals without discipline and order, often only to amuse each other, driven them quite early from our neighborhood and, later on, for the purpose of sacrificing the skins to their covetousness and gambling passion, killed the sea otters and thrown their flesh away, so that towards the end we were obliged to go to the most distant parts of the island to hunt.[382]

[381] The MS has in addition: "I and a few others who were supplied with our own provisions added them jointly to the naval stores and received thereafter even share with the others."

[382] In the MS this section is much more detailed, as follows: "As far as our principal food, viz. the meat of the sea animals was concerned, we were sufficiently supplied, yet not without amazing trouble and labor, which we could have dispensed with if we had had any order among us and had not been living in *statu naturali* [a savage state], on account of envy and ill-will, making the animals shy by constant pursuit both day and night, and from the beginning driving them from the neighborhood. In the chase of these animals everyone tried to defraud everybody else and in every way and manner to cheat the more the nearer spring approached and the hope rose of being able to transport the skins to Kamchatka with great profit. In addition, the sickness had scarcely subsided, when a new and worse epidemic appeared, I mean the wretched gambling with cards, when through whole days and nights nothing but card playing was to be seen in the dwellings, at first for money, now held in low esteem, and, when this was gambled away, the fine sea otters had to offer up their costly skins. In the morning, at inspection, no other topic of conversation was heard than: this one has won a hundred rubles or more, and that one has lost so and so much. He who had totally ruined himself tried to recoup himself through the poor sea otters, which were slaughtered without necessity and consideration only for their skins, their meat being thrown away. When this did not suffice, some began to steal, and stole the skins from the others, whereby hate, quarrels, and strife were disseminated through all the quarters. Though on many occasions [I] remonstrated with the officers about the unfairness of this and that they should prohibit it, I could accomplish nothing, inasmuch as the officers themselves were devotees and tried to stimulate the passion with

The second main effort consisted in transportation of wood, which was regarded as one of the biggest and hardest tasks, since except for the low willow shrubs[383] not a tree was to be found on the whole island, while the driftwood thrown out by the sea, not too common at that, was buried under the snow, sometimes an arshin,[384] sometimes a fathom deep. That which was found in the neighborhood had been gathered early for building the huts and for fuel; in December we were already obliged to drag it in from a distance of four versts, in January and February from about ten versts,[385] and finally in March even from fifteen to sixteen versts. In April, however, when the snow settled[386] this labor came to a sudden stop, because not only did enough driftwood come in sight near by, but from the breaking up of the

---

new-fangled [schemes] when the men had become disgusted, in order to accomplish the double purpose: (1) [to get] the money and the furs of the men; (2) by this vile familiarity to bring the crew to forget the old general hate and former bitterness. In the meantime the gambling passion got the upper hand to such an extent that nobody paid much attention to our delivery, the building of the vessel progressed sleepily, many necessary materials and objects in the vessel were ruined, having been left in the water, such as compasses and the general journal itself, regarding which [I] had made so many admonitions and received so many marvelous answers, so that our delivery might perhaps not have come to pass during the present year, if a few upright petty officers had not with all their might insisted on the total abolition of the gambling, which, when it took place in June, at once brought about an entirely different aspect of affairs."

There then follows in the MS a long description of the sea otter. In the present work this forms the part of Appendix A under that heading (pp. 214-222). In the version published by Pallas it forms part of the Description of Bering Island which he published twelve years earlier than the journal in *Neue Nordische Beyträge*, Vol. 2, 1781, pp. 255-301 (the description of the sea otter is on pp. 279-286).

[383] At least five species of willow (*Salix*) occur on the island. The one here referred to forms low thickets in suitable localities. The species is *Salix arctica* Pallas, recorded under various names, such as *S. pallasii*, *S. crassijulis*, and *S. diplodictya*. (S)

[384] 28 inches.

[385] The MS has: "from six to ten versts."

[386] The MS has in addition: "and disappeared from the beach."

old ship and building of the new vessel there was enough refuse
for heating and cooking purposes. However, we carried[387]
both the sea animals and the wood by means of a piece of wood
across the breast tied with ropes; a common load weighed sixty
and mostly up to eighty pounds, not counting axes, pots, and
shoemaker's and tailor's tools, which everyone always had to
have with him in order to mend the worn-out clothes and shoes
as soon as a tear occurred. For this purpose as well as for soles
the leathern provision sacks and knapsacks were cut up little by
little.[388]

The third task consisted in the management of the household
matters, since cooking had to go on all the time, so that the
workmen, no matter when they came home, might have enough
to eat. In our [household] the arrangement was accordingly
made that daily one or a couple of Germans and Russians went
hunting, while the others went for wood, and one German together with one Russian attended to the kitchen. This arrangement was afterwards copied by all the others. Thus circumstanced, we celebrated all holidays and entertained after our own
fashion.[389]

[387] The MS adds: "on the back."

[388] The MS is somewhat longer, as follows: "We had only a three
months' supply of summer clothing and shoes, but as so much became
torn every day because of the hard work, the Sunday clothes—overcoats
and coats—had to be made into work blouses, the *chamadoxes* into boots,
the leathern provision sacks into soles. Since nobody would work for
money, everyone had to act as shoemaker, tailor, glover, butcher, carpenter, cook, and footman as best he could, so that henceforth they would
have been able to earn an ample living in all these trades."

The word *chamadoxes* of the MS (there spelled, in German transliteration, *Tschamadoxen*) Pallas has rendered by "lederne . . . Tornister,"
military knapsacks of leather. Dr. Golder thinks that the word is intended for "the Russian word *chemodan*, which means box or portman-
teau. The older type, the kind used in Siberia, was usually covered with
skin." (S)

[389] Beginning with the equivalent of the second sentence of this paragraph the MS is considerably more detailed, as follows: "In our *yurt* we
had made an arrangement which thereupon the others adopted and retained as a permanent regulation. Our [household] consisted of five Ger-

wir die Wolluſt einmal wieder Brod zu eſſen. — Das
Wild würden wir ſtets zur Nahrung in Menge, ohne
viele Mühe gehabt haben, wenn nicht die Leute, ohne
Zucht und Ordnung darunter gewüthet und die Thiere
gar bald aus unſrer Nachbarſchaft, oft einander nur zum
Poſſen, verſcheucht, und nachmals, bloß um die Felle
ihrem Geiz und Spielſucht zu opfern, die Ottern geſchla-
gen und das Fleiſch weggeworfen hätten; ſo daß wir endlich in die entfernteſte Gegend der Inſel auf die Jagd zu
gehen genöthiget waren.

Die zweyte hauptſächliche Bemühung beſtand im
Holztragen, welches für eine der gröſten und ſchwerſten
Arbeiten gehalten wurde, da außer niedrigem Weidenge-
büſch nicht ein Baum auf dem ganzen Eilande anzutref-
fen war, das von der See ausgeworfne Holz aber nicht
allzuhäufig, bald eine Arſchin, bald bis auf einen Faden,
unterm Schnee begraben lag. Was davon in der Nähe
vorhanden war, wurde im Anfang ſogleich zum Bau der
Hütten und zum Brennen weggeſamlet; im December
muſten wir es ſchon auf vier Werſte her, im Januar
und Februar wohl auf zehn Werſte, im März endlich
gar 15 bis 16 Werſte ſchleppen. Doch hörte im April,
da ſich der Schnee ſezte, dieſe Arbeit mit einmahl auf,
da nicht allein Holz genug in der Nähe zum Vorſchein
kam, ſondern auch, beym Aufbrechen des Schiffs und
Bau des neuen Fahrzeugs, genug abfiel, um damit
heizen und kochen zu können. Wir trugen aber ſowohl
die Seethiere, als das Holz, vermittelſt eines Querholzes
vor der Bruſt, mit Stricken gebunden und eine gewöhn-
liche Ladung betrug 60 und mehrentheils bis 80 Pfund,
ohne die Aexte, Keſſel, Schuſter- und Schneidergeräth-
ſchaft, die ein jeder bey ſich haben muſte, um die ganz
abgetragne Kleider und Schuhe immer zu flicken, ſo wie
ſich ein Riß daran ereignete; wozu die ledernen Provi-

FIG. 18—Facsimile of page from the published version of Steller's journal (N. N. B., Vol. 6, 1793, p. 11; or book form, substantially p. 118:
see Bibliography) to illustrate editorial changes from the MS by Pallas.
The upper third of this page is an abridgment of the MS between line
16 of fol. 76 (Fig. 19) and line 25 of fol. 77 (Fig. 20), which matter is translated in our footnotes 381 and 382. The equivalent of the lower two-thirds
of this page does not occur in the MS for some folios to come.

FIG. 20—Reduced facsimile of fol. 77 of MS copy of Steller's journal. The section on the sea otter beginning at line 26 of this folio does not appear in the corresponding place in the published version (see Fig. 18) as Pallas had already published it in *Neue Nordische Beyträge* Vol. 2, 1781, pp. 279–286, as part of the Description of Bering Island, to which he had transferred it. The translation of this section is given below in Appendix A under "Sea Otter, pp. 214–222."

On December 26 the scouts whom we had sent out a second time returned with the report that we were on an island which they had walked around in an easterly direction.[390] They had found, however, on the beach so many signs, such as rudders,[391] bottoms of fish barrels, and similar objects, that no other conclu-

mans, three common Kamchatka cossack sons, besides the two servants of the Captain Commander, whose guardian I had become by his last will, consequently altogether ten persons. One of us [Germans] and one of the privates, or in our discretion two of each category, went on the *promysel* [hunt], the others went for wood; one German and one Russian were cooks. We thus had the advantage that we [Germans] did not have to build fires, fetch water, nor open or close the chimney. Furthermore, after meals, the kitchen and table utensils were rinsed and put away by them [the privates], in return for which they received from us kettles, dishes, plates, spoons, tablecloths, and other effects. Besides recognizing that we were head-cooks and they under-cooks, they had at all times to obey us also in all other matters and be at our service so that everything might be done in an orderly manner. Consequently everyone knew at all times his duty and business without having to be reminded of it. This arrangement made all labor bearable and resulted in cheerfulness and good feeling among us and in our having greater abundance of better prepared food and drink than all the other households. At the same time everybody was nevertheless permitted, when we deliberated about something, to express his opinion, and the best advice was taken without respect of persons. Thus circumstanced, we celebrated Sundays and holidays, [including] holy Christmas, as if we were in the [proper] place and situation [at home]. On the public high political [national] holidays we entertained: the officers were invited, and with many pleasant speeches and toasts over the tea, for lack of other kinds of drink, we felt the same enjoyment in this shadowy place as in other places where everything is in abundance."

[390] The log book (see Vol. 1, p. 230, under Dec. 27 and footnote 127) is somewhat more qualified in its reports of the result of this reconnaissance. Khitrov's version reads: "The sailor Timofei Anchiugov returned without bringing any information about the land [we are on]." Yushin's version reads: "The sailor Anchiugov, with the two men from Kamchatka already mentioned, were ordered south to obtain information. He was gone about four weeks but did not learn anything definite. He said that he thought we were on an island. He could not follow the shore for any considerable distance because of the cliffs."

[391] The MS has "Kamchatkan rudders."

sion was possible than that Kamchatka must be a short distance from here.

On January 29 [1742] our company killed the first sea lion.[392] The meat was found to be of such exceptional quality and taste that we only wished soon to get hold of more. The fat was like beef marrow, and the meat almost like veal.

On February 1 a violent northwest gale and very high tide carried our ship so far up on the beach that we experienced no little hopes of being able to float it off to sea at high water, if only we could succeed in raising the anchors again in the spring, because we believed that, as the ship held the water it had taken in, the bottom could not be much damaged. This erroneous belief was due to the fact that the vessel was almost filled with sand inside, so that the water could not run out. Nevertheless, this setting of the ship so high up on the beach saved us much trouble later when we came to break it up.

On February 25 the hitherto mild weather tempted us to send out a third expedition to examine the land to the westward. For this purpose the assistant navigator Yushin and four men were sent off. In six days, however, they only got as far as the headland projecting to the north, sixty versts from our dwellings,[393] and, after the whole exploration had turned into a sea otter hunt, they returned, as the weather by March 8 had again become worse, with the report, afterwards found to be false, that because of the precipitous cliffs extending into the sea they had not been able to go farther.[394]

On March 10 we held another council and decided to order the boatswain, Alexei Ivanov, who was unanimously nominated, to

[392] See, below, footnote 422, especially the last paragraph.

[393] Probably Cape Waxel, the northeastern point of the island, is meant (see map, Pl. II). (S)

[394] In the MS this passage reads: "and, after they had turned the whole exploration into a *bobr* [sea otter] hunt, they returned on March 8 with the bad report, afterwards found to be false, which they now gave out as the cause of their return, that . . ."

The log book confirms March 8 as the date of the return of the party (see Vol. I, p. 232, under that date).

go south across the country at Lyesnaya Ryechka[395] and then to follow the shore until he came either to the end of the island or to the mainland itself, in case it were united with the latter, since it was still believed that we were stranded on Cape Kronotski.[396] These scouts began the trip on March 15 but returned unexpectedly on the 19th, again with the report that they could go no farther in the south because of the steep rocks which extended into the sea. However, they, too, had missed the right way, as I discovered later on my trip. Nevertheless, they brought back two noteworthy pieces of information for us, viz., first, that they had found chips and fragments of the pinnace that had been built in Avacha the winter before; the carpenter Akulev[397] recognized definitely the chips which he had hewn off in Avacha. Next they described to us an animal which they had seen for the first time on land and alive, and which, from their description, we took to be a sea bear [fur seal].[398]

On March 22 this same boatswain with his former companions started off again under the former instructions with the changed order to go on the north side as far as the point projecting north, from there continue his way southward overland, and in case he met obstacles in the south, he should once more go northward across or along the mountains and keep on until he came to some mainland or to the other end of the island. In the latter case all of them should come back quickly in order not to put any further obstacles in the way of the building of the new vessel. If, however, they came to the mainland or to Kamchatka, half of the party should [proceed] to Avacha with the reports, the other half return to the command with the information. With three others from our *yurt* I accompanied these scouts and at Lyesnaya

[395] See, above, footnote 344. By "south" is meant west (see, above, footnote 359).

[396] The headland on the Kamchatkan shore directly opposite in the same latitude (see Vol. 1, Pl. I).

[397] The MS reads: "The carpenter and soldier Akulev." This is probably the soldier whose name is spelled Okulov in the list in Vol. 1, p. 235.

[398] The MS adds: "and with which later on we became well acquainted."

Ryechka went across the island for the first time, where on the same day we effected a great slaughter among the sea otters, as they were feeling secure and lying together in herds,[399] so that we could have killed probably a hundred had we not thought more of the meat and the general welfare than of the precious skins.

Now that in the spring the snow had settled and it was possible for us to go across the land to the south, where the sea otters and seals had not yet been frightened away and were found by us in great numbers, our hopes rose not a little and we visited the new localities frequently, notwithstanding the fact that the way was very long and toilsome because of the mountains. Three times, however, there happened such disastrous accidents on this trail that almost a third of our men might have been lost.—On April 1 constable Roselius,[400] assistant surgeon Betge, guard-marine Sint, and a cossack left our camp as usual to hunt. Towards evening there rose such a violent storm from the northwest that no one could keep on his feet or see a step ahead of him. In addition six feet of snow fell during the night. We had never before had such a tempest here. The men who had gone hunting, about whom we all were greatly worried, came all near perishing. After having passed the entire night lying under the snow, they were hardly able in the morning to dig themselves out and reach the beach. The guard-marine, however, had become separated from the others and seemed lost. Fortunately for all of them the snow stopped falling at the break of day, and we had hardly dug out [a passage] from the entrance to our hut[401] when the three of

---

[399] The MS adds: "killing ten." This may have been at or near the South Rookery (of 1883) shown on Pl. II.

[400] In the published version the name is given as "Rosdig." This would seem to be a misreading of the correct form, Roselius. That this is the correct form is attested by many references in the log book (Vol. 1, pp. 214, 225, 229, 235, 241, 242). The MS also reads Roselius here, although the handwriting makes it plausible how the misreading could occur.

[401] This clause in the MS is expanded to: "The next day we worked several hours before we could dig ourselves out of our quarters when, just as the entrance was fortunately cleaned out, three of our men . . ."

our men who had kept together reached us out of their mind and unable to speak, as stiff as machines, and the assistant surgeon quite blind.[402] We undressed them at once, covered them with feather beds, and revived them with tea.[403] An hour later the guard-marine, in a still more pitiful condition and wandering aimlessly about on the beach, was found by three men and brought to us. During the night he had fallen into a brook[404] and all the clothing on his body and even his limbs were frozen almost solid, so that we feared he would lose his hands and feet. His strong constitution pulled him through, however.[405] But the assistant surgeon did not regain the use of his eyes until eight days after.

Another time, April 5, believing that we were forecasting the weather better,[406] Mr. Plenisner, I, my cossack, and the Captain Commander's servant went[407] hunting, as we were out of meat, the weather being most pleasant and sunshiny. As soon as we reached the beach we killed as many otters as we could carry and seated ourselves near a cliff around a camp fire in order to pass the night. Before we knew it, the same storm [i. e. as on April 1, viz. from NW] rose towards midnight and brought so much snow that we should have been covered in a short time had we not constantly run to and fro and given each other no rest. In the morning, after we had been searching long in vain for a crevice

[402] The equivalent of what follows "as stiff" reads in the MS: "and so stiff from the cold that, like rigid machines, they could scarcely still move their feet, while the assistant surgeon, totally blind, kept walking behind the others without seeing."

[403] The MS has in addition: "and other remedies."

[404] The MS has instead: "During the whole night he had been lying in a brook."

[405] The MS has instead: "God, however, pulled him through without harm."

[406] In the MS the recital of this episode begins as follows: "Although this [experience] alarmed us greatly, we others undertook to handle the matter more skillfully and, when it was imperative to go, to forecast the weather better; hence, on April 5," etc.

[407] The MS has: "went south." The party presumably again went by way of the transverse depression (see, above, footnote 344) to the western shore. (S)

or other refuge and were already quite desperate, the cossack succeeded finally in finding in a cliff a very wide and spacious cave, which apparently had been caused by a great earthquake.[408] Loaded with wood and meat we made ourselves at home there and found a safe refuge against all snow and wind which in the future could be of great use in similar cases. We found there not only room enough but also a side cave,[409] in which we could keep our supplies safe from the thievish[410] foxes, and even a chimney formed by Nature, through which the smoke found an outlet through the cracks in the rock, without in the least annoying us in our quarters, which became properly heated from the fire.[411] Here we spent, with hearts very thankful to Providence,[412] three days in hunting[413] and resting alternately, and returned on the

[408] The account in the MS is much more detailed, as follows: "Towards midnight we got such a violent northwest storm with much snow that, without our being able to get under shelter, the cossack soon lay buried covered deep with snow without moving, while I sat in the snow and by constantly smoking tobacco tried to keep myself warm and banish the bitterness of death, and the other two were running incessantly to and fro like true *hemerodromi* [couriers, coursers], though one could hardly keep on one's feet because of the wind. As day broke, though hardly to be distinguished from the darkest night, and as my other companions would not let me rest under the snow, I finally got up in order to search, together with them, for a cave and crevice in the rocks. After having wandered about for a long time without having found a refuge we came back full of despair and half dead. My cossack, who, when I spoke to him, would not [get up], we dug out of the snow by force. We agreed once more to make an attempt in two parties in order to save our lives in the incessant storm. The cossack, more successful in this than we, after half an hour's search found a very wide and spacious cave in a cliff which without doubt had been caused by a great earthquake. After receiving the news we went there with the greatest expectation."

[409] Thus the published version. The MS has *ambar*, Russian for warehouse, provision chamber. "Side cave" would seem to be Pallas' inference by extension.

[410] The MS adds: "and malicious."

[411] The MS adds: "and in which we could cook conveniently."

[412] The MS has instead: "Here we revived at once, gave thanks to God, and spent. . . ."

[413] The MS has in addition: "as the foxes had devoured our provisions during the storm."

fourth with much booty and good news to our people, who were already fearing that we would never appear again. The cave, as well as the bay, was afterwards named for me.[414] At our first entrance into this cave we found many foxes in it; they retreated into a crevice in the rock through which afterwards the smoke passed from the fire we made so that there started among them such a sneezing and spitting that we had enough to laugh at. At night, however, they gave us no rest, as they pulled off the cap first of one and then of another and performed other tricks.[415]

A few days before us the assistant navigator Yushin had gone hunting with our only ship's carpenter, who had undertaken to build alone a new vessel from the wreck and on whom consequently rested all hope of our delivery, and three other persons. When they, too, were forced by a storm to seek a crevice for shelter and found one close to the water, it happened that they were kept imprisoned there by the high tide for seven days, without provisions and wood, and only returned on the ninth day, at which time we had believed them either drowned or crushed to death by snow dashing down from the mountains.

When we came home on April 8 we were greeted by the glad news that this person,[416] so indispensable to us, had made his appearance again, and furthermore that the boatswain[417] had come back on April 6 with the information that we were really on an island and that they thought they had seen high mountains in the northeast. According to the latitude in which we were, I am of the opinion that these must not be regarded as a part of America but as another island* unknown in Kamchatka.[418]

[414] The MS has in addition: "as it was discovered on my trip." The location of this cave cannot be indicated with certainty. It may have been near Dikaya Bay (Pl. II; see below, p. 197, footnote 35) southeast of the mouth of the transverse depression. (S)

[415] The last two sentences are not in the MS.

[416] The MS has the plural, "these persons. . . ."

[417] Alexei Ivanov, who had left on March 22 (see the journal, p. 169, above).

* Indeed, subsequent events have shown in this case also that Steller's surmise was correct. For these mountains, seen from Bering Island in

Since, according to this, there seemed to be no other way to get away from here and to reach Kamchatka, in default of any forest, than to break up the old vessel and build a smaller one

---

the northeast, were the now well-known Copper Island (Mednoi Ostrov). —P. [On the incorrectness of this interpretation see the next footnote, next-to-last paragraph.]

[418] In the MS this sentence has directly the opposite meaning. It there reads: "And I was of the opinion, according to this latitude, that it could be nothing else than the American mainland, seeing that this [i. e. Bering Island] is an island of which nothing is known in Kamchatka."

Clearly this, and not the published version, represents Steller's opinion. It may be ascribed to the fact, previously referred to (asterisk footnote between 163 and 164, last paragraph, and footnote 260), that the general conception of the members of the expedition was that, in what we now know as the Aleutian Islands, they had been skirting the mainland coast of North America. With Steller's correct inference, from the reports of natives, of the nearness of Asia and America farther north (see the journal, pp. 18 and 99 and footnote 221, above) he may well have believed that the two continents approached closely in this region also (see also the next-to-last sentence of footnote 149 for his conception on the outward voyage, which nothing occurred on the return voyage to change). That this was his belief seems to be confirmed by the 1758 map of the St. Petersburg Academy of Sciences (our Fig. 14), which embodied the expedition's discoveries and conceptions.

The underlying argument of the clause "seeing that Bering Island is an island of which nothing is known in Kamchatka" may possibly be explained as follows: Even Bering Island, presumably close to Kamchatka, is unknown there. All the more reason why a land beyond it would be unknown.

The report of land northeast of Bering Island had already been brought back from Yushin's reconnaissance a month earlier (log book under March 8, Vol. 1, p. 232, and third paragraph from bottom of p. 237). The fallacy of this report has already been pointed out (in the same paragraph on p. 237). In extension of the statement there made it may be said that, even allowing for the probable magnetic declination in that region at that time (given in the log book as 1¼ rhumb, or about 14°, E for a position off the southern end of Bering Island six months later; see Vol. 1, p. 244, "Variation of Compass"), Copper Island could not have been the basis of the report, for it lies east and southeast of the southern end of Bering Island and the position from which the land was reported to have been seen in the northeast was, in the case of both Yushin and Ivanov, the northeastern point of Bering Island, viz. Cape Waxel (see, above, footnote 393 and

from it, such a decision[419] was taken in a council held on April 9 and the following arrangement was made, which was to remain in force from the date when the breaking up should begin until the building of the new vessel should be completed: (1) that the twelve men skilled in the use of the ax should work continuously on the carpenter work; (2) that the others, with the exception only of the two officers and myself, should hunt and work in such a manner that, when one party returned home from the hunt, though indeed having a day for rest, they should nevertheless also attend to the housework and afterwards mend clothing and shoes but on the third and following days they should assist with the work on the vessel, until their turn to hunt came around again; (3) that all meat should be brought to one place and every

---

the journal, p. 169—"the point projecting north"). Furthermore, the height and distance of Copper Island are such that it was in plain view on every clear day from the huts of the shipwrecked crew (see Fig. 21) and

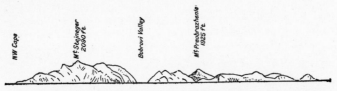

FIG. 21—Copper Island seen from spot near camp of shipwrecked crew on Bering Island marked "Polovina" on Pl. II. Sketch by L. Stejneger, April 21, 1883.
   Because of the deep Bobrovi Valley Copper Island at this distance appears as two islands. Mt. Stejneger was so named and its elevation determined as 637 meters by J. Morozewicz (*Mém. Comité Géol.*, Vol. 72 (N. S.), St. Petersburg, 1912, p. 45).

was therefore known to them. From Cape Waxel it was barely within the arc of visibility, but in an even more southeasterly direction than from the camp.

In conformity with the report an island is shown northeast of Bering Island on Waxel's map (this section reproduced in *Mémoires Acad. Imp. des Sci. de St. Pétersbourg*, Series 7, Vol. 38, No. 7, 1891, and our Fig. 29; modified copy in Dall, *U. S. Coast and Geodetic Survey Rept. for 1890*, Pl. 70, referred to above in footnote 260), a representation which persisted on many of the later maps (e. g. our Fig. 14). (J)

[419] For the wording of that decision see the log book under April 9 (Vol. 1, p. 233).

morning a petty officer should distribute to the cooks of each party their share, so that the carpenters might not suffer want.

After this had been unanimously agreed to and signed, the first preparations were already started on the next day. Everything was taken out of the vessel, and the materials were brought together in one place on the beach; grindstones were dressed and placed in troughs, tools were cleaned of rust and sharpened, a smithy erected, crowbars, iron wedges, and large hammers forged, wood gathered, and charcoal made. This last work was arduous and caused most of the delay.

While many difficulties were expected because the hunting was so far off, since the animals were already frightened away by us for a distance of eighteen to twenty versts, our courage was nevertheless unexpectedly again raised by the following dispensation: on April 18 and 19, namely, two sea bears [fur seals] were killed, each of which, including meat and fat, weighed at least 20 poods, two or three being apparently sufficient to support the command for a whole week. Likewise, since the migrations of these animals, as observed from the coast of Kamchatka, were well known to us, there was hope, which was also soon realized, that more of these animals would shortly follow.[420]

A quite fresh whale caused us still more encouragement and comfort, having been thrown ashore at Kozlovo Pole,[421] five versts to the west of our dwellings, on April 20, the day before we began to break up the old vessel. It was 15 fathoms long, and in two days we collected so much blubber and oil from it

[420] In the MS this sentence is more detailed and is followed by a long passage dealing with the fur seal. This sentence and the subsequent passage are omitted by Pallas in the published version of the journal, inasmuch as he had already published them twelve years earlier (*Neue Nordische Beyträge*, Vol. 2, 1781, pp. 288–290) with Steller's description of Bering Island, as a part of which they are translated below in Appendix A on pp. 225–226. The sentence begins with the words "As I had furthermore already learned in Kamchatka"; the passage ends with the words "cover the way out and back in one day."

[421] For location, see map, Pl. II.

that at our departure a few barrels thereof were left behind.[422]

During the whole of May and half of the month of June we lived on the meat of the young and female sea bears which are much more tender to eat.

On May 5[423] by erecting the sternpost and the stem on the keel the start was made on our vessel and our future deliverance. Lieutenant Waxel thereupon invited all and everybody to him and, in default of other drinks, treated us to Mongolian *saturan*,[424] or tea soup, which is prepared with flour and butter, at

[422] In the MS the following here intervenes: "Shortly after this sea lions, in Kamchatka called *sivuch*, also appeared frequently, but nobody dared to kill this ferocious animal. One which had been wounded in Kamchatka with a *nosok*, or harpoon, and escaped was cast ashore near us dead but still fresh, and we set to work on this one too."

This passage is omitted by Pallas in the journal but occurs (*Neue Nordische Beyträge*, Vol. 2, 1781, p. 290, lines 7–12) in Steller's description of Bering Island as Pallas had published it twelve years previously (see, below, Appendix A, p. 226). The passage is there completed by the following sentences (*loc. cit.*, lines 12–17, and, below, Appendix A, p. 226):

"The most delicate part of this animal is its flippers. When being boiled they swell up a great deal and can then easily be skinned, while when raw it is not possible to remove the skin. I have discussed the main matters of interest concerning this animal in the previously mentioned description of sea animals." [The reference is to Steller's "De bestiis marinis," pp. 360–366 (see also, below, p. 224, footnote 125).]

The sea lion (*Eumetopias jubata* (Schreber)) is known in Kamchatka under the name *sivuch*. The full-grown male is a large and formidable animal. In view of Steller's own statement on p. 168, above, that "on January 29 our company killed the first sea lion" it would appear that the one then killed was a female or young male, a supposition corroborated by his saying that the meat was almost like veal, a quality which even he would hardly attribute to that of the old *sivuch*. (S)

[423] In the log book (Vol. 1, p. 234) this event is dated May 6.

[424] According to Admiral Ferdinand von Wrangell (Expedition to the Polar Sea, New York, 1841, pp. 84–85) the *saturan* is prepared as follows: "The meal is roasted in a pan, and butter or train oil mixed with it so as to bring it to a paste, which is then thinned by the addition of boiling water. When the drink is carefully made, and with good butter, it has an agreeable flavor, and is very nourishing and warming; it may be com-

which, with many wishes and longings, we enjoyed ourselves fairly well. The pleasant spring weather brought us still other advantages, besides the mild air, for, after the snow had thawed, we discovered here and there on the beach so much wood that we felt quite encouraged with regard to the charcoal necessary for the work in the smithy. We furthermore obtained many edible and palatable herbs and roots, which, besides being a change, served as medicine for our emaciated bodies.[425]

---

pared to Rumford's 'spare soup.' It is drunk hot, like tea, out of glasses or cups." (S)

[425] In the MS there is here added an enumeration, omitted in the published version, of these plants and roots. In the following translation the superior letters have been added; they correspond to the botanical identifications given below.

"Among these the following were the most notable: the Kamchatkan sweet grass *Sphondylium*;[a] the bulbs of the *lilium fl. reflexo atro purpureo*,[b] much more plentiful and larger than in Kamchatka; a kind of herb[c] the leaves of which resemble celery in taste and shape while the root resembles parsnip in taste; as well as the roots of *kutakhshu*.[d] Besides these we ate the leaves of *Ceronthe*;[e] the turions [young shoots] of *Chamnaerion speciosum*;[f] the roots of the bistort.[g] Instead of bohea tea we made infusions of the leaves of *Vitis idea buxi folio*,[h] and in place of green [tea], of the leaves of *Pyrola*[i] and, as second choice, of *Veronica humilis montana, flore amplo*.[j] As salad herbs we had *Cochlearia*,[k] beccabunga,[l] and *Cardamine nasturtium*."[m]

In the MS some of the plant names are mutilated by the copyist, but they are nevertheless quite recognizable as just given. The identifications, using modern nomenclature, are as follows:

(a) *Heracleum lanatum* Michx. See also, above, footnote 78.

(b) the Saranna lily, *Fritillaria kamtschatcensis* (L.).

(c) *Conioselinum kamtschaticum* Rupr. (*Selinum benthami* Watson).

(d) the Kamchadal name, variously spelled *kutachtschu* or *koutakschin*, for a kind of angelica, *Coelopleurum gmelini* (D. C.), often erroneously referred to as *Archangelica officinalis*.

(e) the sea lungwort, *Mertensia maritima* (L.), which in some places is extremely abundant on the beaches, a single plant covering a large area.

(f) *Chamaenerion* (or *Epilobium*) *angustifolium* (L.), the purple fireweed. *Chamnaerion* (in the MS the word occurs in the genitive, "*Chamnaerii*") is probably a lapsus for *Chamaenerion*.

(g) *Polygonum viviparum* L.

(h) the upland cranberry, *Vaccinium vitis idaea* L. The word in the

On May 11 and the following days not only did the snow begin to thaw rapidly, but the steady rains that came with south-east winds caused, in addition, such high water that the creeks overflowed so much that we could scarcely remain in our underground homes, which had one or even two feet of water in them. This influenced us after the rain ceased to abandon the winter huts and build summer homes above ground.[426] In the meantime the building of the vessel was likewise delayed for some days, but afterwards it was resumed with increased zeal, the more so because of the headway[427] made in the breaking up of the ship, which in the beginning we had almost despaired of being able to accomplish, as the vessel was new and very well built while

---

MS for what is known in English as "bohea," or black tea, is "Theeboy," which, with "Theeboh" and "Theebuh," are the contemporary German equivalents.

(i) *Pyrola minor* L., one of the true wintergreens, or shinleaves.

(j) *Veronica aphylla* var. *grandiflora* (Gärtn.) (or *kamtschatica* L. fil.), one of the four species of speedwells found on Bering Island.

(k) the scurvy grass, *Cochlearia officinalis* L.

(l) the American brooklime, *Veronica americana* Schwein.

(m) the bitter cress, *Cardamine pratensis* L., as well as *C. hirsuta* L., both of which occur. See also, above, footnote 314.

Upon his return to Kamchatka Steller sent a full catalog of all the plants observed by him on Bering Island, which is preserved in the archives of the Academy of Sciences in Petrograd (under Arkhiv Konferentsia, Bundle 13 C, No. 1 Q: see, above, footnote 119; photostat copies are in the Library of Congress, Washington, and the library of the American Geographical Society). In this "Catalogus plantarum in insula Beringii observatarum, 1742" he enumerated 218 species, some of which, however, are only varieties. Most of these have been relocated by subsequent collectors, and a number of other species added, but a few species recorded by Steller still await verification. Of Spermatophytes and Pteridophytes 252 species were known in 1921 from Bering and Copper Islands, two of which have not been found elsewhere, viz. *Saussurea morozeviczi* Fedtsch. and *Alopecurus stejnegeri* Vasey. Dr. Boris Fedtschenko has published a general account of the plants under the title "Flore des Îles du Commandeur," Cracow, 1906. (S)

[426] The MS has in addition: "although after the water had receded they were again visited."

[427] The MS reads: "because of the unexpected headway."

we were almost without tools.[428] The building of the new vessel made equally good progress daily, and the eagerness to work rose with hope, so that soon there was no doubt that we should be able to start for Kamchatka in the month of August.[429] In order still more to accelerate the work, a beginning was made to facilitate the victualing of the crew by catching the sea cows in the neighborhood, in order to have that much more time and help for building the ship and in order to spare the men, who were already pretty destitute of shoes and clothes, the hard road over the mountains.[430] This chase, so profitable to us, I have recounted in detail in the description of Bering Island.*[431]

As the work thus could be advanced more and more[432] and as

[428] In the MS the last clause reads: "and the necessary tools for breaking up the ship were lacking."

[429] The last clause in the MS after "with hope" is amplified as follows: "As towards the end of the month of May all the frame timbers were ready and set up on the keel, we began no longer to doubt that it would be possible to leave here for Kamchatka in the month of August."

[430] The equivalent of this sentence is somewhat more detailed in the MS, as follows: "Our only concern was how to obviate the difficult transportation of the meat and obtain the food near home by catching the sea cows which were daily present in great numbers before our eyes near the shore. The work would thereby progress much faster in view of the fact that the men were already lacking strength, shoes, and clothes, which were being worn out very much on the extremely toilsome road southward across the country and over the mountains."

* See Part 4 of these *Nordische Beyträge*.—P. [See the next footnote.]

[431] "Part 4" in Pallas' note is a typographical error for Part (or Vol.) 2, published in 1781. The passage on hunting the sea cow is on pp. 290–292. Pallas had transferred it from the MS, where it occurs at this point in chronological order under May 21, and added it to the Description of Bering Island. (The sentence "This chase . . . description of Bering Island" is Pallas' and is therefore not in the MS.) Both in the MS and in the published version (*ibid.*, pp. 292–299) this passage is immediately followed by an account of the natural history of the sea cow. In the present work this passage and account are published in Appendix A under the heading "The Sea Cow," pp. 226–237, below.

[432] In the MS this clause reads: "As now all difficulties both in regard to the breaking up of the vessel and the provisioning were solved and as, in addition, we sometimes for a change got so many fishes in our half-rotted fish nets that we were supplied for eight days from one haul."

the constant efforts and encouragement by Lieutenant Waxel raised the spirit of the men, it came to pass [433] that in the month of July the vessel, 36 feet long at the keel and 42 feet from stem to stern, [434] stood ready on the stocks as far as the hull was concerned. The remaining time until August 13 was consumed in making rigging, trying out tar from old ropes, [435] and finally also in building ways for launching the vessel. This last caused us great trouble since we were so poorly provided with timber and other material. The wood [436] was hauled from the farthest parts of the shore; their stability [i. e. of the ways] was secured by placing the cannons on them. In the meantime some built a magazine in which to store the materials to be left behind; others were occupied in erecting an oven and in baking biscuits for the voyage; some overhauled the casks which had to be bound for the voyage with iron hoops and ropes; [437] some examined the bottom of the bay; [438] and altogether there was no one who wanted to be idle, because everyone was exceedingly anxious for deliverance from this desert island. [439]

[33] The MS reads: "it came to pass, as a result of [the work of] many hands, redoubled courage, and the constant efforts and friendly encouragement of Lieutenant Waxel, that in," etc.

[434] This clause giving dimensions does not occur here in the MS (for its position see, below, footnote 444). The log book under May 6 (Vol. 1, p. 234) states that the vessel was to have "a length of 36 feet, a 12-foot beam, and depth of 5 feet 3 inches." These figures in Khitrov's version of the log book are repeated in Yushin's version (*ibid.*, p. 239, footnote 133). Under August 10, 5 P. M. entry (*ibid.*, p. 240) it is stated that the vessel "measured 36 feet in length, 11 feet in beam, 5 feet in depth, and 41 feet from stem to sternpost."

[435] The MS reads: "in making rigging, spars, and masts, in blacksmithing, in the toilsome trying out of tar from old ropes."

[436] The MS adds: "for the ways."

[437] The MS adds: "because this had previously been neglected in Okhotsk."

[438] The log book gives the reason—to find the anchors (entries of July 1 and July 24; see Vol. 1, p. 234).

[439] The MS has in addition: "Although the hope of procuring more otter pelts made some of the men desirous of spending another winter, at the last moment they did not, for shame, want to acknowledge it."

As on August 8 all was in order and ready for the voyage, a public prayer was offered up in the afternoon, in which we prayed to God for a successful launching of the vessel, which we dedicated to the apostle St. Peter and named after him. Whereupon everybody lent a hand to the launching. To our great consternation the weight of the ship pressed down the too low foundation and she stuck during the launching. However, we lifted her up with jacks, retrieved the error by placing some planks under her, and thus got her off the land. But by that time the high water had already receded, and only on the following day at the next flood could she be completely floated into the sea.

After this, we worked day and night. On the 11th the mast was set and made fast with its shrouds. Water and provisions were next brought on board, and lastly everybody's baggage, a limited amount only being allowed each person.[440] In the meanwhile the carpenters were still at work on a small boat which could be placed on deck.[441] Our supplies consisted of twenty-five poods of rye flour, five barrels of salted sea cow, or manati, meat, two poods of peas, and a barrel of salt beef that in spite of all our want had nevertheless been saved for the home voyage. Each man was handed, in addition, four pounds of butter; and most of the men, who had managed economically, were able to bake for themselves from the stores they had saved up perhaps half a pood of biscuit for the trip; those, however, who could not do this provided themselves with dried manati meat.[442]

On August 13 all left their huts with much inner emotion and went on board the vessel, which was going either to bring us back to our country or to decide our fate in some manner or

[440] Instead of the last clause the MS has: "Everyone had to submit in writing how much in weight he wanted to take; what was in excess of the agreed weight had to be left behind." For the text of the agreement and the list of baggage see the log book (Vol. I, pp. 236 and 235, respectively).

[441] The MS has in addition: "so that we could use it in case of any eventuality."

[442] In the MS this clause reads: "those, however, who had previously lived too luxuriously, made themselves biscuits of dried manati meat."

another.[443] When we were all together on the vessel we realized for the first time how cramped the quarters were and what a hard voyage it would be on that account; we were lying one on the other and crawled over each other. Lieutenant Waxel, Master Khitrov, I, and the son of the Lieutenant had, after all, the best place, in the cabin. The other forty-two men were lying in the hold, which was crammed so full with water casks, supplies, and baggage that the people could hardly lie down between them and the deck. As the crew was divided into three watches, two places were assigned to three men. However, as the space was still too narrow, we began to throw into the sea pillows, bedding, and clothing, which had been brought from land.[444] Meanwhile we watched the foxes on shore ransacking our dwellings[445] with the greatest glee and activity and sharing among themselves what was left of fat and meat.

In the morning of August 14[446] the support of the Almighty was invoked in a special prayer for a good voyage, whereupon the anchors were weighed. Because the west wind helped us to pass the eastern[447] point of the island, it was decided, although the

[443] In the MS the relative clause reads as follows: "which was going to bring us back to the border of Asia and of our beloved country or to decide the outcome of our miserable pilgrimage after so much toil, hope, and longing according to the will of the Almighty."

[444] In the MS the statement of the length of the vessel, which occurs in the published version as here translated on p. 181, above, is inserted at this point, in a paragraph by itself.

[445] The MS continues from here on: "and occupying them as living quarters. It seemed to them very curious that nobody interfered with them as formerly and, in addition, that they had all at once come into secure possession of so much fat and meat left over, a pleasure to which, on our part, they were heartily welcome."

[446] According to the log book (Vol. 1, p. 243) the departure took place on the morning of August 13 (both astronomical and civil date; the discrepancy can therefore in this case not be ascribed to the fact that Steller reckoned by civil time—see, above, footnote 131—and the officers in the log book by astronomical time).

[447] The MS has, more precisely, "southeastern," which term is also used a few lines farther on in the published version. In the August 14 entry of the log book (Vol. 1, p. 244) under 3 P. M., 8 P. M., 12 M., it

mouth of the Kamchatka River was twice as near and our ship hardly in condition to withstand an autumn storm, nevertheless to set a direct course for Avacha Bay. With a light wind we made such progress that in the afternoon we were in the strait between Bering Island and the island five versts[448] opposite to the east and parallel with it, and by evening we had reached the southeastern end of our island. This day[449] was enjoyed very much, as in the clear and pleasant weather we coasted along the island, on which we knew every mountain and valley which with much toil we had climbed so often in search of food or on some other reconnaissance and to which we had given names from various circumstances.[450] Late in the evening we had come, God be praised, so far that we were opposite the extreme point of the island.

On Sunday, the 15th, the wind was light during the forenoon, and the southern side of the island was still in sight. Towards evening the wind increased in force, and, after we had cut adrift the large ship's yawl[451] that had till now done us so much service

is termed the "southern" point. Cape Manati of course is meant (see Pl. II). The name was given at this time (see 12 M. entry of that date in the log book).

[448] The MS has more correctly five miles, i. e. German miles, 15 to a degree of latitude. The shortest distance between Bering Island and Copper Island is about 30 nautical miles (see, above, Fig. 15). Steller's estimate of 5 miles is therefore one-third short.   (J)

[449] The MS has "this afternoon."

[450] The MS has in addition: "and incidents." There then follows this passage, omitted from the published version: "The grace and mercy of God became evident to all, the more particularly [when considering] in what miserable condition we came to this barren island on November 6, how wonderfully we were fed, and how in spite of astounding toil we steadily gained in health and became more and more hardened and strengthened, and the more we gazed at it in parting the plainer appeared to us, as in a mirror, God's wonderful and loving guidance."

[451] The published version has "Schiffs-Zoll." The Z is a misprint for J, as correctly given in the MS.

In the log book (Vol. 1, p. 245) this incident is mentioned under 4 P. M., August 15 (astronomical date). This would be August 14, civil date—the time according to which Steller reckoned. August 15, 1742, is, however, correctly designated as Sunday.

but which was now hindering the progress of our vessel, the island was lost entirely from view. The wind and weather being very favorable, we now continued on the course towards Avacha west by south. However, towards midnight we were suddenly frightened in the extreme, because the ship began filling with water from an unknown leak. Owing to the cramped space and full-loaded condition of the vessel it was very difficult to locate the leak quickly. The pumps, since it had been forgotten to place kettles [strainers?] under them, were soon clogged up with chips which had been left in the hold, and with each minute the danger became greater, as the wind was high and our craft was not too strongly built. Under these circumstances the sails were shortened at once; some moved baggage out of the way in order to look for the leak, others bailed out the water with kettles without stopping, and still others threw into the sea the cannon balls and grapeshot which we had taken with us from shore. To our great good fortune the carpenter, after the ship had been lightened, succeeded in locating the leak, by conjecture, below [452] the water line and plugged it up, so that we were saved this time also from the danger of foundering. Warned by this accident steps were taken to correct the defect and to set kettles [strainers?] under the pumps in the bilge. The leak, however, was really due to the straining of the frame by the action of the jacks while lifting the ship at the launching. [453]

On August 16 we continued on the same course. Early on Tuesday, the 17th, [454] we suddenly caught sight of the mainland

[452] The MS has "above." This diametrically opposite statement possibly implies that through the lightening of the ship the leak had changed in position from below to above the water line.

[453] This sentence is fuller in the MS and reads as follows: "It was also observed that the leak had developed at the time when the vessel had been raised from the sagging ways by means of jacks whose upper parts were placed below the water line, and the planks were displaced the more easily since they were fastened only with iron nails without any wooden pins, in order to hasten the construction."

[454] Here Steller's reckoning coincides with that of the log book (Vol. 1, p. 247, footnote 134), in which the sighting of Cape Kronotski is recorded at 9.30 A. M., August 17 (both astronomical and civil date).

of Kamchatka. We made it just in the neighborhood of Cape Kronotski and on account of the thick and foggy weather did not see it until we were about a mile[455] from shore. Nevertheless, the decision to go to the port [Avacha], from which we were yet 30 miles away, was adhered to. However, as under the lee of Kamchatka we had either complete calm or head winds the whole time, we spent nine days more in tacking, until at last, on the 26th of August, in the night, we arrived at the entrance of the bay [of Avacha], after having used the oars for twenty-four hours without a break, and on the 27th, in the evening, in the long desired harbor [of St. Peter and St. Paul] itself.[456]

Great as was the joy of everybody over our deliverance and safe arrival, nevertheless the news[457] which we received from a Kamchadal[458] at the very entrance caused a much greater excitement.[459] We had been regarded by everybody as dead or lost; the property which we had left behind had fallen into the hands of strangers and had mostly been carried away. Therefore, in a few seconds joy turned to anxiety in the hearts of all of us.[460] However, we were all by this time so much used to

[455] The MS has "scarcely a mile." The log book (Vol. 1, p. 247), 10 A. M. entry on August 17 (both astronomical and civil), gives 3 German miles.

[456] The log book (Vol. 1, p. 256) says that the entrance to Avacha Bay was reached at 5 A. M. on August 26 (both astronomical and civil), that the vessel anchored there until 11 A. M., when she proceeded to the Harbor of St. Peter and St. Paul in the interior of Avacha Bay, reaching the harbor at 2 P. M. on August 27 (astronomical; August 26, civil).

[457] The MS has: "the adverse and unexpected news."

[458] The MS has in addition: "who paddled out to the vessel in his *baidar*." See the log book, August 27, astronomical date, 8 A. M. entry (Vol. 1, p. 256).

[459] The MS has in addition: "and complete forgetting of self."

[460] This sentence in the MS reads: "Therefore joy alternated with sorrow repeatedly in a few seconds according to the nature of the news about general and special happenings." This may possibly be interpreted to mean that some heard that their belongings were still there and could be regained, others that theirs had already been dissipated; also that some, on hearing a general situation described, believed themselves unaffected by loss, but on questioning about their own particular property, found that they had lost it.

Fig. 22 (left)—The harbor of Petropavlovsk seen from the north. Beyond the lagoon in the foreground lies the harbor, enclosed between the land-tied island in the middle distance and the slopes on which the town is built. The spit seen between the two divides the harbor into an inner and outer part. Cf. also with Vol. 1, Figs. 7 and 8. (Photo by N. A. Transehe.)

Fig. 23 (right)—The monument to Bering in Petropavlovsk. The monument is in the town itself, near the New Church. The Old Church is seen in the background. (Sketch by L. Stejneger, Oct. 11, 1883.)

misery and sorrow that, instead of looking forward anew, we only thought of continuing the old life and regarded the present circumstances as in a dream.

The next day, after we had heartily thanked Almighty God in a common prayer for [461] our wonderful preservation and safe return to Asia,[462] the naval officers decided still to proceed to Okhotsk this autumn. I, however, took leave of them and made myself ready to travel the 30 miles to Bolsheretsk Post [463] on foot, in order to get to my own people,[464] arriving there safely on September 5 and joining in the celebration of the august name day[465] of our most gracious monarchess. A few weeks later we received in Bolsheretsk the news that the ship, after starting for Okhotsk, had, because of contrary and heavy winds, put back to the harbor.[466] Meanwhile, the news of our return when received at Bolsheretsk was not forwarded, owing to the negligence of the commander, through the galiot *Okhotsk*, then just ready to sail,[467] although she did not leave until three days after the receipt of the news.[468] In this way we were consequently regarded at headquarters as dead for eight months longer.[469]

[461] The MS here has in addition: "His gracious protection."

[462] The MS here has in addition: "and our respective native lands."

[463] The MS has "to the Bolshaya River," on which lies Bolsheretsk Post, on the other side from Avacha Bay of the here narrow Kamchatka peninsula (see Vol. 1, Pl. I and Fig. 3).

[464] The MS has: "to my own long longed-for people."

[465] Elizabeth, the youngest daughter of Peter the Great, who had become Empress in December, 1741. The name day of St. Elizabeth, her patron saint, falls on September 5 in the Greek church calendar.

[466] The MS adds: "in order to winter." On the return of the vessel to Avacha Bay and the Harbor of St. Peter and St. Paul, see also the log book, under dates of September 3–6 (Vol. 1, pp. 264–268).

[467] "then just ready to sail" does not occur in the MS.

[468] In the MS the last clause reads: "although she did not leave the estuary [of the Bolshaya River] until three days after receipt of the news at the port."

[469] In the MS the last sentence reads: "Through these two circumstances we had to endure being counted among the dead eight months longer than would have been necessary."

APPENDIX A

To give a description of Bering Island and the natural resources found on it is all the more important[2] as thereby in the

[1] The sections on the sea otter and the sea cow (pp. 214–222 and 226–
237, below) have been translated and annotated by Dr. Stejneger. The
remainder of the Description of Bering Island has been translated and,
except where indicated otherwise, annotated by the editor, in which task
he has had the benefit of a reading by Dr. Stejneger. The symbols used
are the same as in the journal (see p. 8).

Pallas introduces the Description of Bering Island with this "Preface.—A man of so thorough learning, unlimited zeal for his science, and
true merit as was the former adjunct of the Imperial Russian Academy
of Sciences, Georg Wilhelm Steller, famed for his voyage to Kamchatka
and America, would have deserved a less partisan and more understanding
biograpber than it was possible for the editor of his 'Beschreibung von
dem Lande Kamtschatka' to be. In Volume 8 of the esteemed *Physikalisch-ökonomische Bibliothek* of Professor Be[c]kmann I have already
refuted the most reprehensible of the tales with which the editor had
tried to darken the last events of the life of this worthy naturalist, and
therefore no longer need to dwell on this matter. But, because that
work of the late lamented on Kamchatka, printed with all its imper-
fections from a mere first draft, which furthermore has been loaded with
copying and typographical errors that are inexcusable and betray
gross ignorance, does not give the most favorable idea of Steller's capa-
bilities, I wish to try and destroy that unfavorable impression by the
publication of another small manuscript of his, which I caused to be
copied in the year 1767 from the original [Urschrift] communicated to
me by the late Professor Fischer, and to demonstrate what one could
have expected of Steller if he had not been prevented by death from
revising his manuscripts at leisure.

"This manuscript is a topographical-physical description of Bering

main[3] a conception may be gained of all the other numerous
islands which lie in the Canal de Pico,* which [islands], so far as

Island, on which Steller, shipwrecked, was forced to winter in the year
17[41–]42 and where Captain Commodore Bering, whose vessel stranded
there, died of scurvy and left his name to this island. This description
really forms the conclusion of Steller's journal of his sea voyage undertaken in Bering's company from Kamchatka for the discovery of the
mainland of America. It, as likewise this journal, has, to be sure, been
inserted in abridged form by the world-renowned State Councilor
Müller in his 'Sammlung Russischer Geschichte'; but it certainly
deserved to be printed in its entirety as Steller put it on paper. The
author seems to have written it down, in complete leisure from first-
hand materials and while fresh in his memory, in Kamchatka, where he
stayed for a while after his return from this island; hence in the original
almost nothing was crossed out. Except for the correction of certain
carelessnesses of style I publish it unchanged so that Steller's powers of
observation may appear unadulterated. Perhaps I shall later let follow
the journal of his sea voyage, a copy from which I also possess. The
following are Steller's words."

The editor of Steller's "Beschreibung von dem Lande Kamtschatka"
was J. B. Scherer (see, above, p. viii and footnote 4 on p. ix). The
"reprehensible tales" against which Pallas protests occur in a life of
Steller with which Scherer introduces the volume. This is written in
a careless and rambling manner and is controversial in tone. Scherer
makes (loc. cit., pp. 15–16) Steller after his return to Russia retrace his
steps from near Novgorod across two-thirds of Siberia to Irkutsk, then
turn westward again and get as far as the vicinity of Moscow, and
finally resume his eastward march, to die in Tyumen in western Siberia.
The facts are, however, as set forth in the biographical note in the
present volume (see above, pp. 3–4). With regard to the immediate
cause of Steller's death Scherer's account does not differ materially from
Pallas' account. In this account Pallas, however, adds valuable authentic
details. Pallas' strictures as to Scherer's careless editing of Steller's
"Beschreibung" are fully justified, although it should be remembered
that this work thus became available to posterity, an advantage which
many of Steller's other manuscripts did not share.

  2 In the MS the description of Bering Island, as stated above, p. vii,
forms an integral part of the account of the expedition, as, indeed, is
stated in its title page (see above, p. 9, footnote 1). The description of
the island follows the narrative of the voyage without even so much as a
paragraph indentation to mark the break. The first few lines, which
Pallas has condensed into the words up to this point, there read: "Now
that the happenings of our voyage from June 5, 1741, to our arrival in

they were met with on our voyage, seemed to have the greatest
similarity with Bering Island.[4] I shall divide this discussion into
two parts, of which one is to deal with the nature of the land and
the other with all the organisms present on it.[5]

[POSITION AND SIZE][5a]

This island, which received the name Bering Island from the
late Captain Commander, chief of the Kamchatkan expedition,
his death and burial,[6] [trends] northwest-southeast [and] lies off
the coast of Kamchatka in latitude 55° to 56°.[7] Its northwestern

Kamchatka have been related, it remains to give a short account of
Bering Island itself, the objects of Nature that are to be found on it,
and her wonderful creatures that were disclosed to us in surprising
numbers." In spite of the implication of these words, of the title page,
of the last sentence of the present paragraph as worded in footnote 5,
and of the paragraph introducing the discussion of the streams of the
island (below, p. 208), the description in the MS does not include—
to use the phraseology of that time—the objects of the vegetable or
animal kingdoms (see, below, footnote 73). The title of "Topographical
and Physical Description" that Pallas supplied also seems, it will be
noted, to reflect this condition.

[3] Instead of "as thereby in the main" the MS has "as from a complete description of this island."

[*] By Canal de Pico Steller means the sea between Kamchatka and
the western coast of America, which he thought is much narrower than
it really is, because a part of the island[s] seemed to him still to belong
to the mainland of America.—P. [See, above, p. 73, footnote 149.]

[4] This relative clause is not in the MS. Its place is there taken by the
following: "all the more so as this account may serve the general interest."

[5] Instead of "with all the organisms present on it" the MS has "with
everything that is present on it."

[5a] The headings are neither in the MS nor Pallas' version but have
been inserted by the present translator.

[6] Instead of ascribing the naming of Bering Island also to his death
and burial, as does Pallas' version, the MS reads: "of whose death and
burial we have told."

[7] For the general relationships and the dimensions of Bering Island,
as compared with those given in this section, see Pl. I in Vol. 1 and
Pl. II in the present volume. In all that follows it should be borne in
mind that Steller calls the northeast- and east-facing coast of the island
the *northern* coast, and the southwest-facing, the *southern* (on this
point see also *Bull. U. S. Fish Comm.*, Vol. 16, 1896, p. 39, footnote 1).

point, due east or east by south of the mouth of the Kamchatka
River or of Cape Kamchatka, is distant about 20, and the southeastern part 60, Dutch miles from Avacha Bay and the Harbor
of St. Peter and St. Paul within it. The island itself is 23½ Dutch
miles, or 165 versts, long and of varying width. The southeastern
end is only 3 to 4 versts wide for two miles of its length toward the
west, to the place which was called by us Ne Obkhodimyi Utes[8]
(The Impassable Rock); from there to the Sivucha Guba[9] (Sea
Lion Bay), 5 versts; at the Bobrovoe Utes[10] (Sea Otter Rock),
6 versts; at Kitova Ryechka[11] (Whale Creek),[12] where a large bay
occurs to the south, likewise 5 versts; directly across from our
dwellings, 7 versts; at Lyesnaya Ryechka[13] (Wood Creek), 8
versts. Thence the width of the island increases slightly[14] more
and more until finally its greatest width, towards Syevernoi
Nos,[15] or the cape extending out to the north, which is 115 versts
from the southeastern cape, amounts to 23 versts, or 3¼ miles.
From here the land likewise continues to the northwest and
gradually decreases in width to such an extent that, 135 versts
from the southeastern cape, it is only 5 versts and, 15 versts
beyond that,[16] only 3 versts across, and so on until it again de-

[8] The *nepropusk* at Peregrebnoi Mys, or Cape Khitrov (*Deutsche
Geogr. Blätter*, Vol. 8, 1885, pp. 255–256). A *nepropusk* is a portion of
the shore at which the rocks descend abruptly into the sea without any
shelf at their foot, making impossible any passage around it by land
(*ibid.*, pp. 236–237). (S)

[9] Serebrenikova Bay? (Pl. II). (S)

[10] Possibly the projecting corner south of Tolstoi Mys, before the
nepropusk (Pl. II). (S)

[11] Possibly the larger stream south of Tolstoi Mys (Pl. II), the "large
bay to the south" being Lissonkovaya B. (S)

[12] The MS has in addition "opposite Alexei Ivanov's *stan*."

[13] The stream debouching at Polovina (Pl. II) from the major transverse valley. See also, above, p. 150, footnote 344. (S)

[14] "slightly" not in the MS.

[15] Meaning Northern Cape. This is Cape Waxel in 55° 18′ (Pl. II). (S)

[16] The words "15 versts beyond that" are changed from the MS
reading of "at a distance of 150 versts," which amounts to the same thing.

creases to the other [northwest] cape[17] to the minimum width of
1 verst. The width of this island therefore bears an entirely
unequal relation to its length; the same holds true of all the other
islands we saw near America and in the Channel.[18]

[TOPOGRAPHY AND GEOLOGY]

Bering Island consists of a series of bare adjoining cliffs and
mountains which, although they are separated from each other
by many north-south[19] trending valleys, rise from the sea like
one single rock mass. The question as to the manner of origin of
this island, whether it is not a remainder of the mainland through
which Asia and America were formerly connected, I leave to
more competent persons to decide.[20] At all events, no little basis
and cause for such conjectures is afforded by the broken shore
line of Kamchatka as well as America, the many rocky headlands
which extend out to sea five to ten miles, the numerous islands in
the Channel, their position and consequent form, as well as the
narrow width of the Channel itself.

Because of its altitude this island in clear weather can be seen

[17] Instead of "to the other cape" the MS has "up to 165 versts, which
constitutes the whole length of the island."

[18] The clause here following the semicolon reads in the MS: "and I
do not recall ever having heard or read that such islands exist in other
parts of the world, although the islands seen by us near America and in
the Channel are without exception so proportioned." On the Channel
see above, p. 73, footnote 149.

[19] i.e. northeast-southwest; in other words, transverse valleys.

[20] It is in the spirit of this frank admission that Steller's following
comment on the geology of the island should be judged. While his
observations on this subject, because it was not his specialty and because
it had not yet reached as high a stage of development, do not have the
same value as his botanical and zoölogical observations, they are of
interest as reflecting to a certain extent the status of geological knowledge
at the beginning of the eighteenth century. They likewise reflect the
universality of knowledge presupposed in the man of science of that time
and, by the range of his observations, how Steller's zeal enabled him to
meet that expectation even in this less familiar field. Incidentally it is
of interest to note the progress in geology in the intervening half century
as revealed in Pallas' footnotes.

at least ten to twelve miles at sea, and it is consequently quite possible that on a voyage from Kamchatka to this island that land as well as this island can be seen simultaneously, although it is not possible to see one from the other. The inhabitants of Kamchatka have long supposed that a land must lie to the east opposite the mouth of the Kamchatka River for the reason that fog was constantly visible there, however clear the rest of the horizon may have been.

The highest mountains on Bering Island are vertically not over 1000 fathoms high.[21] To the depth of half a foot they are covered with common yellow clay, below which to a depth of two to three feet[22] a layer of poor yellowish disintegrated rock is met with, until one reaches, continuing uniformly into the depth, the bed rock proper which can be observed in the steep rocks of the coast.[23] In general the mountains in those parts which face the sea towards the north and the south are solid and undivided in structure, whereas those [parts] which open up inland to the east and west by valleys are cleft and decomposed as a result of the heavy precipitation which in winter through freezing splits the rocks. The mountains throughout maintain the same north-east-southwest strike. The valleys as well as the mouths of the streams and rivulets all open north and south to the sea, and the latter from their source flow from the southeast toward the southeastern end and from the northwest toward the northwestern end,[24] as I invariably observed on my trip around the island and noted day by day in my diary. Inland no level plains are

[21] As the Russian fathom of seven feet seems to be meant, this upper limit of 7000 feet is, of course, much too high. The highest mountain on Bering Island is Mt. Steller, so named by me, about 2200 feet (*Deutsche Geogr. Blätter*, Vol. 8, 1885, pp. 226 and 240; *Bull. U. S. Fish Comm.*, Vol. 16, 1896, pp. 36–37). (S)

[22] The MS reads "23. Schuhen." Pallas' change is, however, probably correct.

[23] From "below which" the end of the sentence seems in the MS rather to read: "below which at a depth of 23 feet a layer of poor yellowish disintegrated rock begins and continues homogeneously down to bed rock [Grund], as [I] observed at the steep rocks on the coast."

[24] The meaning of this is not clear.

Fig. 24—Mt. Steller, the highest mountain on Bering Island, about 2200 feet, as seen from Polovina looking westwards up the main transverse depression of the island; see Pl. II. (Sketch by L. Stejneger, April, 1883.)

FIG. 25 (left).—Cape Manati, the southeastern cape of Bering Island, from the west. (Sketch by L. Stejneger, Aug. 26, 1882.)
FIG. 26 (right).—Steller's Arch, just south of Poludennyi Mys, western shore of Bering Island; see Pl. II. (From sketch by L. Stejneger, Aug. 21, 1882, in *Deutsche Geogr. Blätter*, Vol. 8, 1885.)

anywhere to be found, only high mountains and narrow valleys. Because, however, the valleys are generally occupied by streams, one is forced to pick one's way over the lowest mountains when wanting to go from one side of the island to the other.[25] This was very burdensome to us, as, loaded down with animal [carcasses] and fish,[26] we often had to make our way over them laboriously. Level spots must therefore be looked for only along shore, there where the mountains withdraw half a verst or at the most one verst from the beach in the form of a half circle; and such spots are found wherever streams occur. And the following uniform relationship is to be observed, namely that, wherever a mountain extends southward or northward into the sea in a headland or point, the shore behind it becomes level and wide. The steeper the headland of the mountain, the smaller is the flat behind it; the gentler and the more gradual its slopes, the greater is the plain back of it. This is also the case when the mountains trend southeast-northwest lengthwise with the land. The larger the level area and the lower the mountains, the larger are the streams issuing from it; the steeper the mountains when they reach the shore, the smaller, but also the more numerous, are the streams. Where the shore and the mountains fall off on the landward side as a compact and steep mass, inland lakes are always to be found within one or one-half verst from the shore, which drain to the sea through streams. The reason for this seems to me to be that the water resulting from snow, rain, and fog[27] is precipitated all at once in such steep places and washes away the soft surface deposits down to the bed rock that forms the basin of these lakes; whereby the springs that occur at the foot of these mountains have room to develop such lakes because the mountains recede in these places.[28] Their origin is therefore

[25] The MS reads "when wanting to go to the southern side of the island."

[26] The MS reads "Fleisch," meat, which is more plausible.

[27] The MS reads "Ausdünstung," evaporation; the published version "Nebel," fog.

[28] Instead of "and washes away . . . in these places" the MS has: "but the springs break out at the foot of the mountains, whereby the

to be explained quite differently from that of inland lakes in large plains, which generally have a mucky or clayey bottom.[29] Where, on the other hand, the mountains descend gradually[30] the water forms a continuous valley in the bottom of which a stream flows.

All the mountains of the island consist of a common gray rock (granite). Where, however, they run parallel to the sea the headlands that extend out into the water are generally transformed into a clear, grayish, solid sandstone which can be used for whetstones. This is a circumstance that seems quite remarkable to me, as it almost has the appearance as if the transformation of this rock, whose structure is quite different, were due to contact with the sea water.

In many places the shore below the rocks is so narrow that one can hardly get by at high water; in some one can only pass at low water. In two places, of which one is not far from the southeastern, the other not far from the northwestern point, even this is absolutely impossible. These have probably been caused by earthquakes, high seas, undermining of the land through wave action, and splitting[31] of the rock through freezing of the water. Of this there is evident proof partly in the large boulder heaps and partly in the pillars and rocks that have been torn off from the shore and stand up by themselves in the water, of which many are to be found in such places. The southern shore of the island is in general much more broken,

---

ground becomes soft and porous and from time to time is loosened and washed away, until finally, the upper layer being dispersed, the other, namely the disintegrated rock and gravel, remains, which then constitutes the bed of these shores and rivers." For the word here translated "dispersed" the MS has "verstopft," clogged, obstructed. Probably this is a copyist's error for "verstobt," dispersed.

[29] The MS here has in addition: "but where the mountains are steep and do not gradually descend to the [lower] land, more space remains at the foot of the mountains for water and makes it possible for it to collect, thus supplying the location for a lake."

[30] The MS here has in addition: "to the level land."

[31] The MS has "annual splitting."

rocky, and characterized by cliffs than the northern. On the northern side the shore can everywhere be followed except at the Ne Obkhodimyi Utes[32] and behind the point[33] that extends towards the north, which is very abrupt and along the shore of which there are many cliffs and fallen rocks. Here and in several other places I have met with unusual aspects and effects of nature among these rock ruins,[34] as in the case of the *peshchera* named after me (Steller's Cave),[35] where the mountains closely resemble a wall, and their outliers [resemble] bastions and other parts of a fortress. Back of the cave a number of separate cliffs are dispersed here and there along the shore, which one can imagine to be ruins of walls and columns, vaults, and arches,[36] and under some of which one can walk.

I have also observed the following difference between the opposite shores: that, if on the northern side a bay extends into the land as, for example, near our dwellings, the land lying directly opposite in the south extends out into the sea as a headland; if a section of the northern shore is wide and sandy then the opposite section to the south is all the narrower, rockier, and broken; if on the other hand on the northern side the shore

[32] See, above, footnote 8.

[33] Cape Waxel (see, above, footnote 15).

[34] In the MS this sentence reads to here as follows: "in several other places I have met with similar wonderful, unusual prospects which at first glance were more like the ruins of large cities and buildings than an aspect of nature."

[35] Although in 1882 I identified (*Deutsche Geogr. Blätter*, Vol. 8, 1885, p. 237) the area of ruined natural walls and columns, vaults, and arches back of which Steller states that his cave lay as lying immediately south of Poludennyi Mys (on the western shore in 55°; Pl. II), I do not now hold the opinion that Steller's Cave lay in that vicinity. There is not at present known any cave that corresponds to Steller's description, the nearest approach being the caves on Dikyi Mys farther southeast along the shore (near Dikaya B., Pl. II), and it is more likely that the cave was located in that general neighborhood. (S)

[36] One of these arches I have named Steller's Arch (*loc. cit.*). It lies on the shore immediately southeast of Poludennyi Mys (Pl. II; for views of the arch see the present sketch, Fig. 26, and a photograph, *Bull. U. S. Fish Comm.*, Vol. 16, 1896, Pl. 27b). (S)

is hardly or not at all passable then it is all the more wide, level, and sandy on the southern.

Caves and fissures which seemingly have been caused at different times by earthquakes are to be found in various types and at different places. The cave named after me, just referred to, and Yushin's Sherlop[37] are the most important.

On the highest mountains and their uppermost summits I have observed that a heart or core, as it were, projects from their center and ends in a bare, conical, upright rock, which, while it does not differ from the rest of the rock formation, is at least much softer and purer and in addition has a definite shape. I met with such quartz[38] points in 1739 in the mountains along Lake Baikal and on Olkhon Island, which lies in it. From Anadyrsk I received another kind of rock, green almost like malachite, somewhat transparent and fibrous like stalactites,[39] with the information that this type of rock there also projects from the summits of the mountains in the same manner and that when broken off it is even said to grow again[40]—which, if this is so, would possibly have to be explained by the inward pressure.*

When the land suddenly changes its direction and abruptly continues toward a different region I have always observed that the shore for one or two versts first becomes very rocky and that the mountains extend out to the shore, are very steep, and are broken up at their ends in separate cliffs and columns. Moreover, Bourguet's observation in the Pyrenees, that the surface of the mountains because of many ridges running in

[37] Its location cannot be identified, nor is the meaning clear of "Sher-
[38] The MS has "alabaster."   [lop," which may be a garbled word.
[39] Instead of "green almost like malachite, somewhat transparent and fibrous like stalactites" the MS has "which is like malachite, green, somewhat transparent, and resembles stalactites."
[40] From here to the end of the paragraph the MS reads: "and this seems to be the result of internal movements and especially the pressure of the mountains toward the center, and these points consequently [seem to be] a kind of rock crystal—material, at first pliable but then solidified, which represents the real inner nature of the rock."

* Denudation and erosion of the enclosing rock, whereby such a core may be increasingly exposed, seem to me more natural causes.—P.

the same direction resembles the waves of the sea and that [this configuration] discloses the probable marine origin of the mountains,[41] I have also made in the mountains not only of this island but generally in Kamchatka and Siberia. I also find correct in this part of the world what he says about the development[42] of valleys and the spurs lying opposite the reëntrants,* likewise the deduction drawn from this to the effect that these changes have been caused gradually by high floods, earthquakes, and other circumstances.

As regards the shore of this island, it is so remarkably constituted that without incurring suspicion one may say that we were preserved by a miracle of God on this island and saved from complete destruction. Although the length of the island is 23 Dutch miles there is nevertheless on the whole northern side not a single place that could in any way serve as a harbor, even for a small vessel. For two to three, and in some places four to five, versts out to sea the shore is occupied entirely by rough reefs and rocks, so that at low tide one can walk out to sea dryshod for this distance, which is afterwards covered at high tide; and with the falling tide the waves are so high and

[41] The words here translated by "because of many ridges running in the same direction" in the published version read: "durch viele, nach gewissen Gegenden laufende Absätze."

Louis Bourguet (1678–1742), a French naturalist and archeologist long resident in Neuchâtel, Switzerland, where a chair of philosophy and mathematics was established for him. His theories of the marine origin of mountains and the development of valleys, to which Steller refers, are probably discussed in his "Mémoire sur la théorie de la terre," which forms part of his "Lettres philosophiques sur la formation des sels et des cristaux, etc.," Amsterdam, 1729 (see also Nouvelle Biographie Génerale, edited by Hoefer, Firmin Didot, Paris, Vol. 7, 1855, col. 92: "c'est ainsi qu'un des premiers il fit remarquer la correspondance des angles saillants et des angles rentrants dans les chaînes de montagnes").

[42] The MS has "shape."

* Steller had not been in the higher mountains on the border of Siberia. In mountains of lower and middle elevations, where the valleys have been eroded by rain, streams, and springs, Bourguet's rule is indeed valid.—P.

strike these reefs with such noise that we often could not view it from the land without terror. From the continual pounding the sea water becomes so foamy that it looks like milk. We came to know of only one narrow passage on this side that is free from ledges, so that one can anchor there when the sea is calm, and this is precisely the stretch about 80 fathoms wide to which, as, disheartened and in desperation, we were blindly sailing full tilt on to the land and to our doom, God in his wisdom and love directed us, and also led us out again through the same gate.[43] At this same place, also, is the largest bay on the whole northern shore.

From all circumstances it can be seen that this island in former times was much larger and wider than it is now; and clearly the reefs lying in the sea are the ruins and limits of its original size, which is evident for three[44] reasons. First, the rocks in the sea strike in the same direction as the mountains on the land; second, the course of the streams which debouch from the valleys is continued to sea in an open channel;[45] third, the black, green, and white (from quartz)[46] seams and veins in the reefs in the sea can be followed without interruption to the land and to the foot of the mountains, as a positive indication that they once were one with the land.—Fourth, while it is otherwise an established principle that, where mountains descend gradually to the sea or the land in itself is low and has a sandy shore, the sea is likewise shallow near the land and only gradually grows deeper; where, on the other hand, the shore is steep and abrupt, the sea deepens suddenly quite close to the land and often has a depth of 60 to 80 fathoms in a distance of 20 fathoms—in the case of this island, on the contrary, the sea is not deeper under the abrupt cliffs than it is elsewhere, because the sea floor is filled with fallen cliffs. Finally, we

[43] This is the reef-free sandy stretch at Komandor Bay (Pl. II). (S)

[44] The MS has the numeral 3 changed into a 5, to conform with the five reasons, which there are individually numbered.

[45] In the MS the second reason reads: "the streams debouching from the valleys have an open channel through the reefs also."

[46] Instead of "white (from quartz)" the MS has "of alabaster."

ourselves were witnesses of the gradual decrease in size of this island as, for instance, when in the winter of 1741 at Yushini Pad[47] (Yushin's Valley) a considerable amount of material was washed off the mountains and in the spring, split by the frost, plunged down of its own accord. It also happened that, after I had gone westwards along shore under a cliff on June 18, I found on my return after several days that the whole rock mass had fallen into the sea in this short time and that the whole region had thus acquired a different appearance.

As regards its shore, the southern side of the island is entirely different from the northern; and, although the shore is much more rocky and broken up, there are two places along it where one can land without any danger and, in small or flat boats, for instance skerry boats, can enter the mouths of the streams, or rather of the inland lakes that empty into the sea through a short canal, and find refuge as if in a harbor. The first place is 7 Dutch miles from the southeastern cape in a large bay which can readily be identified at sea from the rock pillar lying at the western headland.[48] It is this place that was called by us Yushini Pad[49] (Yushin's Valley) after its first discoverer, navigator Yushin.

The other place[50] is 115 versts from the southeastern cape and 50 from the northwestern and is still more readily identifiable because the land at this point turns from north to west, in the angle of which a little river[51] empties, which is the largest in the

[47] See, below, footnote 49.

[48] Instead of "at the western headland" the MS reads "at the southeastern end." If the former reading is correct, probably Ostrovnoi Mys (Pl. II) is meant; if the latter, the rocks off the southern entrance to Lissonkovaya Bay. (S)

[49] This is Lissonkovaya Bay (Pl. II; see *Deutsche Geogr. Blätter*, Vol. 8, 1885, p. 245, and *Bull. U. S. Fish Comm.*, Vol. 16, 1896, p. 38). "7 Dutch miles" is probably a copyist's slip for 2 Dutch miles. (S)

[50] The site of the present settlement of Nikolski (Pl. II), the largest on the island. (S)

[51] The stream flowing out of Gavanskoe Ozero, or Gavan Lake (Pl. II; see also *Deutsche Geogr. Blätter*, Vol. 8, 1885, p. 229, and *Bull. U. S. Fish Comm.*, Vol. 16, 1896, p. 38). (S)

island and at high water has a depth of 6 to 8 feet[52] at its mouth. This river flows out of[53] the largest inland lake[54] of the island and increases in depth from the sea to the lake, so that through it without much trouble one can reach the lake, which lies a verst and a half from its mouth, and can find shelter there all the more securely because the lake is surrounded by steep slopes like walls, which afford protection against all winds. I have called this river Ozernaya.[55] The place can also be distinguished by the fact that opposite its mouth to the south lies a small island[56] having a circumference of a mile and lying only a mile away from the mouth of the river. From this point toward the west the shore is sandy, level, even, and devoid of reefs for five versts, because I was never able to observe either at rising or at falling water[57] a movement of the waves (burun) betraying such sunken rocks, although I spent three days at this place for this purpose.

[LAND VISIBLE FROM THE ISLAND]

From the highest mountains of Bering Island one sees in sunshiny and clear weather on the southern side two islands,*

[52] The MS has "6 to 7 feet."

[53] Instead of "flows out of" the MS reads "flows into"—presumably a copyist's error.

[54] Gavanskoe Ozero is not the largest lake of the island. This position is held by Saranna Lake (Pl. II). This incorrect statement by Steller is rather good evidence that he did not visit the part of the island occupied by Saranna Lake, unless possibly when it was covered with ice and snow (*Deutsche Geogr. Blätter*, Vol. 8, 1885, p. 229, and *Bull. U. S. Fish Comm.*, Vol. 16, 1896, p. 38). (S)

[55] Meaning Lake River (*Deutsche Geogr. Blätter*, Vol. 8, 1885, p. 229, footnote 4). (S)

[56] Toporkov Island (Pl. II; see also *ibid.*, footnote 5). (S)

[57] The words "either at rising or at falling water" do not occur in the MS.

* It was forgotten to show these nearer islands, stated to lie off the southern side, on the map of the islands between Kamchatka and America published in Vol. 1 of the *Nord. Beytr.* On the other hand according to several maps by Russian navigators two islands were there shown off the northern side at a somewhat greater distance which presumably

FIG. 27—Yushin's Valley on the western shore of the southern end of Bering Island, seen from mouth of the stream which empties into Lissonkovaya Bay. Over the lower mountains in the left-central background the island may be crossed to Komandor Bay; see Pl. II. This was the shorter route referred to by Steller (p. 226) by which the seal meat was carried across the island to camp. (Sketch by L. Stejneger, Aug. 24, 1882.)

of which one[58] is about a mile in circumference, long in shape, and lies distant from the shore of Bering Island 50 versts, or 7 miles, from [a point] one mile to the south of the north-western cape; the other[59] consists of two high split rocks in the sea which have a circumference of two to three versts and may be about two miles distant from the island. This latter island lies directly opposite the northwestern cape to the southwest.

From the northwestern[60] cape itself very high and snow-covered mountains may be seen to the northeast at a distance of about 15 or 20 miles, and I consider this to be a headland of the mainland of America[61] rather than an island, because these mountains seem too high to belong to an island and also because from our dwellings[62] on the northern side white mountains of equal height were clearly observed many times at the same distance.[63] Indeed, between this surmised mainland and the

---

were the land seen with high mountains which he mentions in what follows. For Steller's opinion that the mainland of America stretches out thus far is now sufficiently disproved by the more recent voyages.—P.

[The map referred to, which shows the status of knowledge in 1780 of the region from the mouth of the Amur to the coast of California and between latitudes 47° and 71°, was compiled by Pallas and accompanies *Neue Nordische Beyträge*, Vol. 1, 1781, as Pl. 4. Its compilation and sources are explained in "Erinnerungen, die beygefügte Karte betreffend" on pp. 265–272.]

[58] Probably Toporkov Island is meant. The MS, namely, has instead: "and lies to the south one mile distant from the shore of this [Bering] island, [at a point] 50 versts, or 7 miles [5 versts, or 1 mile?], from the northwestern cape of this Bering Island." (S)

[59] Allowing for errors in direction and for overestimated distances (see footnote 7, above), this island is undoubtedly Ari Kamen (see Pl. II), as otherwise the description fits it well. (S)

[60] Northeastern? (see, above, footnote 393 and next-to-last paragraph of footnote 418, in conjunction with Vol. 1, p. 232, entries under February 23 and March 8, 1742).

[61] On this point see, above, footnote 418 and Fig. 14.

[62] Instead of "from our dwellings" the MS reads "from the mountains at our dwellings."

[63] The MS has in addition: "and [I] judged from the height and trend of the mountains that it must be the mainland of America."

island another island[64] could several times be seen. And from the southeastern cape I saw, although very indistinctly, in very sunny and clear weather still another island[64] to the southeast. Similarly in the clearest weather I have always observed fog to the west and southwest, namely over Kamchatka, and from this deduced the nearness of this land.

On the northern side there lies opposite Bering Island another considerable island, which we estimated to be 12 to 15 miles long,* likewise trending northwest-southeast and therefore parallel to it. The channel between both is only about three miles wide in the northwest,[65] and the island extends eastward to sea far beyond Bering Island. The mountains on it are lower than those on Bering Island, and at both its capes many high, separate rock chimneys and pointed pillars rise from the sea. It was this island that we first sighted and took to be Kamchatka and, because the channel was obscured from our sight by the land, [thought] it was connected with Bering Island. We did not notice this mistake during the foggy and dark autumn weather until some time after we had been shipwrecked on Bering Island. If we had seen this channel before we had landed we could have satisfactorily concluded that it was not Kamchatka that we had before us, because off its shore in this latitude no such island is known, and we could then have continued our voyage through this channel to Kamchatka just as well as we did in 1742 on our return in the new vessel.[66]

[64] There is no basis in fact for Steller's assumption of the existence of these islands, unless they be the two parts of Copper Island as viewed from Bering Island (see, above, Fig. 21, and Vol. I, p. 237, next-to-last paragraph of footnote 130), although Steller, to judge by the next paragraph, seems to realize quite correctly the general relationships of Copper Island. More probably, as in a similar case (*loc. cit.*, third paragraph from bottom) a cloud bank was taken for land.

* This is the island later become known by the name of Mednoi Ostrov (Copper Island).—P.

[65] The MS here has in addition: "and 5 miles wide opposite the southeastern cape of Bering Island."

[66] On the confused orientation of the members of the expedition as the *St. Peter* was nearing the Commander Islands, see, above, pp. 130–135.

[CLIMATE AND EARTHQUAKES]

As to the weather prevailing on Bering Island, it is not much different from that on Kamchatka. However, the storm winds are much more violent and perceptible because the island lies at sea without any protection and is at the same time very narrow and unforested. Moreover, when the wind blows through the depressions and narrow valleys, its violence is increased to such an extent that one can barely stay on one's feet, and it is accompanied by a terrible whistling and roaring the frightfulness of which is enhanced by the violence of the sea breaking on the rocks on shore and filling the air with its thunder. The most violent storm winds occurred in February and April from the southeast and the northwest. With an east wind we had mild and clear, with a north wind cold and clear weather. The highest stage of the sea occurred on the first of February with northwest winds. The other occurrence of a flood was caused by melting snow and heavy rain in the middle of May.

Earthquakes occurred three times; of these that which occurred on February 7 at one o'clock in the afternoon with a west wind was the most violent and lasted for six whole minutes. I was at the time in our underground hut and, as did others, heard several minutes before this a sound and a strong subterranean wind[67] which seemed to proceed with violent hissing and roaring from south to north and which became stronger the nearer it approached us. After the roaring had stopped the tremor began; it was so violent and perceptible that the posts in our hut moved and everything began to crack. I immediately ran out of the hut to the sea to see what took place in nature. Although

[67] In this reference to a subterranean wind in connection with earthquakes and, to a lesser degree, in the preceding and subsequent references to the direction of the surface wind, there is more than an echo of the seismological views of antiquity (see Montessus de Ballore: La science séismologique, Paris, 1907, pp. 16–17; J. K. Wright: The Geographical Lore of the Time of the Crusades, *Amer. Geogr. Soc. Research Series No. 15*, New York, 1925, p. 32). (J). The sound which I heard accompany an earthquake at Nikolski, Bering Island, in 1922 was like that of a heavy truck moving quickly over a very rough stone pavement. (S)

the tremor continued on land I could not observe the slightest unusual motion in the sea. The air, moreover, was sunny and clear and the weather pleasant. The other earthquake occurred on the first of July towards evening at five o'clock during very clear and pleasant weather with the wind from the east.

We had not the least cause to complain of great cold, and in the two years 1740 and 1741 it did not happen that ice collected in the sea and could be driven here from the mainland, as I had often desired, in order thereby to confirm my opinion that the drift ice in Kamchatka [was derived] from the American rivers and that the sea otters went on it when it was passing the islands of the Channel[68] and was driven about by the wind for a time in their vicinity.

At our arrival on the island on November 6 we did not find any snow except only on the high mountains; by contrast snow up to an arshin deep falls as early as the middle of October not only at Kamchatka but also two degrees farther south on the Kurilian Lopatka [Cape Lopatka] and at Avacha [Bay].[69] But the snow remains all the longer [on Bering Island] and does not melt in the level places before the middle of May, in the mountains not before the end of June, and on their highest summits and the northward slopes not at all. The amount of snow is as in Kamchatka, namely lying on level ground to a depth of about 1½ fathoms. The narrow valleys between mountains are often drifted full of snow from top to bottom because of the violent winds. It happens not infrequently that whole mountains, especially in the spring, divest themselves of their snow at once; we therefore were in no little danger, as necessity forced

[68] See, above, p. 73, footnote 149.

[69] The MS reads: "not only at Kamchatka but also four degrees farther south at Lopatka and about Avacha." By Kamchatka is probably meant Lower Kamchatka Post or its equivalent, the mouth of the Kamchatka River. The difference in latitude between these points and Cape Lopatka is about 5° (see Vol. 1, Pl. I), but Steller believed that the mouth of the Kamchatka River lay in the same latitude as Bering Island, which he knew to be near the 55th parallel (see, above, p. 130). But the mouth of the Kamchatka River lies in 56°; hence his figure.

us constantly to pursue [animals for] our food at their base. It is well known that in Kamchatka many men are lost every year through such accidents while hunting sable and wild sheep.[69a]

From the middle of the month of May to the middle of June we mostly had gloomy weather and rain; the best weather occurred from then to the middle of July. Although during this time considerable heat prevails, the evenings and the nights are so cool that one can stand warm furs. During the whole period of our sojourn on this island we never heard thunder. Aurora borealis I also did not observe.

The greatest changes on this island probably occur as a result of earthquakes and high floods. Clear evidence of the great floods is afforded by driftwood, whalebones, and whole sea cow skeletons which have been swept far inland and into the mountains. From the age of the wood I was able to conclude quite certainly that, at the time of the flood that struck the Kamchatkan shore and the Kurile Islands in 1738, the water rose to a height of 30 fathoms at Bering Island also, a circumstance to which bear witness whole trees which I came across in the mountains at that elevation and also the sand hills and new hillocks that had been deposited near the beach and among which large trees still stand erect without having decayed.* With regard to these hills that had been built up by the floods it seemed to me remarkable that they coincided completely in form, position, number of summits, and valleys with the high mountains at the foot of which they had only recently been formed; hence the dissection and origin of the higher mountains may in all probability likewise be attributed to the force of the waves.[70]

[69a] Instead of "wild sheep" the MS has "mosimont," i.e. *Ovis musimon*, the mouflon. The Kamchatkan species, however, is *Ovis nivicola*. (S)

* As the result of similar but much greater floods is to be explained [the presence of] a large amount of petrified wood in the sandstone strata, deposited as silt, on the western side of the Ural Mountains and elsewhere.—P.

[70] The MS has in addition: "and the origin of the larger may be

[STREAMS]

With regard to the objects of the threefold natural kingdom which occur on this island, the excellent and wholesome water is doubtless the most important among the minerals.

Although the island is narrow compared with its length and no stream has a course of more than five or six versts from its source, the amount of water that occurs on it in the form of springs is remarkable, inasmuch as the number of such streams is over sixty and there are as many streams as there are valleys. Some among them, especially those that flow out of inland lakes, are so large besides that they have a width at their mouths of 8, 10, to 12 fathoms, and a depth at high water of 2 to 3, some few of 4 to 5 feet. The greater number of streams, however, have no depth at their mouth, for the following three reasons: that, although the land slopes down toward the sea, it suddenly rises directly at the shore; that therefore the streams have a rapid flow and at the obstacle at the shore divide into many arms and are too weak to develop a regular channel; and that for this reason they often shift their mouths and are choked here and there[71] by the sand washed up from the sea.

In this respect the month of May is the most convenient to look for a harbor on the island. For, when in July and August the snow has completely melted, most of the streams are so small that they hardly have a foot of water at their mouths. An exception to this is the Ozernaya River, to which reference has been made before.[72] At that time [May], however, the streams rise to such an extent after a continuous rain of two or three days that they overflow their banks.

Among the streams of this island there are many which plunge down from high cliffs and mountains with great noise and afford pleasing prospects. One stream I noticed that falls

---

rationally explained from the casual development of the smaller." The passage referred to on the origin of mountains is above on pp. 198–199.

[71] Instead of "here and there" the MS reads "constantly."

[72] Above, pp. 201–202.

down step by step over a rock which has been worn down in
the form of a wide stairway, as if an artist had sculptured it thus.
All the water, that of the inland lakes as well as the streams, is,
because of the stony bottom and the rapid motion, unusually
cold, pure, and light, in other words, wholesome. Its good effect
on our sick and emaciated bodies we all experienced with great
profit and joy.[73]

[THE BLUE FOX][74]

Of four-footed land animals there occur on Bering Island
only the stone or Arctic foxes (*Lagopus*), which doubtless have
been brought there on drift ice and which, fed on what was cast
up by the sea, have increased indescribably. I had opportunity
during our unfortunate sojourn on this island to become acquainted only too closely with the nature of this animal, which
far surpasses the common fox in impudence, cunning, and
roguishness. The story of the countless tricks that they played
on us can compete successfully with the monkey story of Albertus
Julius on the island of Saxenburg.[75] They crowded into our

[73] The MS ends here. What follows in the description of Bering Island
as published by Pallas has been taken from the preceding part of the
journal and possibly from other of Steller's manuscripts which passed
through Pallas' hands. In so far as can be done, the source will be indicated of the sections now to follow.

[74] From what manuscript of Steller's Pallas took the description of the
blue fox, which begins here and continues to p. 216, is not clear. It may
have been from the report on land animals sent with Steller's report of
July 12, 1743, to the Senate but not received by that body (No. 18 in
Steller's accompanying list; see Pekarskii, *Zapiski Imp. Akad. Nauk*,
Vol. 15, Suppl. 1, 1869, p. 26) or from Steller's descriptions of land
animals listed by his fellow-explorer Krasheninnikov (Nos. 31, 32, 33;
see Pekarskii, Istoriya Akademii Nauk, Vol. 1, St. Petersburg, 1870,
p. 615).

There are numerous references to the blue fox in the journal, thus on
pp. 139, 142, 146–147, 173 (about which see footnote 415), and 183 (see
also note 445), above, and p. 216, below. For the modern zoölogical
identification of this animal see, above, footnote 317.

[75] Steller's allusion to the monkey story of Albertus Julius on the
island of Saxenburg refers undoubtedly to J. G. Schnabel's famous novel
"Die Insel Felsenburg," which was published pseudonymously ("dem
Drucke übergeben von Gisandern") first at Nordhausen, in 1731 (pub-

dwellings by day and by night and stole everything that they could carry away, including articles that were of no use to them, like knives, sticks, bags, shoes, socks, caps, and so forth. They knew in such an unbelievably cunning way how to roll off a weight of several poods from our provision casks and to steal the meat from thence that at first we could hardly ascribe it to them. While skinning [sea] animals it often happened that we stabbed two or three foxes with our knives, because they wanted to tear the meat from our hands. However well we might bury something and weight it down with stones, they not only found it but, like human beings, pushed the stones away with their shoulders and, lying under them, helped each other [do this] with all their might. If we cached something up in the air on a post they undermined the post so that it had to fall down or one of them climbed up it like a monkey or a cat and threw down the object with incredible skill and cunning. They observed all that we did and accompanied us on whatever project we undertook. If an animal was cast up by the sea they devoured it even before one of us could reach it, to our great detriment; and if they could not eat it all up at once they dragged it piecemeal to the mountains, hid it from us under stones, and ran back and forth as long as there was anything left to drag. While doing this others stood guard and watched out for the arrival of any of the men. If they saw someone coming from afar the whole pack combined and dug together in the sand until they had the sea otter or fur seal so well concealed under the ground that no trace of it could be seen. At night when we camped in the open they pulled the nightcaps and the gloves from and under our heads and the sea otter covers and skins from under our bodies.

---

lisher: Johann Heinrich Gross), under the title "Wunderliche Fata einiger See-Fahrer, absonderlich Alberti Julii, eines gebohrnen Sachsen," etc., and has since appeared in numerous editions, the last one a verbatim reprint of the first edition, in 1902 (Deutsche Litteraturdenkmale, Nos. 108-120, B. Behr's Verlag, Berlin). Albertus Julius, the Saxon "Robinson Crusoe," tells, on pp. 237-269 (1902 reprint, pp. 181-205), of his encounters with the monkeys on the island. (S)

When we lay on the sea otters which had just been killed in order to keep them from being stolen by them [the foxes], they ate away from under us the meat and the entrails from the carcass. We therefore always slept with clubs in hand so that when they waked us we could drive them away or knock them down.

Where we sat down by the wayside they waited for us and played innumerable tricks in our sight, became constantly more impudent, and when we sat still came so near that they began to gnaw the straps on our new-fashioned, self-made shoes, and even the shoes themselves. If we lay down as if sleeping they sniffed at our nostrils to see whether we were dead or alive; if one held one's breath they even nipped our noses and were about to bite. When we first arrived they bit off the noses, fingers, and toes of our dead while their graves were being dug; they also attacked the weak and ill to such extent that one could hardly hold them off. One night when a sailor on his knees wanted to urinate out of the door of the hut, a fox snapped at the exposed part and, in spite of his cries, did not soon want to let go. No one could relieve himself without a stick in his hand, and they immediately ate up the excrement as eagerly as pigs or hungry dogs. Every morning these impudent animals were seen patrolling among the sea lions and fur seals that were lying on the beach and sniffing at those who were asleep to see whether there were not some dead among them. If they found one they immediately went at devouring it, and they could all be seen helping to drag it away. Because especially the sea lions often smothered their young while sleeping at night they [the foxes], as if aware of the circumstance, examined [the animals in] the herds one by one every morning and dragged away the dead cubs like scavengers.

Inasmuch as they left us no rest by day or night we indeed became so embittered against them that we killed young and old, did them all possible harm, and, wherever we could, tortured them most cruelly. Whenever we awoke from sleep in the morning two or three that had been killed lay at our feet, and I personally may well have been responsible during my sojourn on the island for having killed over two hundred. The third day after my arrival I killed with an axe within three hours over seventy, from whose skins the roof over our hut was made.—They were so voracious that one could hold a piece of meat before them in one hand and hold an axe or stick in the other to knock them down. We would lay down a seal, stand only two paces away with a stick, and close our eyes as if we did not see them; soon they crawled up on it, began to eat, and were killed without causing the others to take it as a warning and run away. We would then dig a hole or ditch and throw meat or their dead comrades into it; before one was aware of it the whole ditch was full, whereupon we killed everything with clubs. Although we did not care for their fine pelts, of which more than a third here were of the blue variety, nor even skinned them, we were engaged in constant warfare against them as our sworn enemies. Every morning we dragged by their tails for execution before the Barracks our prisoners who had been captured alive, where some were beheaded, others had their legs broken or one [leg] and the tail hacked off. Of some we gouged out the eyes; others were strung up alive in pairs by their feet so that they would bite each other to death. Some were singed, others flogged to death with the cat-o'-nine-tails. It is most ludicrous when, being held by the tail, they pull with all their might and some one then cuts off the tail; they start forward a few steps and, when they miss their tail, turn around in a circle over twenty times. Nevertheless they would not be warned and keep away from our huts; and finally countless numbers could be seen running about the island without a tail or on two or three legs.

When these busybody animals could not do any damage to an article, as for instance clothes which we had taken off, they would befoul them; and then hardly one [of them] would pass by that did not do the same. From all this it could be inferred that they must never have seen a human being here and that fear of man is not inherent in animals but is based on long experience.

In October and November, like the [common] foxes,[76] they

[76] i.e. the common red fox (*Vulpes vulpes* or *vulgaris*). (S)

were in the best condition and their fur was thickest. The three-year-olds seemed to be the best, as is also true of the [common] foxes. In January and February their fur is too thick; in April and May they begin to lose their hair; in June and July they only had the wool on them and looked as if they were going about in shirts. In June they give birth to their young, nine to ten cubs, in caves and crevasses. They specially like to have their lairs up in the mountains or on the edge of the mountains. Their young ones they love so deeply that they betray the location of their burrows by barking at human beings like dogs in order to keep them from their young. This explains the origin of the name *pesets* (little dog), by which name the Russians call this animal. As soon as they notice that their burrow has been discovered they carry away their young in their mouths if not disturbed and endeavor to conceal them at a more secluded place. If you kill the young the mothers follow you with loud howling day and night for a hundred versts or more and do not desist until they have played a trick on [you], their enemy, or have been killed themselves.

They stink much worse than the red foxes. In rutting time they buck day and night and like dogs bite each other cruelly for jealousy. Copulation itself takes place amid much cater-wauling like cats. When there is a storm and much snow falls they dig into the snow, roll into a ball like dogs, and lie there as long as the bad weather lasts. When winter has set in for good they always have their burrows and holes in the snow in deep valleys, at sources and rivers. They are very agile at swimming across rivers. In addition to [securing] what is cast up by the sea or animals that have died they also catch the sea birds that have settled on the cliffs to sleep, and sometimes they clean up a whole rockfull. I once saw a large sea eagle, which had caught a fox in his talons and risen high in the air with him, drop him on the rocky ground and then devour him.[77] The white ger-

[77] This and the next sentence, which, in the reversal of the struggle described, fail to carry out the previous argument, represent observations

falcons[77a] on Kamchatka catch them in the same way as [they do] the [common] foxes and break their necks while they run.

The blue foxes that we found in indescribable numbers on this island are in appearance exactly the same as those which are caught near Olyutora on the mainland; and this species, inasmuch as there are no other land animals on the island, probably came from there or from America on drift ice a long time ago. We also found them in America, but a good deal poorer and smaller than the Siberian blue stone-foxes.

[THE SEA OTTER][78]

With warm-blooded sea animals the Bering Island region is more copiously provided. When we arrived there the sea beavers (or sea otters,[79] *Lutris*) were present in large numbers.[80] In November and December we killed them 3 to 4 versts from our quarters at the so-called Bobrovoe Pole[81] (Beaver [i.e. Sea Otter] Field) and Kozlova Ryechka;[82] in January, 6 to 8 versts at Kitova Ryechka[83] (Whale Creek); in February, 20 versts[84] at

---

made by Steller on Bering Island which for want of a better place have been inserted here, possibly by Pallas.

[77a] *Falco islandus* Brünnich. (S)

[78] The section on the sea otter occurs in the MS after the end of the passage in the MS translated above in footnote 382, pp. 161–162. It is followed by the passages the published version of which is translated above beginning on p. 162. The excision by Pallas from the MS of the section on the sea otter can be traced on the facsimile reproductions above (Figs. 18, 19, 20) of the corresponding pages of the published version and the MS. On the present translation see p. 189, footnote 1.

[79] See above, p. 32, footnote 57.

[80] These are two introductory sentences inserted by Pallas.

[81] On the location of Bobrovoe Pole see, above, footnote 336.

[82] Possibly the short stream debouching into Kozlovo Pole at the southeastern end of the sandy beach at Polovina (Pl. II).

[83] On the location of this stream, see, above, p. 192, footnote 11, and Pl. II.

[84] The MS has "20 to 30 versts."

the Utes[85] and Bolshaya Laida[86] (Large Cliff). In March and April, when the sea otters were driven entirely away from the north side about our quarters, we went overland to the south side and brought the otters by carrying them 12, 20, 30, to 40 versts. The chase of these animals by us took place in the following manner: These animals at all seasons of the year, more, however, during the winter than in summer, leave the sea for the shore in order to sleep, rest, and play all sorts of games with each other. At low tide they lie on the rocks and the uncovered beaches, at high water on land in the grass or on the snow a half[87] or even a whole verst from shore, though mostly near the shore. In Kamchatka and on the Kurile Islands they never, or at least very rarely, go ashore; so that from this also it is evident that on this island they had never been disturbed by man in their quiet and play.[88] Usually in the evening or at night,[89] in groups of two, three, or four persons provided with long and strong poles of birch wood, we went quietly along the beaches as much as possible against the wind, looking diligently about everywhere. When a sea otter was seen lying asleep one [of us] went quietly towards him, even creeping when near by. The others in the meantime cut off his passage to the sea. As soon as he had been approached so closely that it was thought he could be reached in a few jumps, the man sprang up suddenly and tried to beat him to death with repeated strokes on the head.

[85] Probably either Ne Obkhodimyi Utes (above, p. 192, footnote 8) or Bobrovoe Utes (above, footnote 10) is meant.

[86] Probably the same as Bobrovoe Utes.

[87] In the MS this is preceded by "a quarter."

[88] In the MS the two parts of this sentence are in reversed order, and what is here the second part is there stated more fully as follows: "Since they have never seen a human being on this uninhabited island nor been frightened by any, they are quite secure, play their mating game on shore, and bring forth their young there." The equivalent of what is here the first part then follows, beginning with the words: "—different from [what they do] in Kamchatka and the Kurile Islands, where they never" etc.

[89] Instead of "at night" the MS has "at night when the moon was shining."

However, if he ran away before he could be reached, the other men together chased him from the sea farther inland and gradually closed in on him by running, whereupon, no matter how nimbly and adroitly the animal might be able to run, he would finally tire[90] and be killed. If, as often happened, we came upon a whole herd together, each of us selected the animal that seemed nearest to him, in which case the affair went off still better. In the beginning we needed but scant effort, stratagem, and dexterity, as the whole shore was full of them and they were lying in the greatest security. Later on, however, they learned to know our earpicks[91] so well that, when we spied upon them, we saw them go ashore with the greatest care. They first looked well about them everywhere, turned their noses in all directions in order to catch a scent;[92] and, when after long looking about they had settled down to rest, one would sometimes see them jump up again in fright, look about anew, or go back to sea. Watchers were posted by them wherever a herd was lying. The malicious foxes, by waking them out of their sleep violently or keeping them watchful, also thwarted us. We were therefore compelled to search constantly for new places and to go hunting farther and farther away, also to prefer dark nights to light ones and blustering to quiet weather in order to get them, as our maintenance depended upon it.[93] In spite of all these obstacles, from November 6, 1741, to August 17, 1742, over seven hundred

[90] Instead of "he would finally tire" the MS has "he would finally fall into our hands exhausted."

[91] "Ohrlöffel." This word is facetiously used by Steller to designate the clubs with which the sea otters were slain. Professor A. F. W. Schmidt, of George Washington University, kindly furnished me with the following quotation from Grimm's Wörterbuch: "*Bohemian earspoon* or simply *earspoon:* a club-shaped, stout stick, cudgel (the Bohemian peasants formerly carried stout cudgels which at the lower end had a thick knob and because of their shape might be compared to an earspoon)." (S)

[92] Instead of "to catch a scent" the MS has "to ascertain by smell what was hidden from their eyes."

[93] From "in order to get them" to this point the MS reads only "in order to steal upon them."

otters were nevertheless killed by us, eaten, and their skins taken along to Kamchatka as tokens. However, as they were often clubbed needlessly and only for the sake of the skin or even frequently left lying about with pelt and flesh when they were not black enough, matters came to such a pass through our wicked persecution of these animals[94] that we nearly lost hope of being able to build a vessel. For in spring, when the stock of provisions had been consumed and the work was to begin, these animals had been driven away for 50 versts on either side of our dwellings. We would gladly have been satisfied with seals,[95] but these were too crafty to venture farther inland, so that it was great luck when we could steal upon a seal.

The sea otter, which, because of the nature of its fur,[96] has been erroneously regarded[97] as a beaver and therefore called Kamchatka *bobr*, is a real otter and differs from the river otter only in this, that the former lives in the sea, is almost one half larger, and in the beauty of the fur is more like a beaver than an otter. It is indisputably an American sea animal, occurring in Asia only as a guest and newcomer which lives in the so-called Beaver Sea[98] (Bobrovoe More) from [latitude] 56° to 50°, where America is nearest and both continents are possibly[99] separated by a channel* only 50 miles wide,[100] which, moreover, is filled with many islands, making the transit of these animals to Kamchatka possible in this region, as otherwise they are not able

[94] "through our wicked persecution of these animals" is not in the MS.

[95] The MS reads instead "we got along with seals."

[96] "because of the nature of its fur" is not in the MS.

[97] The MS has in addition "by the Russians."

[98] On the Beaver Sea, see also what Steller says in the journal (above, p. 31) and Krasheninnikov's definition (Histoire et description du Kamtchatka, 1770, Vol. i, p. 238).

[99] "possibly" is not in the MS.

* This is based on the assumption, to which Steller greatly inclined, that most of the coasts seen on Bering's voyage were parts of the mainland of America.—P. [On this point see, above, footnote 149; asterisk footnote between footnotes 163 and 164; and footnote 260.]

[100] Instead of "only 50 miles wide" the MS has "40 to 50 miles wide."

to cross a wide sea.[101] According to information derived from the Chukchi nation I am certain that these animals are to be met with opposite in America from 58° to 66°, and pelts from there have also been received in trade by way of Anadyrsk. That on the Kamchatkan coast, however, no sea otter is to be found above 56° is possibly due to the fact that Kamchatka from there on may extend more northerly but America more easterly,* whereby the sea lying between them assumes a greater width and depth[102] than these animals, which only find food on the bottom of the sea and, because they can not long endure without inhaling air, must not let themselves down to a great depth,[103] are able to cross; particularly as perhaps no islands occur there, which is all the more probable because all islands must be regarded as remnants of the mainland.[104] From 56° to 50° we found sea otters on the islands in sight of the American mainland and on 60° near the mainland, at Cape St. Elias itself, 500 miles east of Kamchatka. Probably[105] this sea otter is the same animal which the Brazilians on the western[106] side of America according to the testimony of Marggraf[107]

[101] The migration of the sea otter Steller also discusses in the journal (pp. 31–32, above; see also p. 32, footnote 57).

* According to what is now known of the sea between the two continents the reason for this lies in the chain of islands which abuts just in the region where the sea otters arrive in Kamchatka and [thus] leads these animals over.—P.

[102] "and depth" is not in the MS.

[103] The words from "which only find food" to this point are not in the MS.

[104] The relative clause in the MS reads: "which is natural to believe, as the islands must be regarded as remnants torn from the mainland by certain accidents." It is not at all sure, therefore, that Steller generalized the origin of all islands as rendered by Pallas. (J)

[105] Instead of "Probably" the MS has "Without any doubt."

[106] Thus both in the MS and Pallas. Should be "eastern"; see also a few lines below.

[107] The MS has in addition "and of Ray," i.e. John Ray (for some of his works see above, p. 2, footnote 2, and p. 108, footnote 244).

called *jiya*[108] and *cariguebeju*;* and consequently this animal occurs, if not in all, at least in most places on the western as well as the eastern side of America.—Accordingly, my former hypothesis would now also seem to be confirmed as a truth, that the sea otters which in winter and spring time arrive in great numbers with the drift ice at the Kamchatkan coasts have been brought hither not only from the mainland of America itself but also mostly from the islands in the Channel which the ice must pass. For I have seen with my own eyes how much these animals like to lie on the ice; and, although on account of the mild winter the ice floes were thin and few, they were nevertheless carried on them, asleep or awake,[109] towards the sea by the ebbing tide.

The sea otter is usually 5 feet long and 3 feet in circumference at the breast bone, where the body is thickest. The largest weighed, with the entrails, 70 to 80 Russian pounds. In shape it resembles an otter, the hind feet only excepted, which are smooth[110] and agree in structure with the hind flippers of seals.** The entrails are likewise conditioned as in the otter. The skin, which lies as loose on the flesh as in dogs and shakes all over when [the animal is] running, so far surpasses in length, beauty,

[108] The MS perhaps reads *icya*. Georg Marggraf (Historiae rerum naturalium Brasiliae libri octo, in G. Piso: Historia naturalis Brasiliae, Leyden, 1648) has *jiya*.

* I am fully convinced that Marggraf's sea otter is an entirely different animal.—P. [The Brazilian otter described by Marggraf is an entirely different animal, as correctly surmised by Pallas. It is a river otter known as *Pteronura brasiliensis* (Blumenbach). On Steller's reference to this question in the journal see, above, p. 31 and footnote 57 on p. 32. (S)]

[109] From "and although on account of" to this point the MS reads: "and are carried, asleep or awake, with the few soft and thin winter ice floes."

[110] The Pallas version reads "glatt," smooth; the MS "platt," flat. The MS is correct.

** This is not the place to explain the relationship of the Kamchatkan sea otter to the seal. With respect to the teeth, the feet, and the [other] characteristics it is so considerable that this animal may be declared an intermediate between seals and otters, almost more closely related to the former.—P.

blackness, and gloss of the hair [that of] all river beavers that the latter cannot be compared with it. The best pelts bring in Kamchatka 20 rubles, in Yakutsk 30, in Irkutsk 40 to 50,[111] and at the Chinese frontier, in exchange for their wares, 80 to 100 rubles. The meat is fairly good to eat and palatable;[112] the females, however, are much tenderer, and, against the course of nature, are most fat and delicious shortly before, during, and after parturition. The suckling otters which, because of their poor skin, are called *medvyedki*, or young bears, can, because of their daintiness, both roasted and boiled, at any time compete with suckling lambs. The male has a bony penis like [sea-]dogs [= seals] and all other warm-blooded[113] marine animals. The female has two mammae beside the genitals. They copulate in the human manner. Altogether, in life it is a beautiful and pleasing animal, cunning and amusing in its habits, and at the same time ingratiating and amorous. Seen when they are running, the gloss of their hair surpasses the blackest velvet. They prefer to lie together in families, the male with its mate, the half-grown young, or *koshloki*, and the very young sucklings, *medvyedki*. The male caresses the female by stroking her, using the fore feet as hands,[114] and places himself over her; she, however, often pushes him away from her for fun and in simulated coyness, as it were, and plays with her offspring like the fondest mother.[115] Their love for their young is so intense that for them they expose themselves to the most manifest danger of death. When [their young are] taken away from them, they cry bitterly like a small child and grieve so much that, as we observed from rather

[111] The MS has only 40.

[112] On this point, see, above, footnote 343.

[113] "warm-blooded" is not in the MS.

[114] Instead of "wie Hände," as hands, the MS has "wie Hunde," like dogs.

[115] In the MS this sentence ends with "for fun," and the clause about playing with the offspring is part of the next sentence, which there begins as follows: "As to playing with their offspring even the fondest mother cannot approach them, and they love their young to such a degree that," etc.

authentic cases,[116] after ten to fourteen days they grow as lean as a skeleton, become sick and feeble, and will not leave the shore. In flight[117] they take the suckling young in the mouth, but the grown-up ones they drive before them. If they have the luck to escape they begin, as soon as they are in the water, to mock their pursuers in such a manner that one cannot look on without particular pleasure. Now they stand upright in the water like a man and jump up and down with the waves and sometimes hold the fore foot over the eyes, as if they wanted to scrutinize you closely in the sun;[118] now they throw themselves on their back and with the front feet rub the belly and the pudenda as do monkeys;[119] then they throw the young ones into the water and catch them again, etc. If a sea otter is overtaken[120] and nowhere sees any escape it blows and hisses like an angry cat. When struck it prepares itself for death by turning on the side, draws up the hind feet, and covers the eyes with the fore feet. When dead it lies like a dead person, with the front feet crossed over the breast.

The food of the sea otter consists of marine crustaceans, mollusks, small fishes, a little seaweed, also meat. I have no doubt that if one were not to grudge the expense,[121] a few of these animals could be brought to Russia and made tame; indeed, they would multiply perhaps in a pond or river, for they care but little for the sea water, and I have seen that they stay for several days in lakes and rivers for the fun of it. Moreover, this animal deserves from us all the greatest reverence, as for more than six months it served us almost exclusively as food and at the same time as medicine for the scurvy-stricken.[122]

[116] Instead of "as we observed from rather authentic cases" the MS has "as [I] came to know on several occasions."

[117] Instead of "In flight" the MS has "When frightened."

[118] Instead of "as if . . . in the sun" the MS has "and look at you as if the sun troubled them."

[119] After "front feet" the MS has only "rub the nose."

[120] Instead of "overtaken" the MS has "attacked."

[121] The MS has "the slight expense."

[122] Instead of "for the scurvy-stricken" the MS has "for the sick."

Those wishing detailed information about this animal may find it in my "Beschreibung von Seethieren."*

[HUNTING THE SEA OTTER][123]

Because in the year 1743 I went to sea myself in a *baidar* at the nearer Kurile Islands in order to see how these animals are hunted, at which time the above-mentioned "Beschreibung" had already been completed, I believe it is not out of place here incidentally to describe this chase also.—The Kurile Islanders in spring go to sea for a distance of 10 versts or more in leather boats or *baidars*, in which there are six oarsmen, one steersman, and one hunter. When they see a sea otter they row towards it with all their strength, but the otter also spares no effort to escape. When they are near enough, the steersman and the hunter, who sits in the bow, shoot at the otter with arrows; if they do not hit the animal right away they force it to dive and do not let it rise without immediately again shooting an arrow at it in order to prevent it from getting air. From the rising

* As is known, this excellent work of the late Steller, to which he also was not able to give the finishing touches, is printed in Latin in Vol. 2 of *Novi Comment. Petropol.*, and the German translation is separately printed: G. W. Steller's ausführliche Beschr. von sonderbaren Meerthieren, Halle, 1753, 8vo with copper plates.—P. [On these works and Walter and J. E. Miller's English translation see the Bibliography below, p. 255. The section on the sea otter is on pp. 367–398 of "De bestiis marinis" and pp. 161–208 of the German edition. Only pp. 382–398 are included in the English translation, viz. on pp. 210–218.]

[123] This section is not in the MS. As in it are incorporated observations made in 1743 was probably written later not only than the "De bestiis marinis," as Steller says, but also than the journal and the description of Bering Island. It may have formed part of No. 53, on the method of hunting various animals, of the Steller manuscripts listed by Krasheninnikov (Pekarskii, Istoriya Akademii Nauk, Vol. 1, St. Petersburg, 1870, p. 616). In that list the observations made by Steller in 1743 are represented by at least two documents (No. 38, on birds; No. 41, on fishes). The corresponding section on hunting the sea otter in "De bestiis marinis," of which the present is in the nature of an amplification, is on pp. 386–391; German edition, pp. 191–198; English translation, pp. 212–215.

bubbles they constantly notice in which direction the animal goes, and the steersman steers the boat thither; the man in the bow, however, with a pole to which there are fastened small crosspieces like a brush, fishes up the arrows from the water as they appear. If the animal has a young one with it, this first loses its breath and drowns, as the mother, in order to be able more easily to save herself, throws it from her. The young one is picked up, and generally it revives in the *baidar*. Finally the mother or the male animal also becomes so breathless and exhausted that it cannot stay under water for a minute. Then they dispatch it either with an arrow or often, when near by, with the lance.

When sea otters get into the nets, in which it is also customary to catch them, they are seized with such desperation that they bite each other terribly: at times they bite off their own feet either in rage or, because these are entangled, in desperation.

Nothing is more terrible to see than the arrival of the so-called *prival*, or ice drift, at which time the sea otters are hunted on the ice drifting in from the sea and are killed with clubs. Generally such a storm and blizzard then reigns that one can hardly keep on one's feet, but nevertheless the hunters do not hesitate to use the night time. Also, they run along on the ice without heed, even when it is drifting and is being lifted on the waves to such an extent that they appear now to be on a mountain and then to plunge into an abyss. Each man has a knife and a stick in hand and long snowshoes laced to his feet, to which are attached bone hooks or horns to prevent sliding on the ice or falling from it where it piles up. The skins must be taken off immediately on the ice, and in this the Kurile Islanders and the Kamchadals are so skillful that they often flense 30 to 40 [animals] in two hours. If luck is with them they [are able to] bring these spoils on land; sometimes, however, when the ice is being driven completely away from the shore, they must abandon everything in order to try to save themselves. In that case they resort to swimming and tie themselves with a small rope to their dog, which by swimming faithfully drags them to shore. However, in this chase they pay close attention to ebb and flood tide and as to whether the wind blows toward the land. In favorable weather they run so far out on the ice that they lose sight of land; indeed [they run] across the channel between the first two Kurile Islands.[124]

But I return to the sea animals which I had the best opportunity to observe on Bering Island.

[THE SEA LION AND THE FUR SEAL][125]

The sea lion and the sea bear [fur seal], the most formidable of the marine animals there, have been dealt with in detail in my above-mentioned treatise. Sea lions[126] occur indeed at all times of the year and during the winter in lesser numbers on the steepest rock shores of the island, but the real migration comes in the spring at the same time as [that of] the sea bear or somewhat later.

Our men killed the first sea bear[127] on April 18 and another on the 19th. Each, including fat and meat, weighed at least 20 poods (800 Russian pounds). It was a great consolation to

[124] The northernmost, i.e. Shumshu and Paramushir (see Vol. 1, Pl. I, where they are spelled somewhat differently).

[125] The first and last paragraphs of this section do not occur in the MS and may have been added by Pallas. The long second paragraph, on the fur seal, is on fols. 88 and 89 of the MS, at the point where, in Pallas' version of the journal, occur the words "on April 18 and 19, namely, two sea bears were killed" (above, p. 176). The first two sentences of the third paragraph occur soon after in the MS at the point indicated by footnote 420, above. The rest of the paragraph seems to have been derived from some other source.

The sections on the sea lion and on the fur seal in "De bestiis marinis" are respectively on pp. 360–366 and 331–359; German edition, pp. 152–161 and 107–151. Pages 361–366 and 346–359 are included in the English translation, on pp. 208–210 and 201–208.

[126] On the sea lion see, above, footnotes 129 and 422.

[127] i.e. fur seal, *Callotaria ursina* (Linnaeus). An exhaustive account of this animal was given by David Starr Jordan and associates in "The Fur Seals and Fur Seal Islands of the North Pacific Ocean," 4 vols., Treasury Dept., Washington, 1898–1899. A supplementary report on the fur seals of the Pribilof Islands was published in *Bull. Bur. of Fisheries*, Vol. 34, 1914, by W. H. Osgood, E. A. Preble, and G. H. Parker. (S)

us to find[128] that our command could be sustained a whole week on two or, at the most, three such animals. As I had furthermore already learned in Kamchatka that these animals migrate in herds every spring to the east upwards [northwards] past the Kurile Islands and the coast of Kamchatka and in September back again from there to the south, also that the females are generally all found to be pregnant during the first part of the migration,[129] I immediately concluded that these and other islands in the Channel[130] must doubtless be the summer grounds of these animals where they bear their young, and I now surmised that these were only an advance guard of a larger movement. In this hope we later indeed were not deceived,[131] as soon countless herds followed and within a few days covered the whole beach to such an extent that it was not possible to pass without danger to life and limb; indeed, in certain places where they completely covered the ground they often forced us to make a detour over the mountains. But with this unexpected abundance and blessing a twofold difficulty shortly arose. The first was that the animals landed only on the south side of the island, [namely] that facing Kamchatka; consequently, they had to be dragged not less than 18 versts from their nearest grounds to our huts. In the second place the meat of these animals smelled like fresh white hellebore, thereby became repulsive to the taste, and in the case of many of the men induced violent vomiting with diarrhea. Soon, however, we found out that another, smaller, kind of sea bear, grayish in color,[132] which appeared in even greater numbers, had much more tender

[128] Instead of "It was a great consolation to us to find" the MS has "We saw."

[129] The words "during the first part of the migration" do not occur in the MS.

[130] Instead of "these and other islands in the Channel" the MS has "these islands." On the Channel see above, p. 73, footnote 149.

[131] In the MS a parenthetical clause here intervenes, as follows: "and with the assistant surgeon I later killed another."

[132] This was not a different species, only the younger males and the females. The old males arrive on the island a long time ahead of these. (S)

and palatable meat, devoid of odor, which therefore could be eaten without distaste. Furthermore, later we also discovered a shorter route just abreast of our quarters to the south which amounted to less than half the former one [in length].[133] It was therefore decided to keep two men there constantly in shifts who were to kill the sea bears and always have enough meat on hand so that the men who were sent there daily could immediately pack it on their backs and cover the way out and back in one day.

The sea lions finally also appeared in numbers during May, but no one liked to try to kill these ferocious animals. But we soon set to work on and devoured one that had been wounded in Kamchatka and escaped and was cast up by the sea dead but quite fresh.[134] The most delicate part of this animal is its flippers. When being boiled they swell up a great deal and can then easily be skinned, while when raw it is not possible to remove the skin. I have discussed the main matters of interest concerning this animal in the previously mentioned description of sea animals.

Of seals there occur around Bering Island all the different species which are found on the eastern coast of Kamchatka and to discuss which would here lead us too far. All species very soon became frightened at us and no longer dared go on accessible reefs.

[THE SEA COW][135]

Along the whole shore of the island, especially where streams flow into the sea and all kinds of seaweed are most abundant,

[133] This route lay up the right branch of the south-flowing stream emptying into Komandor Bay and across the divide leading to Yushin's Valley (Lissonkovaya Bay; see Pl. II and Fig. 27). (S)

[134] For the exact wording of these two sentences in the MS, see, above, footnote 422.

[135] The whole of this section, except for the first two sentences ending in "more easily from them," occurs on fols. 90 to 96 of the MS at the point in the journal indicated by footnote 431, above, which see for further details. On the present translation see p. 189, footnote 1.

The section on the sea cow in "De bestiis marinis" is on pp. 294–330; German edition, pp. 48–107; English translation, pp. 182–201.

the sea cow[136] (*morskaya korova*), so called by our Russians, occurs at all seasons of the year in great numbers and in herds. After the supplying of ourselves with provisions began to become difficult because of the frightening away of the sea otters from the northern side, we considered ways and means to secure these animals and, because they were near to us, to derive our nourishment more easily from them. On May 21, therefore, the first attempt was made to throw a large manufactured iron hook, to which was fastened a strong and long rope, into this powerful and large sea animal and haul it ashore; but in vain, because the skin was too tough and firm and the hook was much too dull.[137] It was changed in different ways, and several other attempts were made; but these turned out still more poorly, so that the animals escaped from us out to sea with the hook and the rope attached to it. Finally necessity forced us to make preparations for harpooning.[138] For this purpose towards the end of June the yawl, which had been badly damaged on the rocks in the autumn, was repaired, a harpooner with a steersman and four oarsmen[139] put into it, and a harpoon given to the first together with a very long line, coiled in proper order as in whaling,[140] its other end being held on shore by the other forty men. We now rowed very quietly towards the animals, which were browsing in herds along the shore in the greatest security. As soon as the harpooner had struck one of them the men on shore gradually pulled it toward the beach; the men in the yawl

[136] On the zoölogy of the sea cow, see, above, footnote 318.

[137] The words "and the hook was much too dull" do not occur in the MS.

[138] This sentence in the MS reads more fully: "Finally, extreme necessity forced us to invent the most effective means, as the men for the above reasons were not able to continue the former hunting any more."

[139] Instead of "with a steersman and four oarsmen" the MS reads: "with five other men to row and steer."

[140] Instead of "and a harpoon . . . as in whaling" the MS reads: "who had lying in it a very long line coiled in proper order in the same manner as in the Greenland whale fishery, of which one end was fastened to the harpoon, its other end being held," etc.

rushed upon it and by their commotion tired it out further; when
it seemed enfeebled they jabbed large knives and bayonets into
its body until it had lost almost all its blood, which spouted
from the wounds as from a fountain, and could thus be hauled
on the beach at high tide and made fast. As soon as the water
went out again and the animal lay on the dry beach the meat
and fat were cut off everywhere in pieces[141] and carried with
rejoicing to our dwellings, where the meat was kept in barrels
and the fat hung up on high frames. We now soon found ourselves so abundantly supplied with food that we could continue
the building of our new vessel without hindrance.[142]

This sea animal, which became so valuable to us, was first
seen by the Spaniards in America and described with many
intermingled untruths by the physician Hernandez.[143] The
Spaniards called it manati, the English and Dutch have named
it sea cow.[144] It is found both on the eastern and on the western

[141] The MS has "in large pieces."

[142] In the MS this sentence reads: "At last we found ourselves relieved
at one stroke from all trouble and enabled to continue the building of
the new vessel with twice the number of workmen."

[143] In the MS this sentence is completed by the following: "and after
him by Carolus Clusius and others."

Francisco Hernández was physician to Philip II of Spain, by whom
he was sent to New Spain (1571–1577) to examine its natural resources.
His main published work incorporating the results of this investigation
is "Quatro libros de la naturaleza y virtudes de las plantas y animales
que estan recevidos en el uso de medicina en la Nueva España," Mexico,
1615, of which an abridgment was published in Rome, 1651, under the
title of "Rerum medicarum Novae Hispaniae thesaurus, seu plantarum,
animalium, mineralium mexicanorum historia, etc." The discussion of
the manati constitutes Book 4, Part I, Ch. 8, on leaves 183–184, of the
Mexico, 1615, edition. There are two modern reprints of this edition,
one by Antonio Peñafiel, Mexico, 1888, the other by Nicolás León,
Morelia, 1888.

Carolus Clusius is the Latin form of the name of the French botanist
Charles de Lécluse (1526–1609). The reference to the manati is presumably in his "Exoticorum libri decem, quibus animalium, plantarum,
aromatum, aliorumque peregrinorum fructuum historiae describuntur,"
Antwerp, 1605.

[144] In the MS this sentence reads: "The English either call it, The

Fig. 28.—Steller makes the first measurement of a sea cow, Bering Island, July 12 (O. S.), 1742 (the date and measurements are given in his "De bestiis marinis," pp. 294-296). (Reconstructed by L. Stejneger.)

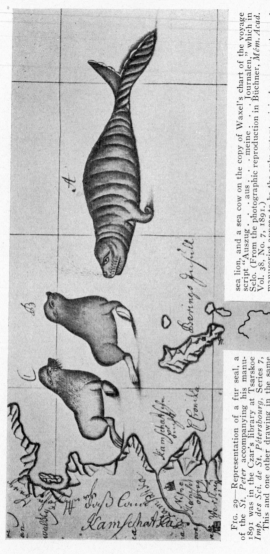

Fig. 29.—Representation of a fur seal, a sea lion, and a sea cow on the copy of Waxel's chart of the voyage of the *St. Peter* accompanying his manuscript "Auszug . . . aus . . . meine . . . Journalen," which in 1801 was in the Czar's library at Tsarskoe Selo. (From the photographic reproduction in Büchner, *Mém. Acad. Imp. des Sci. de St. Pétersbourg, Series 7, Vol. 38, No. 7, 1891*.)

This and one other drawing in the same manuscript appear to be the only extant original representations of a sea cow prepared under the instructions of one who had seen the animal himself (Waxel). as the drawings which Steller caused to be made, presumably by Plenisner, are lost, which also accounts for the absence of an illustration of this animal in his "De bestiis marinis" (see Büchner, *op. cit.*, pp. 12-13).

The section of the map shown here (all that Büchner reproduces) is also of interest geographically in representing the expedition's conception of Bering Island, its relation to the mainland, and the land seen from it. At least one copy made from this map is known; the one with nomenclature predominantly in English, located by Middendorff in 1867 in the map archives of the St. Petersburg Academy of Sciences (Büchner, *op. cit.*, pp. 17-18). This copy is probably the same as the one reproduced by Dall as Pl. 70 of *U. S. Coast and Geodetic Survey Rept. for 1890*. Hence the outlines of the lands supposed to have been seen from Bering Island have here been added from it to give a complete reproduction of this area on the map.

side of America and has been observed by Dampier [145] with sea
bears and sea lions in the southern hemisphere and by me and
others in the northern.* The largest of these animals are 4
to 5 fathoms (28 to 35 English feet [146]) long and 3½ fathoms
thick about the region of the navel, where they are thickest. To
the navel this animal resembles the seal species; [147] from there on
to the tail, a fish. The head of the skeleton is in general shape
not different [148] from the head of a horse, but when covered with

----

Sea Cow, with the Dutch, or Mannetes, with Dampier, from the Spanish
language."

[145] The MS here adds: "which is very remarkable."

Dampier's observations on the manati all, except one, relate to the
tropics within the northern hemisphere. Steller's impression that
Dampier describes this animal as occuring at the island of Juan Fernandez
in the southern hemisphere is not correct (see, below, footnote 177).
Dampier's main discussion of the manati is found in his "A New Voyage
Round the World," London, 1697, Ch. III (pp. 33–37 in 3rd edit., 1698;
pp. 64–67 of Vol. 1 in Dampier's Voyages edited by John Masefield,
2 vols., London, 1906), where he says that, along the Gulf of Mexico
and the Caribbean, he has observed them near the mouth of the Tabasco
River, in the Gulf of Campeche (separate discussion: Masefield edit.,
Vol. 2, p. 205), on the Mosquito coast of Nicaragua, at the Bocas del
Toro west of the Chiriqui Lagoon, and among the keys on the southern
side of Cuba, and, in the East, at Mindanao in the Philippines and on
the coast of Australia (this was on the west coast in about 17° S.). He
also says he had heard of their being found on the north of Jamaica and
in the rivers of Dutch Guiana.

* State Councilor Schreber has quite correctly observed in his excellent work on mammals, Part 2, p. 276, that Steller's sea cow of the
western sea of America has, to be sure, a great resemblance with the
manati of the Spaniards but must certainly be considered a separate
species, [as it is] differentiated by distinct characters.—P. [The work
referred to is J. C. D. von Schreber's (1739–1810) "Naturgeschichte der
Säugetiere," Erlangen, 1775–1824 (continued by Goldfuss and Andreas
Wagner).]

[146] The transformation into English feet is not in the MS. The conversion factor applied by Pallas is evidence that he considered the
fathom used by Steller to be the sazhen of 7 feet (see, above, p. 8).

[147] Instead of "the seal species" the MS reads "a land animal."

[148] Instead of "is in general shape not different" the MS reads "is
not in the least different."

skin and flesh it resembles in some measure a buffalo head, particularly as concerns the lips. In the mouth it has on each side[149] in place of teeth two wide, longish, flat, loose[150] bones,[151] of which one is fastened above to the palate, the other to the inside of the lower jaw. Both are provided with many obliquely converging[152] furrows and raised welts with which the animal grinds up the seaweeds, its usual food. The lips are provided with many strong bristles, of which those on the lower jaw are so thick that they resemble quills of fowls and clearly demonstrate by their internal hollowness the structure of the hairs.[153] The eyes of this animal in spite of its size are not larger than sheeps' eyes [and are] without eyelids. The ears are so small and hidden

[149] "on each side" is not in the MS.

[150] "longish, flat, loose" is not in the MS.

[151] The two "flat bones" mentioned by Steller were in reality horny structures, as demonstrated by Professor J. F. Brandt of the St. Petersburg Academy of Sciences, who, finding part of these plates attached to a skull in the collections of the Academy, has made and published a thorough microscopic examination of their minute structure. He demonstrated the cellulo-epithelial and partly tubulo-papillar nature of these plates and correlated them with the horny tuberculate plates in the mouths of the dugong and manati (J. F. Brandt: Über den Zahnbau der Steller'schen Seekuh, *Mémoires de l'Acad. Imp. des Sci. de St. Pétersbourg*, Ser. 6, Vol. 2, 1833, pp. 103–118; Symbolae Sirenologicae, Fasc. ii et iii, 1868, pp. 102–108).

[152] Instead of "obliquely converging" the MS has "krumm," crooked, curved.

[153] Instead of "the structure of the hairs" the MS reads: "the real nature of hairs in general, which likewise are hollow." A piece of the skin of the Bering Island sea cow was discovered by Dr. Alexander Brandt in 1871 among some miscellaneous old collections in the Academy of Sciences, St. Petersburg. In the elaborate paper describing it he shows that the structure of the skin does not essentially differ from that of the other known sirenians. It is constructed of elongate filamentary cuticular papillae, which Steller mistook for hairs (Alexander Brandt: Über die Haut der nordischen Seekuh, *Mémoires de l'Acad. Imp. des Sci. de St. Pétersbourg*, Ser. 7, Vol. 7, 1871, 28 pp. with 1 pl.; James Murie: On the Skin etc. of the Rhytina, Suggested by a Recent Paper by Dr. A. Brandt, *Annals and Magaz. of Nat. Hist.*, Ser. 4, Vol. 9, London, 1872, pp. 306–313, with Pl. 19).

that they cannot at all be found and recognized among the many grooves and wrinkles of the skin until the skin has been taken off, when its polished blackness reveals the ear opening, which, however, is hardly large enough for the insertion of a pea. Of the external ear there is not the slightest trace. The head is connected with the rest of the body by a short neck not set off from it. On the underside the unusual forefeet and the breasts are worthy of observation. The feet consist of two joints, the extreme end of which has a rather close resemblance to a horse's hoof; they are furnished underneath with many short and closely set bristles like a scratch brush.[154] With these front feet, on which neither fingers nor nails can be distinguished,[155] the animal swims ahead, knocks the seaweeds from the rocks on the bottom, and, when lying on its back getting ready for mating, one embraces the other as with arms. Under these forefeet are found the breasts, with black, wrinkled, two-inch long teats, at the extreme end of which innumerable milk ducts open. When pulled hard these ducts give off a great amount of milk, which surpasses the milk of land animals in sweetness and richness but is otherwise not different.—The back of this animal is formed almost like that of an ox. The median crest of the backbone is raised up high. Next to this [projection] on both sides there is a flat hollow along the back. The flanks are oblongly rounded. The belly is roundish and very distended and at all times stuffed so full that at the slightest wound the entrails at once protude with much whistling. Its relative size is like the belly of a frog. From the genitals on the body suddenly decreases greatly in circumference. The tail itself, however, becomes gradually thinner towards the flipper, which serves as hind feet; yet immediately in front of the flipper it is still two feet wide. Moreover, this animal has no other fin than the tail

[154] The MS here has in addition: "and I hesitate whether to call them hands or feet for the reason that with the exception of the birds we do not have a single two-footed animal."

[155] "on which neither fingers nor nails can be distinguished" is not in the MS.

flipper [and none] on the back,[156] in which it differs from the whales.[157] The tail flipper is horizontal[158] as in the whale and the porpoise. The organ of the male is like that of an ox in [relative] length,[159] almost a fathom long and with the sheath fastened under the navel; in shape and nature it is like that of a horse. The female organ is [situated] immediately over or before the anus, nearly elongate quadrangular and at the anterior part provided with a strong, sinewy clitoris an inch and a half long.

These animals, like cattle,[160] live in herds at sea, males and females going together and driving the young before them about the shore. They are occupied with nothing else but their food. The back and half the body are always seen out of the water. They eat in the same manner as the land animals, with a slow forward movement. They tear the seaweed from the rocks with the feet and chew it without cessation. However, the structure of the stomach taught me that they do not ruminate, as I had at first supposed. During the eating they move the head and neck like an ox, and after the lapse of a few minutes they lift the head out of the water and draw fresh air with a rasping and snorting sound after the manner of horses. When the tide falls they go away from the land to sea but with the rising tide go back again to the shore, often so near that we could strike and reach them with poles from shore. They are not afraid of man in the least, nor do they seem to hear very poorly, as Hernandez asserts[161] contrary to experience. Signs of a wonderful intelligence, whatever Hernandez may say,[162] I could not observe, but indeed an uncommon love for one another, which even ex-

---

[156] Instead of "on the back" the MS reads "on the back or on the sides."

[157] Instead of "in which it differs from the whales" the MS has "in which it again differs from the whales and other sea animals."

[158] Instead of "horizontal" the MS has "parallel with the sides."

[159] The MS here has in addition "and situation."

[160] The MS reads "like cattle on land."

[161] Work cited above, p. 228, footnote 143, Mexico, 1615, edition, leaf 184 recto.

[162] ibid., leaf 183 verso.

tended so far that, when one of them was hooked, all the others were intent upon saving him. Some tried to prevent the wounded comrade from [being drawn on] the beach by [forming] a closed circle [around him]; some attempted to upset the yawl; others laid themselves over the rope or tried to pull the harpoon out of [his] body, in which indeed they succeeded several times. We also noticed, not without astonishment, that a male came two days in succession to its female which was lying dead on the beach, as if he would inform himself about her condition. Nevertheless, no matter how many of them were wounded or killed, they always remained in one place.

Their mating takes place in June, after protracted preludes. The female flees slowly before the male with continual turns about, but the male pursues her without cessation. When, however, the female is finally weary of this mock coyness[163] she turns on her back and the male completes the mating in the human manner. When these animals want to take a rest on the water they turn on their backs in a quiet place in a bay and allow themselves to drift on the water like logs.[164]

These animals are found at all seasons of the year everywhere around the island in the greatest numbers, so that the whole population of the eastern coast of Kamchatka would always be able to keep itself more than abundantly supplied from them with fat and meat.

The hide of the sea cow has a dual nature. The outer skin or coating is black or blackish brown, an inch thick and of a consistency almost like cork, full of grooves, wrinkles, and holes about the head. It consists entirely of perpendicular fibers which lie close upon one another, as in fibrous gypsum.[165] The bulbs of the individual fibers stand out round on the inner side of this coating and fit into delicate cavities in the skin

[163] Instead of "mock coyness" the MS reads "mock flight and fruitless incitations."

[164] Instead of "like logs" the MS has "in that position."

[165] Instead of "as in fibrous gypsum" the MS reads "as in a cross-sectioned Spanish reed or cane."

underneath, which thereby almost looks like the surface of a thimble. This outer coating, which can easily be detached from the skin, is, in my opinion, a crust that has coalesced from juxtaposed transformed hairs, which type I have also found in whales.[166] The inner skin is somewhat thicker than an oxhide, very strong and white in color. Under both of these the whole body of the animal is surrounded by a layer of fat or blubber[167] four fingerbreadths thick, after which comes the meat. The weight of this animal with skin, fat, meat, bones, and entrails I estimate at 1200 poods, or 480 long hundred-weights. The fat of this animal is not oily or flaccid, but somewhat hard and granular, snow-white and, when it has been lying a few days in the sun, as agreeably yellow as the best Holland butter. The fat itself when boiled surpasses in sweetness and taste the best beef fat; when tried out, it is like fresh olive oil in color and liquidity and like sweet almond oil in taste and is of such exceptionally good flavor and nourishment that we drank it by the cupful without experiencing the slightest nausea. In addition it has the virtue that when taken somewhat often it acts as a very mild laxative and diuretic, for which reason I consider it a good remedy against protracted constipation as well as gallstone and retention of the urine. The tail consists wholly of fat which is much more agreeable even than that found on the other parts of the body. The fat of the calves is entirely like the meat of young pigs; the meat itself, however, like veal. It is boiled through in half an hour and swells up to such an extent that it takes up twice as much space as before. The meat of the old animals is not to be distinguished

[166] These two sentences in the MS read: "The individual bulbs of the fibers are round underneath, and the upper crust can therefore easily be detached from the true skin. In the skin itself, however, the *acetabula bulborum* [cavities of the bulbs] remain and cause the surface of it to appear like the top of a thimble. In my opinion the outer skin is consequently a composite of many hairs into a *continuum corpus crustae* [continuous crustal body]." See also, above, p. 230, footnote 153.

[167] Instead of "by a layer of fat or blubber" the MS reads "by the *paniculus adiposus*, i.e. a layer of fat."

from beef; but it has this remarkable property[168] that, even in the hottest summer months and in the open air, it will keep for two full weeks and even longer without becoming offensive, in spite of its being so defiled by the blowflies as to be covered with worms all over. This property of the meat would seem to be attributable in part to the diet of the animal. It also has a much deeper red color than the meat of all other animals and almost looks as if it had been reddened by saltpeter.[169] All of us who had partaken of it soon found out what a salutary food it was, as we soon felt a marked improvement in strength and health; this was the experience especially of those among the sailors who until then had constant relapses of scurvy[170] and who until that time had not been able to recover. With this sea cow meat we also provisioned our vessel for the voyage—[a problem] that we surely should not otherwise have known how to solve.[171]

With regard to the internal structure of this wonderful creature I refer the interested reader to my elaborate description of the sea cow.[172] Here I will only note briefly that the heart of this animal is, contrary to the usual order, divided or double[173] and that the pericardium does not surround it directly but forms a distinct cavity; furthermore, that the lungs are enclosed in a

[168] Instead of "but it has this remarkable property" the MS reads: "and it differs from the meat of all land and sea animals by this remarkable property," etc.

[169] The equivalent of these two sentences reads in the MS: "I attribute this to the diet of [sea]weeds and the saltpeter salt commonly incorporated in them, from which also the meat itself acquires a more reddish color than the meat of land animals and carnivorous sea animals."

[170] "of scurvy" is not in the MS.

[171] This sentence reads in the MS: "On this account the doubts were now also dismissed as to the kind of provisions with which we were to go to sea; through sea animals it pleased God to strengthen us who had come to grief through the sea."

[172] Of the section of "De bestiis marinis" devoted to the sea cow (see above, p. 226, footnote 135), pp. 309–318 deal with its internal structure (German edition, pp. 71–88; English translation, pp. 190–195).

[173] Instead of "divided or double" the MS reads "divided into two parts and consequently double."

strong tendinous membrane and are situated at the back, as in birds, for which reason it [the sea cow] can remain longer under water without drawing breath. In the third place it has no gall bladder, but only a wide gall duct after the fashion of horses; also its stomach and entrails have some similarity to the intestines of a horse; and, finally, the kidneys, like those of [sea] calves and [sea] bears, are composed of very many small kidneys, each of which has its own ureter, pelvis, traps [?],[174] and papillae, and they weigh 30 pounds and are 2½ feet long. From the head of their manati the Spaniards are said to take out[175] a stone-hard bone, which among druggists goes under the erroneous name of *lapis manati*. This I have vainly searched for in so many animals that I have come to think[176] that our sea cow may be a different kind of these animals.[177] Moreover, it has caused me no little wonder that, notwithstanding that I made careful inquiry about all animals while in Kamchatka before my voyage and never heard anything about the sea cow, nevertheless after my return I obtained the information that this animal is known from Cape Kronotski to Avacha Bay, and that it is occasionally

[174] The MS has "Fallen," plural of "Falle," a trap; Pallas' version has "Fallklappe," a trap board or trap door. There being no valves, it is possible that Steller by "Fallen" meant the renal calyces. In his "De bestiis marinis," p. 318, the word *arteriola*, little artery, takes its place, and in a separate sentence the pelvis [renalis] is said to be "as in the elephant."

[175] Instead of "are said to take out" the MS reads "are in the habit of taking out."

[176] The MS here has in addition "that the climate may be the cause of it or" etc.

[177] In the MS the sentence is concluded with "especially since the inquiring Dampier mentions two kinds at the island of St. Ferdinand." The island is called John Fernando by Dampier: Juan Fernandez in the South Pacific is meant. This statement of Steller's rests apparently on a mistaken remembrance of Dampier's account, who (A New Voyage Round the World, 3rd edit., London, 1698, p. 90; Masefield edit., 1906, Vol. 1, p. 118) on the island of Juan Fernandez found, besides seals, only the sea lion, but not the manatee.

thrown ashore dead. For lack of a special name the Kamchadals[178] have given it the name "cabbage eater."[179]

[BIRDS AND FISHES][180]

The sea birds and the migratory birds that I had opportunity
to observe on Bering Island are almost the same as those one
meets with on the eastern coast of Kamchatka. However, a
special kind of large sea raven[181] with a callow white ring about
the eyes and red skin about the beak, which is never seen in
Kamchatka, occurs there but only on the rocks near Steller's
Cave. Of rarer birds not seen on the Siberian coast I have met
with a special sea eagle[182] with white head and tail [and] the white
sea raven[183] (*Pelec. Bassanus*). It is impossible to reach the latter
because it only alights singly on the cliffs facing the sea; the
former nests on the highest rocks, and at the beginning of June

[178] Instead of "the Kamchadals" the MS reads "they."

[179] "Krautfresser" in the German; this is a translation of the Russian
kapustnik, cabbage eater, the sea cow being so called because of its
feeding on seaweeds, in Russian *morskaya kapusta*, or sea cabbage.

[180] The source of this section is not known. Several of Steller's manuscript reports listed by Pekarskii deal with this topic (in *Zapiski Imp.
Akad. Nauk*, Suppl. 1, 1869, p. 26; No. 9, on birds; Nos. 7 and 8, on
fishes; in Istoriya Akademii Nauk, Vol. 1, St. Petersburg, 1870, pp.
614–615: No. 21, on plants, animals, birds, and fishes; Nos. 36 and 45,
on birds; Nos. 39, 42, and 43 on fishes).

[181] The spectacled cormorant, *Phalacrocorax perspicillatus* Pallas,
extinct since about 1850. See Stejneger, *U. S. Natl. Museum Bull. 29*,
1885, pp. 180–181, and *Proc. U. S. Natl. Museum*, Vol. 6, 1883, p. 65,
and Vol. 12, 1889, pp. 83–88. (S)

[182] *Haliaeetus leucocephalus* (Linnaeus). See Stejneger, *U. S. Natl.
Museum Bull. 29*, 1885, pp. 209–213, and *Proc. U. S. Natl. Museum*,
Vol. 6, 1883, pp. 65–67. The northwestern race of this bird indicated by
me (*loc. cit.*) has since received the subspecific name *H. l. alascanus*
Townsend. Steller describes this eagle also in his "Beschreibung von
dem Lande Kamtschatka," 1774, pp. 193–194. (S)

[183] See, above, footnote 244. As in the case there discussed the Latin
name had been added by Pallas, it is probable that "*Pelec. Bassanus*"
here, too, is an addition by Pallas. The bird he had in mind is not
identifiable. (S)

they have young ones that are completely covered with white down.

The sea in this region likewise has no fishes or other products of the sea that do not occur in the waters laving the Kamchatkan coasts.

[PLANTS]184

Of plants I was not able to find more than 211 species during my ten months' sojourn on this island although I spent the greater part of a summer there and had to travel through all parts of the island frequently. Among these there are over one hundred that this island has in common not only with Siberia but also with the mountain regions of Europe; the rest are likewise to be found practically in all of eastern Siberia, at least on the mountains, or else about Okhotsk and in Kamchatka; and among the latter there are several that Kamchatka has in common with America and that, because they disappear towards the interior of Siberia, seem to be of American origin. But at Cape St. Elias I collected several plants that are to be met with neither on this island nor on Kamchatka.* Of shrubs there are to

184 The source of this section is also not positively known. However, unless it is a verbatim copy from some manuscript of Steller's, it may be permissible to conjecture that it was in part abstracted by Pallas from Steller's "Catalogus plantarum in insula Beringii observatarum 1742" (see, above, p. 179, footnote 425). The plants enumerated in the present section are listed in Steller's "Catalogus," and the number of species there listed (218) agrees quite closely with the number here given (211). Many of the edible plants and roots here enumerated are mentioned in the passage in the MS journal quoted and annotated in footnote 425, above.

* Of this type [there are known to me *or* there have come into my hands (the verb is missing)] from Steller's collection of plants especially *Mimulus luteus, Tiarella trifoliata, Heuchera*, a prickly kind of *Croton*, and several *Potentillae*. Plants that are common to Kamchatka and North America and that seem to be of American origin are especially the following: *Trillium erectum, Helleborus trifolius, Claytonia, Sanguisorba canadensis, Fumaria cucullaria, Pteris pedata, Polypodium fragrans, Lycopodium rupestre*, besides several other species partly not yet described.—P. [Pallas, in separating out these categories, may also have

be found on the whole island only in that part where it is widest, not far from the northern point, a few pointed-leaved alder shrubs[185] that are able to rise above the ground; in the same place wild roses[186] are also to be found. Occasionally there are to be found the small round-leaved birch[187] (*Betula nana*) in the swamps, very small juniper bushes[188] on the hills, and equally small mountain ash[189] (*Sorbus aucuparia*). Of low shrubs there are the Kurile tea[190] (*Potentilla fruiicosa*), Labrador tea[191] or *Ledum*, *Andromeda polifolia*,[192] huckleberries,[193] bearberries[194] (*Uva ursi*), cranberries[195] and crowberries[196] (*Empetrum*), and the yellow-flowered snow rose[197] (*Chamaerhododendros laurifolio, flore flavo*). Also blackberries[198] (*Rubus arcticus*) and yellow raspberries[199] (*Chamaemorus*) and *Cornus herbacea*[200] are there in abundance, and of edible roots and plants the Kamchatkan sweet grass[201] (*Sphondylium*), whose root resembles parsnip and is as

---

used Steller's manuscript "Catalogus plantarum intra sex horas in parte Americae septentrionalis iuxta promontorium Eliae observatarum anno 1741 die 21 Iulii sub gradu latitudinis 59" (see above, p. 58, footnote 119).]

[185] *Betula ermani* Cham. (Footnotes 185 to 218 inclusive are by Dr. Stejneger.)

[186] *Rosa cinnamomea* L.

[187] *Betula nana* L.

[188] No juniper has been found on the island by later collectors. The probability is that some ericaceous plant was mistaken for it.

[189] *Sorbus sambucifolia* (Cham. et Schlecht.).

[190] *Potentilla fruticosa* L. Not recorded from the island by later collectors.

[191] *Ledum palustre* L.

[192] The wild rosemary, *Andromeda polifolia* L.

[193] *Vaccinium uliginosum* L.

[194] *Arctostaphylos arctica* (L.).

[195] Upland cranberries, *Vaccinium vitis idaea* L.

[196] *Empetrum nigrum* L.

[197] *Rhododendron chrysanthum* Pallas.

[198] *Rubus stellatus* Smith.

[199] *Rubus chamaemorus* L.

[200] *Cornus suecica* L.

[201] *Heracleum lanatum* Michx. See also, above, p. 45, footnote 78.

eatable as the stalk; a species of *Angelica*,[202] which in Kamchatka
is called *kutakhshu; Ulmaria*,[203] used in Kamchatka under the
name of *shalamai;* the Kamchatkan brown lily;[204] the Alpine
bistort[205] (*Polygonum viviparum*); the purple fireweed[206] (*Epilobium angustifolium*); wormwood;[207] the common goose grass;[208]
sorrel;[209] and a species of celery.[210] Of herbs we used for salads
there were *Pulmonaria maritima*,[211] watercress, *Cochlearia
danica*,[212] beccabunga,[213] and several cardamines.[214] Instead of
tea we made an infusion with cranberry leaves,[215] with *Pyrola*,[216]
with a special large-flowered speedwell,[217] and with Kurile tea[218]—
so that we lacked nothing for the bare maintenance of our health;
and for fuel enough wood drifts ashore even if it cannot grow on
the island itself.

[CONCLUSION][219]

Not without the keenest realization of the miraculous and
loving guidance of God did we all leave this island; and surely we

[202] *Coelopleurum gmelini* (D. C.). See also, above, footnote 425, under
(d). Also discussed by Steller in his "Beschreibung von dem Lande
Kamtschatka," 1774, p. 88.

[203] *Filipendula kamtschatica* (Pallas).

[204] *Fritillaria kamtschatcensis* (L.).

[205] *Polygonum viviparum* L.

[206] *Epilobium angustifolium* L.

[207] *Artemisia vulgaris* L.

[208] *Potentilla anserina* L.

[209] *Rumex arcticus* Trautv.

[210] *Conioselinum kamtschaticum* Rupr.

[211] *Mertensia maritima* (L.). See also, above, footnote 425, under (e).

[212] "Brunnenkresse, die *Cochlearia danica*," probably meant for the
same plant (*C. officinalis* L.), as the true Brunnenkresse, *Nasturtium
officinale*, is not found on the island. In 1882 I collected *Nasturtium
palustre* (Leysser) at Komandor, near Bering's grave.

[213] *Veronica americana* Schwein.

[214] *Cardamine pratensis* L. and *hirsuta* L.

[215] See, immediately above, footnote 195.

[216] *Pyrola minor* L. See also, above, footnote 425, under (i).

[217] *Veronica aphylla* L. var. *grandiflora* (Gärtn.).

[218] See, immediately above, footnote 190.

[219] This concluding paragraph is probably based on the passage in the
MS quoted above, p. 184, footnote 450.

could be all the more thankful not only for our rescue from the most imminent perils of the sea but also for our preservation on this barren island in view of our miserable arrival there in November, 1741, and the wonderful manner in which Providence nourished us there not only but strengthened us greatly also and in spite of the prodigious labor made us increasingly well and hardened us more and more.

APPENDIX B

Honored and Respected Doctor, Esteemed Friend and Patron:

Your Highness' last letter from Krasnoyarsk I received at Bolshaya River, Kamchatka, in September, 1742, and was glad to learn from it of Your Highness' health and recall to St. Peters-

---

[1] Published in the original German in: Joannis Georgii Gmelini . . . Reliquias quae supersunt commercii epistolici cum Carolo Linnaeo, Alberto Hallero, Guilielmo Stellero et al., Floram Gmelini sibiricam ejusque Iter sibiricum potissimum concernentis, ex mandato et sumtibus Academiae scientiarum Caesareae Petropolitanae publicandas curavit Dr. Guil. Henr. Theodor Plieninger, Stuttgart, 1861, pp. 181–185, with facsimile of beginning and end of letter (the latter reproduced in our Fig. 30).

The letter is reprinted from the above in Otto Gmelin, edit.: Johann Georg Gmelin, 1709–1755, der Erforscher Sibiriens: Ein Gedenkbuch, Munich, 1911, pp. 128–132.

Johann Georg Gmelin (1709–1755), who had come in 1727 from his native Tübingen to St. Petersburg and became in 1731 professor of chemistry and natural history at the newly founded St. Petersburg Academy of Sciences, was one of the three scientists originally appointed to join Bering's second expedition, the other two being the historian Gerhard Friedrich Müller and the astronomer Louis Delisle de la Croyère (see Vol. 1, p. 32). The scientists began their journey in August, 1733, and in the next four years Gmelin explored the Irtysh and Ob region, Transbaikalia to the Chinese frontier at Kyakhta, and the Lena valley down to Yakutsk. The plan was to continue to Kamchatka. But news arrived that the authorities might not be able to provide sufficient provisions. Hence Gmelin, who was discouraged by the passive resistance to which the scientists had constantly been subjected by the local Siberian officials, considered abandoning the journey to Kamchatka. He retraced his steps up the Lena, went to Irkutsk to try to get the officials to act, but, failing in this, he continued down the Angara and Upper Tunguska to Yeniseisk. It was here that Steller, who had been appointed as his assistant in natural history, joined him in January, 1739 (see above, p. 2). Steller's voluntary offer and zeal to undertake the investigation

burg,[2] on which I extend hearty congratulations and can wish nothing better than to see Your Highness there soon.

On the American voyage that I undertook I have been more than abundantly penalized for my curiosity and hardly escaped with my life, but nothing hurt and distressed me more than to have had the most excellent opportunities for being able to accomplish something worth while and not to have been permitted to make use of them owing to the lazy and pompous conduct of the officers Waxel and Khitrov, who played nothing short of a tragedy, which opened airily and joyfully and ended mournfully with the wreck of our ship on an unknown and uninhabited island. We landed on the island on November 6, 1742.[3] Thirty[4] of our party died miserable and pitiable deaths, among them the Captain Commander, who died miserably under the open sky on December 8, almost eaten up by lice. Had my proposal been accepted, based, as it was, on accurate and carefully collected information in Kamchatka, we should, on the second

---

of Kamchatka, which was part of the task allotted to the scientists, and his obvious competence and fitness, removed a great burden from Gmelin's mind. He decided to leave this work to Steller and to request permission to return to St. Petersburg. This was granted. The return journey consumed three years, as on it Gmelin continued his investigations. It included the descent of the Yenisei to Turukhansk near the Arctic Circle, the crossing of the Baraba Steppe between the upper Irtysh and the upper Ob, a study of the Caspian region, and a detailed investigation of the mineral districts of the Urals. He reached St. Petersburg in February, 1742 (Robert Gradmann, prefatory life of Gmelin in Otto Gmelin, *op. cit.*, pp. 7–11).

Gmelin's main contributions were in the field of botany. His main work, which contains many geographical and phytogeographical observations, is "Flora sibirica," 4 vols., St. Petersburg, 1747–69. His travels were described in his "Reise durch Sibirien," 4 vols., Göttingen, 1751–52.

[2] As the preceding footnote shows, Gmelin's recall was solicited. It came as a great relief to him.

[3] This should, of course, be 1741.

[4] This count tallies with Steller's statement in his journal (above, p. 154) but not with Waxel's official list (Vol. 1, pp. 281-282; but see there p. 282, footnote 6).

day after our departure, have found the islands in the Channel[5] between Kamchatka and America, which is not over forty miles due east of the mouth of the Kamchatka River. But as the exalted spirit of the navigators would not listen to reason and they first wanted to locate Company Land and wanted to find America outside of the Channel, we found it, to be sure, but five hundred Dutch miles from Avacha, whence we had sailed, in latitude 59°, after having roamed about the sea for over seven weeks and run all the time under and along the land. On a northerly course any day within twenty-four hours we could have reached land, which I constantly suspected from innumerable signs at sea and [which procedure] was repeatedly but in vain suggested by me as well as others. I was not a little astonished at the behavior of the Captain Commander, who was ever eager to go home but allowed neither me nor any one else to do anything worth while. What I did, I did alone at the risk of my life and without any assistance, although this constituted the most important part of their discoveries, for which, into the bargain, they wanted to deny me the credit and which they wanted to claim for themselves.

Especially is it worthy of note how we lived and sustained ourselves through the winter on the island on which we were wrecked, how we built a vessel in the spring and were delivered from the island. The island is twenty miles from the mouth of the Kamchatka River and sixty from the port of Avacha. With Mr. Plenisner[6] I built the first hut, [making use of] driftwood for lack of forests, established a colony, and placed all of us on an orderly footing; this was copied by the others, and in this manner forty-six[7] of us spent the winter in five huts. We lived on sea

[5] See, above, p. 73, footnote 149, and Fig. 14.

[6] Plenisner in the baggage allotment list (Vol. 1, p. 235) is listed as "Corporal of Okhotsk Harbor." Steller (above, p. 21) calls him surveyor. He was a compatriot of Steller's (see above, p. 148, footnote 337) and seems to have accompanied him on most of his hunting and exploring expeditions.

[7] The list of survivors as given in Khitrov's version of the log book (Vol. 1, p. 235) contains forty-five names.

otters or *bosop*,[8] sea lions or *sibucha*,[9] sea bears or *kot*,[10] as Dampier calls them, sea dogs,[11] sea cows or manati, all kinds of sea birds and plants. We brought back nine hundred sea otter skins, of which I alone received eighty as my share. These animals and their characteristics I have described[12] in such a manner that it will be impossible to add anything, because, so to speak, we had constant intercourse with them, at all times and of all ages. I only regret that I was not able to make real anatomical observations; these were impossible in our dark underground huts and, without adequate assistance, because of the size of these animals.

The Channel between Kamchatka and America is not over forty to fifty miles in width and full of islands on which such an abundance of sea animals is to be met with that from them the costs of the most expensive expedition could be regained without much trouble in a few years. These sea animals live on the islands in large numbers and in security just like land animals, because since the beginning of the world they have never seen a human being or been disturbed. I would not exchange the experience of nature that I acquired on this miserable voyage for a large capital, and I regret that, owing to the lack of a ship, I was not able to bring to Kamchatka my collections, rare skeletons, and skins [exuvia]. For my part I did not spend an idle moment: I refer Your Highness to my detailed description of the

[8] This may be a misreading of Steller's handwriting, as the Russian word for sea otter is *bobr*.

[9] The word is written in Russian *sivuch*.

[10] Strictly *morskoi kot*, sea cat, i.e. the fur seal. Dampier (work cited in Appendix A above, p. 229, footnote 145) nowhere calls the fur seal *kot*, although he discusses seals in various passages. Probably in copying Steller's letter this phrase became displaced from its original position. It probably read "sea bears or *kot*, sea dogs, sea cows or manati, as Dampier calls them." This would correspond to the facts (see, above, p. 229, footnote 145).

[11] i.e. seals.

[12] In Steller's "De bestiis marinis" (see, above, Appendix A, p. 222, asterisk footnote preceding footnote 123).

voyage,[13] which I will despatch from here in the spring of 1743. Just now I am sending a small portion of the seeds collected in America that I was able to save from spoiling; the remainder I will forward in the spring of 1743, together with the plants and other noteworthy objects, of which Your Highness shall have your share. I have christened a new genus of plants in America with your most worthy name and called it *Gmelina* in order to regain your eternal friendship[14] by means of a scientific god-fathership. If, however, by a hard and inevitable fate I am consigned to be an anonymous one of your friends or a pseudo-friend I should feel it all the more keenly as I see Linnaeus in his "Critica botanica" quite rightly taking strong exception to the matter.[15] When Fortune shall deliver me into your hands you will learn from me the whole secret, my rashness, and my innocence; and, although the mistake I committed was against my will, yet, in keeping with my regard for Your Highness and your merits, I will most gladly concede whatever reparation you may claim. In the meantime the assurance of a pardon would give me great peace of mind and promote my affairs.

I should also like to report that Professor Fischer has not yet

---

[13] i.e. the journal which forms the main part of the present volume.

[14] It seems that relations between Gmelin and Steller had been strained for a time because Steller sent his reports directly to St. Petersburg instead of to Gmelin, to whom he had been assigned as assistant (Otto Gmelin, *op. cit.*, p. 130, second footnote). (J)

The genus named *Gmelina* by Steller is now called *Lagotis* Gärtner and the species he collected, *Lagotis glauca* var. *gmelini* (Cham. et Schlecht.). It is described by him in one of the five manuscript documents in Latin referred to above, p. 58, footnote 119, namely as the first entry in the "De-scriptiones L. plantarum rariorum in insula Beringi 1742 observatarum una cum catalogo plantarum omnium in dicta insula obviarum" (see Bibliography below, p. 254). (S)

Linné, however, as he states in a letter to Gmelin dated April 4, 1744 (Otto Gmelin, *op. cit.*, p. 137, and Plieninger edit., p. 19), in the second edition of his "Genera plantarum," Leyden, 1742, had bestowed the generic name *Gmelina* upon *Gmelina asiatica* L., and Steller's American *Gmelina* therefore had to withdraw before Linné's Asiatic genus. (J)

[15] The "Critica botanica" was published at Leyden in 1737.

arrived [16] and that I shall not detain the artist Berkhan,[17] unless unavoidable necessity and the interest of the Academy force me to do so, should I be obliged to wait longer for the same [Fischer (?)] than there is work for me and him [Berckhan (?)] to do at the Sea of Penzhina.

The excerpt on marine plants from Ray's "Synopsis"[18] which was sent from Krasnoyarsk on February 28, 1740, I have not yet received and am eagerly waiting for it.

That the student Gorlanov [19] was in great need, as he wrote to Your Highness as well as to Professor Müller, is a gross lie, and I assure Your Highness that all my affairs are in the best of order and regularity and that no one in my party can complain of being in want, notwithstanding the fact that we received our first [allowance of] provisions from the general fund only in 1742. Never before has Gorlanov had a year's pay on hand at the end of the year, as he has now, never before has he been out of debt as now, and never before has he had such good clothes and linen as now. But he surely deserves no credit for this. That he may at times be short of brandy, I admit willingly that I am the cause of that, and most diligently so. How clear my conscience is and how justified my diligence is apparent from the fact that when I unexpectedly found a copy of that letter at his quarters [bei ihm] I did not even deign to call to account this imprudent

[16] Johann Eberhard Fischer (1697–1771) replaced G. F. Müller as historian on the Siberian expedition, when Müller, who with Gmelin had asked to be relieved, returned to Russia. Fischer's appointment dated from May, 1738, and was confirmed by the Senate in March, 1739, whereupon Fischer set out upon his journey (Pekarskii, Istoriya Akademii Nauk, Vol. 1, St. Petersburg, 1870, pp. 617–618).

[17] Johann Christian Berckhan was one of the artists assigned to the expedition. His zealous and accurate work in depicting the plants and animals found on the expedition led, on his return, to his appointment as an adjunct, or assistant, of the St. Petersburg Academy of Sciences (preface to J. G. Gmelin's "Flora sibirica," as reprinted in Otto Gmelin, op. cit., pp. 66–67).

[18] Probably John Ray: Synopsis methodica stirpium britannicarum, London, 1690 (2nd edit., 1696; 3rd edit., 1724), is meant. (S)

[19] Gorlanov was a student assistant.

person but admonished him to report only the truth about my whole behavior. I yield to none in [the protection of] the honor of my institution, my services, or the welfare of the general fund,[20]

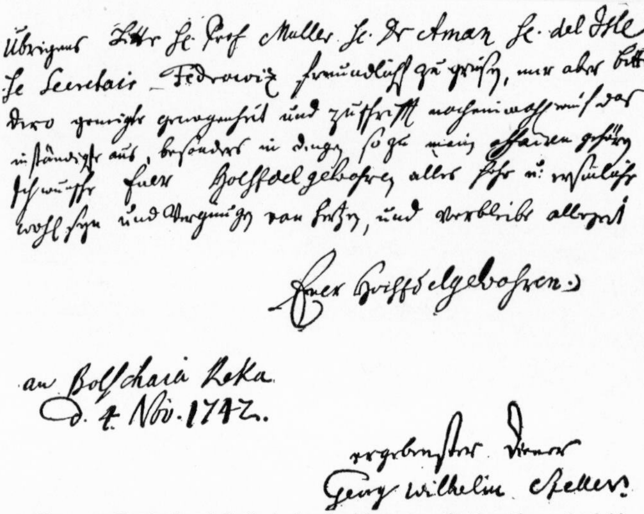

FIG. 30—Facsimile of Steller's handwriting, constituting the end of his letter to Gmelin of November 4, 1742. (From Plieninger, Reliquiae . . . commercii epistolici, Stuttgart, 1861.)

and on my return I regard it as my greatest riches that I shall leave behind in Siberia neither sighs, nor debts, nor a bad reputation, nor accusations.

May I beg Your Highness to be good enough to see to it that I at least receive from the chancellery of the Academy an assurance as to whether they received my reports and collections.[21] To date I do not know whether they got a single one from me,

[20] This passage in German reads: "ich vergebe weder der Ehre meines Collegii, meiner Dienste, noch dem Interesse der Cassa das Geringste."

[21] It is difficult to identify these. The Academy received a report from Irkutsk dated February 13, 1740, and two reports from Kirensk Post dated April 30, 1740 (Pekarskii, *Zapiski Imp. Akad. Nauk*, Vol. 15,

although I have already sent five. This winter I will have clean copies made of all my observations and will send them in the spring. In the summer I intend to go to Lower Kamchatka Post and in the [following] winter to Anadyrsk. Should I, however, be recalled I should be quite content also. My field notes I will send in the rough because I have neither the time nor the skill of a formal historiographer, nor, moreover, is that my function. Mr. Plenisner has been recalled and is spending the winter with me at Bolshaya River. He is a great *fur temporis* [thief of time]. He and Mr. Berkhan wish to be remembered kindly to Your Highness. Also please give my kindest regards to Professor Müller,[22] Dr. Amman,[23] Mr. Delisle,[24] and Secretary Fedrowiz.[25] I ask again most earnestly for your gracious favor and a word from you, especially about matters that concern me.

With hearty good wishes to Your Highness for all possible health and pleasure, I remain,

Your Highness' most humble servant,
GEORG WILHELM STELLER

Bolshaya River
  Nov. 4, 1742[26]

Suppl. No. 1, 1869, p. 28). Steller sent to Gmelin for transmission to the Senate a report and some plants from Okhotsk on August 20, 1740 (Plieninger, Reliquiae . . . commercii epistolici, 1861, p. 173). In his report to the Senate of November 16, 1742, Steller mentions (Pekarskii, *op. cit.*, p. 13) that he had sent a report to the same body on March 31, 1741, from Bolsheretsk. Some of these reports may be among those here referred to.

[22] G. F. Müller. See, above, this appendix, footnote 1.

[23] Johann Amman (1707–1741), member of the St. Petersburg Academy and professor of botany.

[24] Joseph Nicolas Delisle. See Vol. 1, p. 32, and the present volume, p. 70, footnote 148.

[25] This person cannot be identified. As he is not mentioned in Pekarskii, Istoriya Akademii Nauk, Vol. 1, St. Petersburg, 1870, no secretary of the St. Petersburg Academy of Sciences seems to be meant.

[26] The letter was received by Gmelin on October 29, 1743. Gmelin was by that time in St. Petersburg.

BIBLIOGRAPHY

Biographical Material on Steller

STÖLLER, AUGUSTIN. [Life of Steller.] *Ergötzungen der Vernünftigen Seele aus der Sittenlehre und der Gelehrsamkeit Überhaupt*, Vol. 5, No. 1, Leipzig, 1747 or 1748. [This biographical sketch by Steller's brother (the name was originally spelled Stöller) is reliable for the period to Steller's departure for Russia but not for his subsequent activities, partly because it was written before authentic news of Steller's last movements had reached Germany. This sketch was reprinted or copied in contemporary German newspapers and periodicals, thus in the *Hamburgische Correspondent*, Nos. 199–202, the *Frankfurtische Zeitung*, and the *Beyträge zur Historie der Gelahrtheit* (see below).]

Geschichte des Herrn Georg Wilh. Stöller, der Russisch-Kayserl. Academie der Wissenschaften zu St. Petersburg Adjuncti und Mitgliedes. *Beyträge zur Historie der Gelahrtheit Worinnen die Geschichte der Gelehrten Unserer Zeiten Beschrieben Werden*, Hamburg, Vol. 1, 1748, pp. 111–124. [Reprinted from Augustin Stöller's biographical sketch of his brother; see above.]

Leben Herrn Georg Wilhelm Stellers, gewesnen Adjuncti der Kayserl. Academie der Wissenschaften zu St. Petersburg, worin die bisher bekanntgemachten Nachrichten von dessen Reisen, Entdeckungen und Tode theils widerlegt, theils ergäntzt und verbessert werden. Frankfort, 1748. 38 pp. [Although the authorship of this book is attributed to Johann Georg Gmelin by contemporary and other sources, there is at least grave doubt as to this from internal evidence, according to a note in Otto Gmelin, edit.: Johann Georg Gmelin, Munich, 1911, p. 145. Copies are rare: there is one in the Prussian State (formerly Royal) Library in Berlin and one in the Kiel University library. There is a Russian translation in the library of the St. Petersburg Academy of Sciences (Pekarskii, Istoriya Akademii Nauk, Vol. 1, p. 587), Manuscript Division, under the archival designation No. 17.8.8.]

GMELIN, JOHANN GEORG. [Two passages dealing with Steller in his] "Flora sibirica," 4 vols., St. Petersburg, 1747–69, and "Reise durch Sibirien," 4 vols. in two, Göttingen, 1751–52. [Both passages easily accessible in Otto Gmelin, edit.: Johann Georg Gmelin, Munich, 1911, pp. 68–71 and 114–117 respectively.]

REICHARD, ———, transl. Die heutige Historie, oder der gegenwärtige Staat aller Nationen in Europa (translated from the English of H. Salmon and H. von Hoch), Altona and Leipzig, 1752. [Pp. 574–578

deal with the life of Steller. Reichard, who was a pupil of Steller's at
the University of Halle, corrects errors in Augustin Stöller's account
(see above) but is himself inaccurate as to the circumstances under
which Steller died.]

S[CHERER], J. B. Leben Herrn Georg Wilhelm Stellers, gewesenen Mitgliedes und Adjuncti der Russisch-Kayserlichen Academie der Wissenschaften. In G. W. Steller: Beschreibung von dem Lande Kamtschatka,
dessen Einwohnern, deren Sitten, Nahmen, Lebensart und verschiedenen Gewohnheiten, herausgegeben von J. B. S[cherer], Frankfort
and Leipzig, 1774, pre-pp. 1–24. [This is an uncritical and discursive
account, unreliable in many details. Beckmann states (*Physikalisch-
ökonomische Bibliothek*, Vol. 6, 1775, p. 192) that the author was
Scherer, who had lived several years prior to 1774 in St. Petersburg
and been in touch with Professor J. E. Fischer (see above p. 247,
footnote 16) and others who knew Steller. It was mainly to rectify the
errors in this account that Pallas wrote the letter listed in the after-
next entry.]

BECKMANN, JOHANN. [Review of Steller's "Beschreibung von dem Lande
Kamtschatka," Frankfort and Leipzig, 1774.] *Physikalisch-
ökonomische Bibliothek, Worinn von den Neuesten Büchern, Welche die
Naturgeschichte, Naturlehre, und die Land- und Stadtwirthschaft Betreffen,
Zuverlässige und Vollständige Nachrichten Ertheilet Werden, von Johann
Beckmann*, Göttingen, Vol. 6, 1775, pp. 191–202. [On pp. 193–196 are
given certain details about Steller's life and the manner of his death,
to correct misstatements in Scherer's life of Steller (see above).]

[PALLAS, P. S.] Zuverlässige Nachrichten von den letzten Schicksalen
desHerrn Georg Wilhelm Steller. *Physikalisch-ökonomische Bibliothek
... von Johann Beckmann*, Göttingen, Vol. 8, 1777, pp. 453–464.
[Additional details on Steller's life and last days called forth by the review of Steller's "Beschreibung von dem Lande Kamtschatka" (see
above) and sent to Beckmann by Pallas in a letter dated July 27, 1777.
The letter contains a transcript of Steller's testament (pp. 461–463),
which he gave Professor J. E. Fischer near Solikamsk when he was
ordered to return to Irkutsk and report for trial (see, above, p. 4). This
is the note to which Pallas refers in his preface to Steller's description of
Bering Island (see, above, p. 189, footnote 1).]

[Scattered references to Steller in:] "Allegemeine Historie der Reisen zu
Wasser und Lande," Leipzig, Vol. 19, about 1772, p. 79; *A. F. Büsching's
Wöchentliche Nachrichten*, 1774, No. 21, pp. 163–167, and No. 24, pp.
185–187; *Allgemeine Deutsche Bibliothek*, Berlin and Stettin, Vol. 25,
1775, pp. 537–543.

PEKARSKII, PETR. [Biography of] Georg Wilhelm Steller, naturalist.
In his "Istoriya Imperatorskoi Akademii Nauk v Peterburgye,"
Vol. 1, Division of Russian Language and Literature of the Imperial

Academy of Sciences, St. Petersburg, 1870, pp. 587–616. [This is the best study of Steller. It is based on the sources; these are discussed critically on pp. 587–588.]

Steller's Works

(Steller wrote numerous botanical, zoölogical, and other reports during the expedition. Some of these he sent to St. Petersburg, some were transmitted to the authorities there by others after his death, some never reached their destination. At the present day it is therefore difficult to reconstruct a list of them, still more so to indicate their whereabouts. Those that were published are listed below under (b); those in manuscript form whose location is known are listed immediately below, under (a). As regards the large remainder, several references afford a clue to their identity: (1) list of the reports sent to the Senate by Steller with his communication of July 12, 1743 (Pekarskii, *Zapiski Imp. Akad. Nauk*, Vol. 15, Suppl. No. 1, 1869, p. 26), a number of which could not be located when an investigation was made in 1746 (*ibid.*, p. 26); (2) list by Krasheninnikov of reports by Steller transmitted to the Academy of Sciences by the painter Berckhan after Steller's death (Pekarskii, Istoriya Akademii Nauk, Vol. 1, 1870, pp. 613–616); (3) reports mentioned in the biographies of Steller in *Beyträge zur Historie der Gelahrtheit*, Vol. 1, 1748, p. 120, and in "Beschreibung von dem Lande Kamtschatka," 1774, pre-p. 20 (the latter probably taken by Scherer from the former or its equivalent). Several of Steller's zoölogical reports, including the "Ornithologia sibirica" and the "Ichthyologia sibirica" were in Pallas' hands in 1777, so he tells us (*Physikalisch-ökonomische Bibliothek von Johann Beckmann*, Vol. 8, 1777, pp. 459–460). He likewise says that J. G. Gmelin had utilized the botanical reports. Pallas himself incorporated statements from Steller's reports, as indicated by numerous passages in his "Zoögraphia rosso-asiatica," 1811–1831; likewise Krasheninnikov in his "Histoire et description du Kamtchatka," 1770.

(a) Manuscript

II. Zweyte auf Russisch hohen Kayserlichen Befehl unternommene Kamtschatzkische Expedition, das ist Beschreibung der Reise des Hn. Capitain Commendeur Behrings welche zur Untersuchung der von Kamtschatka Nord Ostlich gelegenen Länder angestellet, auch derjenigen Insuln worauf an Land zu gehen Gelegenheit gehabt und wo wir 1742 überwintert. Dabey nebst unsern Schicksaalen die darauf befindlichen Subjecta des 3. fachen Natur Reiches recensiret werden. Von Georg Wilhelm Steller, Adjuncto Historiae Naturalis Academiae Scientarum Petrop. 1743. Title page and III pages. Archives of the Academy of Sciences, Petrograd. [This is the MS copy of the journal located in 1917 and used in the present translation in comparison with the published version. Photostat copies are in the Library of Congress, Washington, D. C., and the libraries of the University of Washington, Seattle, Wash., and the American Geographical Society.]

[Translation from German into Russian of Steller's journal of his voyage from Kamchatka to America.] 87 pp. Archives of the Academy of Sciences, Petrograd, Manuscript Division, No. 120.32.13.13. [This translation, by V. Lebedev, is referred to by Pekarskii, Istoriya Akademii Nauk, Vol. 1, p. 597. It is also listed in Golder's "Guide to Materials for American History in Russian Archives," p. 147, and Dall and Baker's "Partial List of Charts, Maps, and Publications Relating to Alaska," p. 352. The Russian translation used by Pallas to replace pages missing from the German original (see above, p. viii and asterisk footnotes on pp. 63 and 110) may have been this document or a copy from it.]

Catalogus plantarum intra sex horas in parte Americae septentrionalis iuxta promontorium Eliae observatarum anno 1741 die 21 Iulii sub gradu latitudinis 59. 11 pp. Academy of Sciences, Petrograd, Arkhiv Konferentsia, Bundle 13C, No. 5Q. [Photostat copies in the Library of Congress and the American Geographical Society.]

Catalogus plantarum in insula Beringii observatarum 1742. 18 pp. Academy of Sciences, Petrograd, Arkhiv Konferentsia, Bundle 13C, No. 4Q. [Reprinted in Fedtschenko, Flore des Îles du Commandeur, 1906, pp. 23–29. Photostat copies in the Library of Congress and the American Geographical Society.]

Descriptiones L. plantarum rariorum in insula Beringi 1742 observatarum una cum catalogo plantarum omnium in dicta insula obviarum, autore Georgio Wilhelmo Stellero, Academiae Scientiarum Petropolitanae Adjuncto. 76 pp. Academy of Sciences, Petrograd, Arkhiv Konferentsia, Bundle 13C, No. 8Q. [Photostat copies in the Library of Congress and the American Geographical Society.]

Mantissa plantarum minus aut plane incognitarum. 14 pp. Academy of Sciences, Petrograd, Arkhiv Konferentsia, Bundle 13C, No. 6Q. [Photostat copies in the Library of Congress and the American Geographical Society.]

Catalogus seminum anno 1741 in America septentrionali sub gradu latitudinis 59 & 55 collectorum quorum dimidia pars d. 17 Nov. 1742 transmissa. 7 pp. Academy of Sciences, Petrograd, Arkhiv Konferentsia, Bundle 13C, No. 7Q. [Photostat copies in the Library of Congress and the American Geographical Society.]

(b) *Published*

STELLER, G. W. De bestiis marinis. *Novi Commentarii Academiae Sci-entiarum Imperialis Petropolitanae*, Vol. 2 for 1749, St. Petersburg, 1751, pp. 289–398, with Pls. 15 and 16.

STELLER, G. W. Georg Wilhelm Steller's ausführliche Beschreibung von sonderbaren Meerthieren, mit Erläuterungen und nöthigen Kupfern versehen. Halle, 1753. 218 pp. [A German translation of the "De bestiis marinis." Only pp. 41–208 constitute this translation. After a "Vorbericht dieser Ausgabe" and "Inhalt dieser Ausgabe" without pagination, pp. 1–35 are occupied by "Zur Einleitung: Anatomie eines Meerkalbes, von Johann Adam Kulmus, in *Actis Nat. Cur.* Vol. I. Obs. 5;" pp. 36–40 by "Auszug der kayserlichen Academie zu Peters-burg von G. W. Stellers Beschreibung sonderbarer Meerthiere," a prefatory summary of Steller's work; pp. 208–218 by "Anhang: Er-fahrungen vom Meereinhorn, *Narhual.*"]

MILLER, WALTER, and J. E. MILLER, transls. The Beasts of the Sea, by George William Steller. In: The Fur Seals and Fur-Seal Islands of the North Pacific Ocean, by D. S. Jordan and associates, Vol. 3, Washington, 1899, pp. 179–218. ["A translation of those parts of Steller's report which treat of [zoögeography, pp. 289–293], the manatee or sea cow (Vol. II, pp. 289 [294]–330), and the natural history of the sea bear (fur seal) (pp. 346–359), sea lion (pp. 361–366), and sea otter (pp. 382–398). The measurements and descriptions of the last three are omitted" (translators' preface, p. 179).]

STELLER, G. W. G. W. Stellers vormaligen Adjunkts bey der Kaiserl. Akademie der Wissenschaften Tagebuch seiner Seereise aus dem Petripauls Hafen in Kamtschatka bis an die westlichen Küsten von Amerika und seiner Begebenheiten auf der Rückreise. *Neue Nordische Beyträge zur Physikalischen und Geographischen Erd- und Völker-beschreibung, Naturgeschichte, und Oekonomie,* St. Petersburg and Leip-zig, Vol. 5, 1793, pp. 129–236, and Vol. 6, 1793, pp. 1–26 (second title page reads *Neueste Nordische Beyträge, etc.,* Vols. 1 and 2 respectively). [P. 129 is the title page, p. 130 is blank, and pp. 131–132 are occupied by Pallas' preface; Steller's words begin on p. 133. Translated in the present work, pp. 9–187.]

STELLER, G. W. G. W. Steller's ehemal. Adjunkts der kays. Akademie der Wissenschaften zu St. Petersburg Reise von Kamtschatka nach Amerika mit dem Commandeur-Capitän Bering. Ein Pendant zu dessen Beschreibung von Kamtschatka. St. Petersburg, 1793. 133 pp. [The journal issued in book form from the type in *Neue Nordische Beyträge,* Vols. 5 and 6. Except for slightly different running heads the pages in the periodical version and the book form coincide exactly as far as and including *N.N.B.,* Vol. 5, p. 235, and book form p. 107.

Page 108 in the book contains the matter on p. 236 of Vol. 5 and all but the last seven lines of Vol. 6, p. 1. Thence this discrepancy is as follows: p. 111 four lines short of p. 4; p. 112 three lines short of p. 5; pp. 113–121 two lines short of pp. 6–14; p. 122 three lines short of p. 15; pp. 123–132 two lines short of pp. 16–25; p. 133 two lines in excess of p. 26. The title page of the periodical version serves as the half title of the book.]

COXE, WILLIAM, transl. Steller's journal of Beering's voyage of discovery from Kamtchatka to the coast of America in 1741. In his "Account of the Russian Discoveries between Asia and America," 4th edit., London, 1803, octavo impression, pp. 30–93; quarto impression, pp. 24–72. [See above, pp. ix–x, footnote 8.]

STELLER, G. W. Topographische und physikalische Beschreibung der Beringsinsel, welche im ostlichen Weltmeer an der Küste von Kamtschatka liegt. *Neue Nordische Beyträge zur Physikalischen und Geographischen Erd- und Völkerbeschreibung, Naturgeschichte, und Oekonomie*, St. Petersburg and Leipzig, Vol. 2, 1781, pp. 255–301. [Pp. 189-190 and part of 191 are occupied by Pallas' preface; Steller's words begin on p. 191. Translated above, pp. 189–241. See there also footnotes 1 and 2, pp. 189–191.]

STELLER, G. W. Georg Wilhelm Stellers gewesenen Adjuncto [*sic*] und Mitglieds der Kayserl. Academie der Wissenschaften zu St. Petersburg Beschreibung von dem Lande Kamtschatka, dessen Einwohnern, deren Sitten, Nahmen, Lebensart und verschiedenen Gewohnheiten, herausgegeben von J. B. S[cherer]. Frankfort and Leipzig, 1774. [viii]+28 +384+72 pp. [As to the identity of the editor as here indicated see above, p. ix, end of footnote 4 and footnote 5.]

STELLER, G. W. Steller's Briefe [an J. G. Gmelin]: I, [von] Irkutsk, 10. Mai 1739; II, [von Irkutsk], 17. Nov. 1739; III, [von] Ochotsk, 20. Aug. 1740; IV, [von] Bolschaja Reka, 1. März 1741; V, [von] Bolschaja Reka, 4. Nov. 1742. In: Joannis Georgii Gmelini . . . Reliquias quae supersunt commercii epistolici cum Carolo Linnaeo, Alberto Hallero, Guilielmo Stellero et al., Floram Gmelini sibiricam ejusque Iter sibiricum potissimum concernentis, ex mandato et sumtibus Academiae scientiarum Caesareae Petropolitanae publicandas curavit Dr. Guil. Henr. Theodor Plieninger, Stuttgart, 1861, pp. 157–185. [Letter V is translated above, pp. 242–249. Letters II and V are reprinted in Otto Gmelin, edit.: Johann Georg Gmelin, Munich, 1911, pp. 123–132.]

Publications Relating in General to the Commander Islands (Bering and Copper Islands) and Adjacent Regions

NORDENSKIÖLD, A. E. Et Besög paa Beringsöen. *Geografisk Tidsskrift*, Copenhagen, Vol. 3, 1879, pp. 117–120.

NORDENSKIÖLD, A. E. [Account of Bering Island in] "The Voyage of the Vega Round Asia and Europe," 2 vols., London, 1881 (listed in Bibliography of Vol. 1, p. 370), Ch. 15 in Vol. 2, pp. 257-295.

ANUCHIN, D. G. Sbornik glavnyeishikh offitsialnykh dokumentov po upravleniyu vostochnoyu Sibiriyu. Izdaetsya po rasporyazheniyu General-Gubernatora Vostochnoi Sibiri D. G. Anuchina. (Collection of the most important documents on the government of Eastern Siberia. Published by order of the Governor General of Eastern Siberia, D. G. Anuchin.) Vol. 3: Kamchatka i Komandorskie Ostrova (Kamchatka and the Commander Islands), Part 2-i: Komandorskie Ostrova (The Commander Islands). Irkutsk, 1882. 170 pp.

GREBNITSKII, N. A. Zapiska o Komandorskikh Ostrovakh (Note on the Commander Islands). In: D. G. Anuchin, Sbornik glavnyeishikh offitsialnykh dokumentov po upravleniyu vostochnoyu Sibiriyu, Vol. 3, Part 2, Irkutsk, 1882, pp. 43-124.

ALEKSYEEV, ————, and EGERMANN, ————. Lotsmanskiya zamyetki (Pilot notes). Morskoi Sbornik, St. Petersburg, 1884, No. 11, pp. 1-19.

BEKLEMISHEV, ————. O Komandorskikh Ostrovakh i kotikovom promyslye (About the Commander Islands and their seal industry). St. Petersburg, 1884.

DYBOWSKI, B. I. Soobshchenie o Komandorskikh Ostrovakh v ekonomicheskom i statisticheskom otnoshenii (Account of the Commander Islands in an economic and statistical sense). Izvyestiya Imp. Russ. Geogr. Obshchestva, Vol. 20, 1884, pp. 196-201. [Abstract of a lecture held before the society, March 7, 1884.]

GUILLEMARD, F. H. H. [Account of Bering Island in] "The Cruise of the Marchesa to Kamchatka & New Guinea" (listed in Bibliography of Vol. 1, p. 370), 1st edit., London, 1886, Ch. 9 in Vol. 1, pp. 187-208.

TÖRNEBOHM, A. E. Under Vega-Expeditionen insamlade Bergarter, petrografisk beskrifning. In "Vega-Expeditionens Vetenskapliga Iakttagelser," Vol. 4, Stockholm, 1887, pp. 113-140. [Bering Island discussed on pp. 135-138.]

KLYKOV, M. A. Gidrograficheskii obzor russkikh beregov Vostochnago Okeana: Komandorskie Ostrova (Hydrographic synopsis of the Russian coasts of the Eastern Ocean: Commander Islands). St. Petersburg, 1888. 243 pp.

DAWSON, G. M. Geological notes on some of the coasts and islands of Bering Sea and vicinity. Bull. Geol. Soc. of America, Vol. 5, 1894, pp. 117-146. [The Commander Islands are discussed on pp. 123-127.]

SAVICH, K. I. Otchet po komandirovkye v 1893 godu na Komandorskie Ostrova prichislennago k Departamentu Torgovli i Manufaktur Ministerstva Finansov Konstantina Savicha (Account of the mission in 1893 to the Commander Islands of the attaché of the Department of

Commerce and Manufactures of the Ministry of Finance, Constantine
Savich). [St. Petersburg], 1894. 78 pp.

SLYUNIN, N. Promyslovyya bogatstva Kamchatki, Sakhalina i Komandorskikh Ostrovov: Otchet Dra N. Slyunina za 1892–1893 gg. (Economic resources of Kamchatka, Sakhalin, and the Commander Islands:
Account of Dr. N. Slyunin in 1892–1893). Ministry of Government
Domain, St. Petersburg, 1895. 117 pp.

STEJNEGER, LEONHARD. Aleut baidarkas in Kamchatka. *Science*, Vol.
2 (N. S.), 1895, pp. 62–63.

[SLYUNIN, N.] Syevero-Vostochnaya Sibir, II: Komandorskie Ostrova
(Northeast Siberia, II: The Commander Islands). *Pravitelstvennyi
Vyestnik*, St. Petersburg, 1897, No. 27, 2/14 Feb., p. 2.

GREBNITSKII, N. A. Komandorskie Ostrova: Ocherk k vystavlennym
fotografiyam N. A. Grebnitskago (The Commander Islands: Note on
the photographs exhibited by N. A. Grebnitskii). Dept. of Agric.,
Ministry of Agric. and Domain, St. Petersburg, 1902. 41 pp.

GREBNITSKII, N. A. Commander Islands. Translated by Louise
Woehlcke, Dept. of Agric., Ministry of Agric. and Domain, St. Petersburg, 1902.

MOROZEWICZ, J. [On the occurrence of copper on the Commander
Islands]. *Mém. Comité Géol.*, St. Petersburg, Vol. 72 (N.S.), 1912. 88 pp.

SUVOROV, E. K. Komandorskie Ostrova i pushnoi promysel na nikh
(The Commander Islands and the fur industry on them). Dept. of
Agric., St. Petersburg, 1912. 342 pp. [With a bibliography, pp. 320–
324.]

Publications Relating to the Botany and Zoölogy of the Commander Islands and Adjacent Regions

PENNANT, THOMAS. [More plants of Behring's Isle]. Suppl. to "Arctic
Zoology," London, 1787, p. 38.

PALLAS, P. S. Zoögraphia rosso-asiatica, sistens omnium animalium in
extenso imperio rossico et adjacentibus maribus observatorum recen-
sionem, domicilia, mores et descriptiones, anatomen atque icones
plurimorum. 3 vols., St. Petersburg, 1811–1831.

DALL, W. H., and H. M. BANNISTER. List of the birds of Alaska, with
biographical notes. *Trans. Chicago Acad. of Nat. Sci.*, Vol. 1, 1869,
pp. 267–310.

PEKARSKII, PETR. Arkhivnyya razyskaniya ob izobrazhenii nesushchestvuyushchago nynye zhivotnago Rhytina borealis. (Archival researches
concerning pictures of the now non-existent animal Rhytina borealis).
Zapiski Imp. Akad. Nauk, Vol. 15, Suppl. No. 1, St. Petersburg, 1869.
[Aside from its zoölogical interest, this paper is important because it
publishes Steller's report to the Senate of Nov. 16, 1742 (pp. 13–24),
part of his report of July 12, 1743, to the same body (pp. 25–28),

and the portion of Khitrov's log book dealing with Bering Island (pp. 28–31; translated in Vol. 1, pp. 236–238.]

FINSCH, O. Zur Ornithologie Nordwest-Amerikas. *Abhandl. Naturwiss. Ver. Bremen*, Vol. 3, 1872, pp. 17–86.

DALL, W. H. Notes on the avi-fauna of the Aleutian Islands, from Unalashka eastward. *Proc. California Acad. of Sci.*, Vol. 5, 1873–74, pp. 25–35.

DALL, W. H. Notes on the avi-fauna of the Aleutian Islands, especially those west of Unalashka. *Proc. California Acad. of Sci.*, Vol. 5, 1873–74, pp. 270–281.

BEAN, T. H. Notes on birds collected during the summer of 1880 in Alaska and Siberia. *Proc. U. S. Natl. Museum*, Vol. 5, 1882, pp. 144–173.

STEJNEGER, LEONHARD. Fra det yderste Östen: [I, no separate title], *Naturen*, Christiania, Vol. 6, 1882, pp. 177–183; II, Andre fjorten Dage i Kamtschatka, *ibid.*, Vol. 8, 1884, pp. 5–10; III, Ostrof Mednij, *ibid.*, Vol. 8, 1884, pp. 33–40 and 49–57; IV, Kapitlet om Berings-Öen i Nordenskiöld's "Vega-faerden," *ibid.*, Vol. 8, 1884, pp. 65–69; V, En Baadtur rundt Beringsöen, *ibid.*, Vol. 9, 1885, pp. 150–157 and 167–174, and Vol. 10, 1886, pp. 33–36 and 49–52. [Incompletely listed in Vol. 1, p. 365.]

KJELLMAN, F. R. The algae of the Arctic Sea: A survey of the species, together with an exposition of the general characters and the development of the flora. *Kongl. Svenska Vetensk. Akad. Handl.*, Stockholm, Vol. 20 (N. S.), 1882–83, No. 5, pp. 1–350.

RIDGWAY, ROBERT. Descriptions of some birds, supposed to be undescribed, from the Commander Islands and Petropaulovski collected by Dr. Leonhard Stejneger, U. S. Signal Service. *Proc. U. S. Natl. Museum*, Vol. 6, 1883, pp. 90–96.

STEJNEGER, LEONHARD. Notes on the natural history, including descriptions of new cetaceans (Contribs. to the History of the Commander Islands, No. 1). *Proc. U. S. Natl. Museum*, Vol. 6, 1883, pp. 58–89.

DALL, W. H. Report on the Mollusca of the Commander Islands, Bering Sea, collected by Leonhard Stejneger in 1882 and 1883 (Contribs. to the History of the Commander Islands, No. 3). *Proc. U. S. Natl. Museum*, Vol. 7, 1884, pp. 340–349.

STEJNEGER, LEONHARD. Investigations relating to the date of the extermination of Steller's sea-cow (Contribs. to the History of the Commander Islands, No. 2). *Proc. U. S. Natl. Museum*, Vol. 7, 1884, pp. 181–189.

STEJNEGER, LEONHARD. Diagnoses of new species of birds from Kamtchatka and the Commander Islands. *Proc. Biol. Soc. of Washington*, 1884, pp. 97–98.

STEJNEGER, LEONHARD. Überblick über meine Reise nach Kamtschatka und den Commander-Inseln (1882 und 1883). *Deutsche Geogr. Blätter*, Bremen, Vol. 7, 1884, pp. 106–108.

DYBOWSKI, B. Wyspy Komandorskie. Lwow, 1885.

G. g. Die Commodore-Inseln. *Ausland*, Vol. 58, 1885, p. 777.

GRAY, ASA. Notes upon the plants collected on the Commander Islands (Bering and Copper Islands) by Leonhard Stejneger (Contribs. to the History of the Commander Islands, No. 4A). *Proc. U. S. Natl. Museum*, Vol. 7, 1885, pp. 527–529.

NORDENSKIÖLD, A. E. Bemötande af anmärkningar, som riktats mot min skildring af Vegas färd kring Asien och Europa. *Ymer*, Stockholm, Vol. 5, 1885, pp. 246–267. [On pp. 254–258 a reply to Stejneger's criticism of Nordenskiöld's discussion of the date of extermination of the sea cow.]

NORDENSKIÖLD, A. E. Reply to criticisms upon "The Voyage of the Vega Around Asia and Europe." *Bull. Amer. Geogr. Soc.*, Vol. 17, 1885, pp. 267–298. [Translation of the *Ymer* article, above. Date of extermination of sea cow dealt with on pp. 279–285.]

STEJNEGER, LEONHARD. Additional notes on the plants of the Commander Islands (Contribs. to the History of the Commander Islands, No. 4B). *Proc. U. S. Natl. Museum*, Vol. 7, 1885, pp. 529–538.

STEJNEGER, LEONHARD. Eine Umsegelung der Berings Insel, Herbst 1882. *Deutsche Geogr. Blätter*, Bremen, Vol. 8, 1885, pp. 225–273.

STEJNEGER, LEONHARD. Results of ornithological explorations in the Commander Islands and in Kamtschatka. *U. S. Natl. Museum Bull. 29*. Washington, 1885.

TRUE, F. W. Description of a new species of Mesoplodon, M. stejnegeri, obtained by Dr. Leonhard Stejneger in Bering Island (Contribs. to the History of the Commander Islands, No. 5). *Proc. U. S. Natl. Museum*, Vol. 8, 1885, pp. 584–585.

DALL, W. H. Report on Bering Island mollusca collected by Mr. Nicholas Grebnitzki (Contribs. to the Natural History of the Commander Islands, No. 6). *Proc. U. S. Natl. Museum*, Vol. 9, 1886, pp. 209–219.

KJELLMAN, F. R. Ueber die Phanerogamenflora der Kommandirski Inseln. *Botan. Centralblatt*, Cassel, 1886, No. 14, p. 31.

STEJNEGER, LEONHARD. On the extermination of the great northern seacow (Rytina). *Bull. Amer. Geogr. Soc.*, Vol. 18, 1886, pp. 317–328.

STEJNEGER, LEONHARD. "Toporok" tufted puffin (Lunda cirrhata) Pall. *Random Notes on Nat. Hist.*, Providence, R. I., Vol. 3, 1886, 17–19.

TRAUTVETTER, E. R. Plantas quasdam in Insulis Praefectoriis nuper lectas lustravit. *Acta Horti Petropolitani*, St. Petersburg, Vol. 9, fasc. 2, 1886.

ALMQUIST, ERNST. Die Lichenenvegetation der Küsten des Beringsmeeres. In "Vega-Expeditionens Vetenskapliga Iakttagelser," Vol. 4, Stockholm, 1887, pp. 509–541. [Bering Island discussed on pp. 518–519, 521, and 529–531.]

KJELLMAN, F. R. On Kommandirskiöarnas fanerogamflora. In "Vega-Expeditionens Vetenskapliga Iakttagelser," Vol. 4, Stockholm, 1887, pp. 281–309.

LILLJEBORG, W. On the Entomostraca collected by Mr. Leonhard Stejneger on Bering Island, 1882–1883 (Contribs. to the Natural History of the Commander Islands, No. 9). *Proc. U. S. Natl. Museum*, Vol. 10, 1887, pp. 154–156.

NELSON, E. W. Report upon natural history collections made in Alaska between the years 1877 and 1881. War Dept., Washington, 1887.

SAHLBERG, JOHN. Coleoptera och Hemiptera, insamlade af Vega-Expeditionens medlemmar på Beringsöen den 15–18 Augusti 1879. In "Vega-Expeditionens Vetenskapliga Iakttagelser," Vol. 4, Stockholm, 1887, pp. 59-71.

STEJNEGER, LEONHARD. How the great northern sea-cow (Rytina) became exterminated. *Amer. Naturalist*, Vol. 21, 1887, pp. 1047–1054.

STEJNEGER, LEONHARD. Revised and annotated catalogue of the birds inhabiting the Commander Islands (Contribs. to the Natural History of the Commander Islands, No. 7). *Proc. U. S. Natl. Museum*, Vol. 10, 1887, pp. 117–145.

STEJNEGER, LEONHARD. Lundefuglene i det Stille Hav. *Naturen*, Christiania, Vol. 11, 1887, pp. 33–38.

VASEY, GEORGE. Description of Alopecurus stejnegeri, a new species of grass from the Commander Islands (Contribs. to the Natural History of the Commander Islands, No. 8). *Proc. U. S. Natl. Museum*, Vol. 10, 1887, p. 153.

WESTERLUND, C. A. Land- och sötvatten-mollusker. Insamlade under Vega-Expeditionen af O. Nordquist och A. Stuxberg. In "Vega-Expeditionens Vetenskapliga Iakttagelser," Vol. 4, Stockholm, 1887, pp. 141–220. [Bering Island discussed on pp. 161–162 and 219–220.]

TURNER, L. M. Contributions to the natural history of Alaska: Results of investigations made chiefly in the Yukon district and the Aleutian Islands, conducted under the auspices of the Signal Service, U. S. A., extending from May, 1874, to August 1881. *U. S. A. Signal Service Arctic Ser. No. 11*, Washington, 1886.

KJELLMAN, F. R. Om Beringhafvets algflora. *Kongl. Svenska Vetensk. Akad. Handl.*, Stockholm, Vol. 23 (N. S.), 1888–89, No. 8, pp. 1–58.

LUCAS, F. A. Description of some bones of Pallas' cormorant (Phalacrocorax perspicillatus) (Contribs. to the Natural History of the Commander Islands, [No. 10]B). *Proc. U. S. Natl. Museum*, Vol. 12, 1889, pp. 88–94.

STEJNEGER, LEONHARD. Contributions to the history of Pallas' cormorant

(Contribs. to the Natural History of the Commander Islands, [No. 10]A). *Proc. U. S. Natl. Museum*, Vol. 12, 1889, pp. 83–88.

BÜCHNER, EUGEN. Die Abbildungen der nordischen Seekuh (Rhytina gigas Zimm.), mit besonderer Berücksichtigung neu aufgefundener handschriftlicher Materialien in Seiner Majestät Höchst Eigenen Bibliothek zu Zarskoje Sselo. *Mémoires Acad. Imp. des Sci. de St. Pétersbourg*, Series 7, Vol. 38, No. 7, 1891. [Aside from its zoölogical interest, of value because it calls attention to Waxel's manuscript journal (see below, p. 264, and above, Fig. 29).]

RIDGWAY, ROBERT. Catalogue of a collection of birds made in Alaska by Mr. C. H. Townsend during the cruise of the U. S. Fish Commission steamer "Albatross" in the summer and autumn of 1888. *Proc. U. S. Natl. Museum*, Vol. 16, 1893, pp. 663–665.

STEJNEGER, LEONHARD. Skeletons of Steller's sea-cow preserved in the various museums. *Science*, Vol. 21 (N.S.), 1893, p. 81.

STEJNEGER, LEONHARD. Arctic notes on the habits of certain rare northern birds in Commander Islands and Kamtchatka. *Museum*, Albion, N. Y., Vol. 1, 1894–95, pp. 53–58, 85–87, and 101–102.

TANNER, Z. L. Report upon the investigations of the U. S. Fish Commission steamer "Albatross" for the year ending June 30, 1892. *Rept. U. S. Fish Commission*, 1892, pp. 1–64. [Commander Islands discussed on pp. 35–42.]

LUCAS, F. A. The cranium of Pallas's cormorant (Contribs. to the Natural History of the Commander Islands, No. 11). *Proc. U. S. Natl. Museum*, Vol. 18, 1895, pp. 717–719.

BEAN, T. H., and B. A. BEAN. Fishes collected at Bering and Copper Islands by Nikolai A. Grebnitski and Leonhard Stejneger (Contribs. to the Natural History of the Commander Islands, No. 12). *Proc. U. S. Natl. Museum*, Vol. 19, 1896, pp. 237–251.

COVILLE, F. V., and FREDERICK FUNSTON. Botany of Yakutat Bay, Alaska. *Contribs. U. S. Natl. Herbarium*, Vol. 3, 1896, pp. 325–353. [Field report by Frederick Funston, pp. 325–333; botanical report by F. V. Coville, pp. 334–351.]

STEJNEGER, LEONHARD. The Russian fur-seal islands. *Bull. U. S. Fish Commission*, Vol. 16, 1896, pp. 1–148. [Also issued separately, Washington, 1896. Also in "Seal and Salmon Fisheries of Alaska" in four volumes, Vol. 4, Washington, 1898, pp. 613–754. Reviewed in *Geogr. Journ.*, Vol. 9, 1897, pp. 322–324.]

[BARRETT-HAMILTON, G. E. H.]. The draught dogs of the Kommandorski Islands. *Our Dogs*, 1897, Dec. 18, p. 1502.

GERASIMOV, A. Komandorskie Ostrova i kotikovyi promysel na nikh, po knigye Leonh. Stejneger'a: "The Russian fur-seal islands" (The Commander Islands and the seal hunting on them, after Stejneger's book, etc.). *Izvyestiya Vostochno-Sibirskago Otdyela Imp. Russ. Geogr. Obshchestva*, Irkutsk, Vol. 28, 1897, pp. 109–135.

ASHMEAD, W. H., edit. Reports upon the insects, spiders, mites, and myriapods collected by Dr. L. Stejneger and Mr. G. E. H. Barrett-Hamilton on the Commander Islands. In Jordan's "The Fur Seals and Fur-Seal Islands of the North Pacific Ocean" (4 vols., Washington, 1898–99), Vol. 4, pp. 328–351.

COVILLE, F. V., and J. N. ROSE. List of plants collected by Dr. and Mrs. Leonhard Stejneger on the Commander Islands during 1895 and 1897. In Jordan's "The Fur Seals and Fur-Seal Islands of the North Pacific Ocean" (4 vols., Washington, 1898–99), Vol. 4, pp. 352–361.

STEJNEGER, LEONHARD. The Asiatic fur-seal islands and fur-seal industry. Constituting Vol. 4 of Jordan's "The Fur Seals and Fur-Seal Islands of the North Pacific Ocean" (4 vols., Washington, 1898–99). 384 pp. [With a bibliography, pp. 232–236.]

STEJNEGER, LEONHARD. The rookeries of the Commander Islands. In: Second Preliminary Report of the Bering Sea Fur-Seal Investigations, by D. S. Jordan, assisted by Leonhard Stejneger, F. A. Lucas, and G. A. Clark, *Treasury Dept. Doc. No. 1994*, Washington, 1897, pp. 35–38.

STEJNEGER, LEONHARD. Report on the rookeries of the Commander Islands, season of 1897. *Treasury Dept. Doc. No. 1997*. Washington, 1897.

JORDAN, D. S., and C. H. GILBERT. The fishes of Bering Sea. In Jordan's "The Fur Seals and Fur-Seal Islands of the North Pacific Ocean" (4 vols., Washington, 1898–99), Vol. 3, pp. 433–492.

KISHINOUYE, K. A new species of stalked medusae, Haliclystus stejnegeri (Contribs. to the Natural History of the Commander Islands, No. 13). *Proc. U. S. Natl. Museum*, Vol. 22, 1900, pp. 125–129.

COVILLE, F. V. Harrimanella, a new genus of heathers. *Proc. Washington Acad. of Sci.*, Vol. 3, 1901, pp. 569–576.

ALLEN, J. A. The hair seals (family Phocidae) of the North Pacific Ocean and Bering Sea. *Bull. Amer. Museum of Nat. Hist.*, Vol. 16, 1902, pp. 459–499.

CARDOT, J., and I. THÉRIOT. The mosses of Alaska. In "Harriman Alaska Expedition," Vol. 5, New York, 1904, pp. 251–328. [Originally published in 1902 in *Proc. Washington Acad. of Sci.*, Vol. 4, pp. 293–372.]

COVILLE, F. V. Arcterica, the rarest genus of heathers. *Botanical Gazette*, Vol. 37, 1904, pp. 298–302.

CUMMINGS, C. E. The lichens of Alaska. In "Harriman Alaska Expedition," Vol. 5, New York, 1904, pp. 65–152.

EVANS, A. W. The Hepaticae of Alaska. In "Harriman Alaska Expedition," Vol. 5, New York, 1904, pp. 339–372. [Originally published in 1900 in *Proc. Washington Acad. of Sci.*, Vol. 2, pp. 287–314.]

OSGOOD, W. H. A biological reconnaissance of the base of the Alaska Peninsula. *North Amer. Fauna No. 24.* U. S. Dept. of Agric., Washington, 1904.

SACCARDO, P. A., C. H. PECK, and WILLIAM TRELEASE. The fungi of Alaska. In "Harriman Alaska Expedition," Vol. 5, New York, 1904, pp. 11–54.

SAUNDERS, DE ALTON. The algae of the expedition. In "Harriman Alaska Expedition," Vol. 5, New York, 1904, pp. 153–250. [Originally published in 1901 in *Proc. Washington Acad. of Sci.*, Vol. 3, pp. 391–486.]

TRELEASE, WILLIAM. Alaskan species of Sphagnum. In "Harriman Alaska Expedition," Vol. 5, New York, 1904, pp. 329–337.

TRELEASE, WILLIAM. Ferns and fern allies of Alaska. In "Harriman Alaska Expedition," Vol. 5, New York, 1904, pp. 373–398.

FEDTSCHENKO, BORIS. Flore des Îles du Commandeur. Acad. of Sci., Cracow, 1906. [With a bibliography.]

GRINNELL, JOSEPH. Birds of the 1908 Alexander Alaska Expedition, with a note on the avifaunal relationships of the Prince William Sound district. *Univ. of California Publs. on Zoölogy*, Vol. 5, 1910, pp. 361–428.

KEELER, CHARLES. Days among Alaska birds. In "Harriman Alaska Expedition," Vol. 2, Washington, 1910, pp. 205–234.

ADDENDA TO BIBLIOGRAPHY OF VOL. I

Bering's Expeditions: Accounts of Participants or Persons Directly Concerned

(a) *Manuscript*

WAXEL, SVEN. Auszug So wohl aus meine als aus andere Officiers, auf den kamschatsischen Expedition halltende Journalen, welche A° 1733 Von St. Petersburg abgefärtiget würde; worinnen Ist in der Kürtze angeführet die Absichten dieser Expedition, dessen fortsetzung, neue Entdeckungen, Zustossende unglücksfälle und Endigung; welches durch ein geschicktere Feder wie der meinige deutlicher, umständlicher, wie auch weitläuftiger kan ausgeführet werden, ohne etwas Von der Materia oder Sache an sich selbsten zu verendern. Von Swen Waxell, Capitain von der Flotte zu Russland. At least 185 pp. In 1891 in the Czar's library at Tsarskoe Selo. [This manuscript was located about in 1891 in the library indicated (Büchner, *Mémoires Acad. Imp. des Sci. de St. Pétersbourg*, Series 7, Vol. 38, No. 7, 1891, who also cites certain passages on pp. 22–24). It is longer than Waxel's report of Nov. 15, 1742, to the Admiralty College on the voyage of the *St. Peter* (our Vol. 1, Ch. 6). It is accompanied by a map showing the results of the expedition (see caption of Fig. 29, above, third paragraph) and a larger drawing of a fur seal, a sea lion, and a sea cow. An earlier map by Waxel (archives of the Hydrographic Section of the Ministry of Marine No. 1940) accompanied his report of Nov. 15, 1742. On these appeared cruder pictures of the sea animals (reproduced by Pekarskii, *Zapiski Imp. Akad. Nauk*, Vol. 15, Suppl. 1, St. Petersburg, 1869) and the picture of the Aleut in his *baidarka* reproduced in our Vol. 1, Fig. 12.]

(b) Published

[WAXEL, SVEN.] A letter from a Russian sea-officer to a person of distinction at the court of St. Petersburgh, containing his remarks upon Mr. de l'Isles's chart and memoir relative to the new discoveries northward and eastward from Kamtschatka, together with some observations on that letter by Arthur Dobbs, Esq., Governor of North Carolina. To which is added Mr. de l'Isle's explanatory memoir on his chart, published at Paris and now translated from the original French. London, 1754. 83 pp. [This is the English translation of Waxel's "Lettre d'un officier de la marine russienne" listed in the Bibliography of Vol. 1, p. 362. The booklet consists of the following: pp. 1–33, the letter; pp. 37–51, "Observations upon the Russian Discoveries Mentioned in a [the] Letter" by Arthur Dobbs; pp. 56–71, J. N. Delisle's "An Explanation of the Map of the New Discoveries Northward of the South Sea" (translation of Delisle's 1752 memoir listed in Vol. 1, p. 360); pp. 72–81, Admiral de Fonte's letter (see Vol. 1, top of p. 361); pp. 82–83, extract from the register of the Paris Academy of Sciences, Jan. 13, 1751.]

KRASHENINNIKOV, S. P. Histoire et description du Kamtchatka, contenant I, Les moeurs & les coutumes des habitants du Kamtchatka, II, La géographie du Kamtchatka et des pays circonvoisins. Traduit du russe. 2 vols., Amsterdam, 1770. [This is the French translation mentioned in the Bibliography of Vol. 1, p. 360, third item.]

GMELIN, OTTO, edit. Johann Georg Gmelin, 1709–1755, der Erforscher Sibiriens: Ein Gedenkbuch. Munich, 1911. [To a biographical sketch by Robert Gradmann (pp. 3–20) are added the preface (1747) from Gmelin's "Flora sibirica" and from his "Reise durch Sibirien" (see Bibliography in Vol. 1, p. 360, first item) and excerpts from the latter. Letters that passed between Gmelin and Linné, Steller, Haller are also reprinted.]

Near-Contemporary Accounts of Bering's Expeditions, and Compendiums

ROBERTSON, WILLIAM. The history of America. 2 vols., London, 1777. [In Book IV, on pp. 273–277, of this history, which was widely read at the time, the Russian discoveries are discussed, based partly on Müller but also on direct connections of the author with St. Petersburg.]

Modern Discussions of Bering's Expeditions

BERG, L. S. Otkrytie Kamchatki i Kamchatskie Ekspeditsii Beringa. (The Discovery of Kamchatka and the Kamchatka Expedition of Bering.) Biblioteka Puteshestvii, Series 3, edited by Prof. A. A. Kruber, No. 4, Moscow and Petrograd, 1924. 246 pp. [Important recent study of Bering's second expedition. Discussion of sources, with bibliography, pp. 227–234.]

INDEX TO BOTH VOLUMES

ERRATA

Vol. I

p. 2, line 12 from bottom: *transpose* came *to beginning of next line.*

p. 2, lines 11–9 from bottom: *Instead of sentence beginning with "One of these" read:*
The two southernmost of these, Kunashiri and Itorup, he thought were one island, which he named State Island and the other, Urup (which he thought to be part of the American continent), Company Land.

opp. p. 20, title of Fig. 6, next-to-last line: *for* August 22–September, 1727 *read* August 22–September 2, 1727.

p. 22, line 13 from bottom: for *baidaras* read *baidars.*

p. 32, large type, line 7 from bottom: *for* Pizarev *read* Pisarev.

opp. p. 35, title of Fig. 8: *As evident from the description of the* St. Peter *and the* St. Paul *on p. 34, the ships in the view are not these vessels. Add to* From an old engraving *the words* practically identical with an engraving in Steller's "Beschreibung von dem Lande Kamtschatka," 1774, opp. p. 17.

p. 98, two last lines of footnote 38: *for* 1806, Part II, pp. 52–53 *read* 1807, Vol. 2, p. 25.

p. 120, line 7 from bottom: *for* Khatianintsov *read* Khotyaintsov.

p. 148, line 4 of footnote 91: *for* Fig. 11 *read* Fig. 12.

p. 237, line 11: *for* cape *read* camp.

p. 256, 11 A. M. entry: *for* went into *read* proceeded to.

p. 311, re loss of Chirikov's men: *Pallas says* (Neue Nordische Beyträge, Vol. 1, 1781, p. 272) *that on Heceta's expedition of 1775, in lat. 56° near the coast, a party of very white and blond natives in thirty canoes was met with, and he queries whether these might have been descendants of Chirikov's men.*

p. 324, last line: for *sleep* read *deep.*

p. 325, lines 12–7 from bottom: *The quotation from Steller's journal is not literally coincident with the same passage in the present volume (p. 61) because it was taken from Dr. Golder's and not Dr. Stejneger's translation (see above, p. x).*

p. 335, line 8: *for* Chiginigak *read* Chiginagak.

p. 339, line 3 from bottom, and Pl. I: *interpretation of track of* St. Peter *on approaching Bering Island from the east should be modified according to Fig. 15 and footnote 300a of the present volume.*

p. 357, line 10: *for* Mikhael *read* Mikhail.

p. 360, line 4: *for* 1795 *read* 1793.

p. 364, line 13: *for* 67° 18′ N. *read* 65° 30′ N.

p. 365, line 2 from bottom: *for* Vol. 3, 1885, *read* Vol. 8, 1885.

p. 365, line 23: *for* svyedenie *read* svyedyenie.

p. 367, line 8: *for* Fig. 5 *read* Fig. 6.

p. 370, line 7 from bottom: *for* SLUININ *read* SLYUNIN.

p. 371, line 7: *for* dyyl *read* dyel.

Vol. II

p. 6, line 7 from bottom; p. 60, line 3 from bottom; p. 91, line 6 of footnote 206: *for* Pekarski *read* Pekarskii.

p. 38, line 3 of title of Fig. 1: *for* leaves *read* pages.